INTRODUCTION TO
PROBABILITY AND RANDOM VARIABLES

McGraw-Hill Series in Probability and Statistics

DAVID BLACKWELL, *Consulting Editor*

Introduction to
PROBABILITY AND
RANDOM VARIABLES

GEORGE P. WADSWORTH

DEPARTMENT OF MATHEMATICS
MASSACHUSETTS INSTITUTE OF TECHNOLOGY

JOSEPH G. BRYAN

WEATHER SYSTEM DIVISION
THE TRAVELERS INSURANCE COMPANY

Formerly with Central Research Laboratory
American Machine and Foundry Company
and Statistics Laboratory
Massachusetts Institute of Technology

McGRAW-HILL BOOK COMPANY, INC.

New York   Toronto   London

1960

PREFACE

Probability, the "laws of chance," has had a colorful history dating back at least to the early Renaissance, when commercial insurance against risks was established in the Italian cities. The mathematical study of probability was stimulated by questions of practical concern: how to hedge against the uncertainty of individual events by taking advantage of the paradoxical rule of regularity en masse—an empirical discovery.

Pioneering work on probability was done in the seventeenth century by Galileo, Pascal, Fermat, Huygens, J. Bernoulli, and Halley—to mention only the most famous. The roster of contributors since then includes the greatest mathematicians and some of the greatest scientists of each generation. Perhaps the most outstanding contribution of any one individual was that of Laplace, whose celebrated work entitled "Théorie analytique des probabilités" was published in 1812 and dedicated to Napoleon.

The astronomer Edmund Halley, distinguished as the first person ever to predict the return of a comet, made an important application of probability to actuarial science in 1693 by showing how premiums for life insurance could be calculated from mortality tables. Laplace, Legendre, and Gauss were cofounders of the theory of errors—an application of probability to the subject of variations among repeated measurements of the same quantity. The great physicist J. C. Maxwell derived the gas laws in 1860 on the basis of the probability distribution of molecular velocities. In 1900, Max Planck presented his quantum theory of radiation in terms of probability. Under the leadership of Karl Pearson and R. A. Fisher, rapid progress has been made in the field of statistics since the beginning of the twentieth century through the application of probability to problems concerning valid inference from limited—but adequate—data. Problems of this sort arise in quality comparisons of all kinds, sampling inspection of manufactured articles, design of experiments to guide product development when important factors cannot be subjected to laboratory control, market surveys, public-opinion polls, and statistical prediction. World War II opened new fields of application when probability was applied to the theory of search for enemy submarines, bomber defense against fighters, and questions concerning the best tactics in combat or the best use of new weapons.   The men responsible for these applications designated their work as "operations research" —a rapidly developing field which has since gained wide industrial acceptance.   Thus through operations research, probability, which owes its origin to commerce, is at last being brought to bear vigorously and competently on the uncertainties of business operations.

Despite its long history of engaging the greatest intellects of successive generations and proving its value in many fields, probability has been neglected in the college curriculum until very recently.   Within the last decade, however, it has emerged in its true light as a subject of broad application both to science and industry, and it is now beginning to receive due recognition in the technical training of scientists and engineers.

The authors' primary purpose has been to supply a text for a short undergraduate course, with a prerequisite of elementary calculus.   However, they feel it equally important to present the material in a form which will be suitable for self-study on the part of practicing engineers and research workers whose mathematical background does not include a substantial course in probability.   Both for the sake of readers without previous grounding in probability and others who would like a review, much space has been devoted to discussion of concepts and detailed solution of illustrative problems.

The material of this book has been class-tested in mimeographed form for eight years at the Massachusetts Institute of Technology.   There it has served as the text for a one-semester course offered twice a year by the Department of Mathematics and has had the benefit of being used by seven members of the staff.   Considerable revision has taken place during this period, but the contents have remained substantially unaltered for the last two years.   Abbreviations and specialized symbols have been avoided to a large extent because the beginning student finds the use of such shorthand an obstacle to comprehension.

Statistical concepts are developed where they arise as direct applications of the topics in probability under consideration.   In this way the student receives an early but brief introduction to tests of significance, confidence limits, and the major sampling distributions, without interruption to the main theme.   The last chapter is the only one exclusively devoted to statistics.   There the student is instructed in the principal uses of four major distributions—the normal, chi-square, t, and F—and is given a clear statement of their relationships and distinct provinces.

It is our hope that this text will serve two purposes: first, instruction both in university classrooms and the technical professions; second, promotion of greater awareness and appreciation of the potential values of probability to science and industry.

George P. Wadsworth
Joseph G. Bryan

CONTENTS

CHAPTER 1

PRELIMINARY MATHEMATICS

1-1. Introduction. In most elementary courses in calculus the following topics in mathematics are not usually included, and therefore the parts of these topics which are used in this book are discussed. Differentiation with respect to a parameter is very useful in the maximization and minimization of expressions which are the results of models best represented by means of integrals, while some elementary knowledge of permutations and combinations is essential in many probability considerations. Beta and gamma functions represent the areas under certain curves, and these curves are not only important in mathematical statistics but are extremely useful in representing mathematical models in many applied problems.

1-2. Differentiation of an Integral with Respect to a Parameter. A function $\phi(\alpha)$ of a parameter α can be defined by means of a definite integral such as, for example,

$$\phi(\alpha) = \int_0^1 (\alpha x + \alpha^2 x^2)\, dx = \left[\frac{\alpha x^2}{2} + \frac{\alpha^2 x^3}{3}\right]_0^1 = \frac{\alpha}{2} + \frac{\alpha^2}{3}$$

provided the integral converges for the range of values of α in which we are interested, even if one or both of the limits of integration are infinite. If we now differentiate $\phi(\alpha)$ with respect to α, we have

$$\frac{d\phi(\alpha)}{d\alpha} = \frac{1}{2} + \frac{2\alpha}{3}$$

It is possible, however, in most practical cases to differentiate under the integral sign first and integrate afterward as

$$\frac{d\phi(\alpha)}{d\alpha} = \int_0^1 (x + 2\alpha x^2)\, dx = \left[\frac{x^2}{2} + \frac{2\alpha x^3}{3}\right]_0^1 = \frac{1}{2} + \frac{2\alpha}{3}$$

provided again that this new integral is convergent and that the function under the integral sign is also continuous in both x and α. In some of the problems considered, we will be maximizing or minimizing with respect to α, and thus may wish to calculate the derivative directly, as it is simpler to carry out the formal procedures in this way.

1

In the previous example the limits on the integral sign were constant, but often they are functions of α also. We still can define, under certain mathematical restrictions, a function of α such as is indicated in the following example:

$$\phi(\alpha) = \int_\alpha^{\alpha^2} (1 + \alpha x)\, dx = \left[x + \frac{\alpha x^2}{2} \right]_\alpha^{\alpha^2} = \left(\alpha^2 + \frac{\alpha^5}{2} \right) - \left(\alpha + \frac{\alpha^3}{2} \right)$$

If we now differentiate $\phi(\alpha)$ with respect to α, we have

$$\frac{d\phi(\alpha)}{d\alpha} = 2\alpha + \frac{5\alpha^4}{2} - 1 - \frac{3\alpha^2}{2}$$

The general formula for differentiation with respect to a parameter, when the limits are functions of the parameter also, is given here without proof. If

$$\phi(\alpha) = \int_a^b f(x,\alpha)\, dx$$

where a and b are functions of α, and if some general restrictions are placed on $f(x,\alpha)$ and $\partial f(x,\alpha)/\partial \alpha$, then

$$\frac{d\phi(\alpha)}{d\alpha} = \int_a^b \frac{\partial}{\partial \alpha} [f(x,\alpha)]\, dx + f(b,\alpha)\frac{db}{d\alpha} - f(a,\alpha)\frac{da}{d\alpha}$$

If we apply this formula to the same example, namely,

$$\phi(\alpha) = \int_\alpha^{\alpha^2} (1 + \alpha x)\, dx$$

then $\quad \dfrac{d\phi(\alpha)}{d\alpha} = \displaystyle\int_\alpha^{\alpha^2} x\, dx + (1 + \alpha^3)2\alpha - (1 + \alpha^2)(1)$

$$= \frac{\alpha^4}{2} - \frac{\alpha^2}{2} + 2\alpha + 2\alpha^4 - 1 - \alpha^2 = \frac{5\alpha^4}{2} - \frac{3\alpha^2}{2} + 2\alpha - 1$$

which checks the previous result.

1-3. Gamma Functions. The value of the integral $\int_0^\infty x^{n-1}e^{-x}\, dx$ is dependent upon the value of n and represents a finite quantity for values of n greater than zero. This particular function of n is called the *gamma function*, written $\Gamma(n)$, and has two common forms:

$$\Gamma(n) = \int_0^\infty x^{n-1}e^{-x}\, dx \qquad (n > 0) \qquad (1\text{-}1)$$

$$\Gamma(n) = 2\int_0^\infty y^{2n-1}e^{-y^2}\, dy \qquad (n > 0) \qquad (1\text{-}2)$$

Equation (1-2) can be derived from Eq. (1-1) by making the change of variable $x = y^2$. Actually it makes no difference whether the variable is called x or y, since the value of the integral of a given function depends only on the limits, which are constant.

integration by parts : $\int u \, dv = uv - \int v \, du$

Unless n is a positive integer, the value of $\Gamma(n)$ must be obtained by series expansion or some type of numerical integration. For this reason, tables of the gamma function have been worked out for various values of n. Commonly, however, the tables are confined to values of n between 1 and 2, inasmuch as the function can be determined for other values of n by means of a recurrence formula, which we shall now derive. If Eq. (1-1) is integrated by parts, we have

$$\Gamma(n) = \int_0^\infty x^{n-1}e^{-x}\,dx = [-x^{n-1}e^{-x}]_0^\infty + (n-1)\int_0^\infty x^{n-2}e^{-x}\,dx$$
$$= (n-1)\Gamma(n-1)$$

since the integrated part vanishes at both limits. Therefore if the gamma function is tabulated for values of n between two consecutive integers, say 1 and 2, the function can be computed for values outside of the table by repeated use of the recurrence formula.

On the other hand, if n is a positive integer, the gamma function of n reduces to the ordinary factorial of $n - 1$ as defined in algebra. To begin with, we determine $\Gamma(1)$ from the defining integral, that is,

$$\Gamma(1) = \int_0^\infty e^{-x}\,dx = 1$$

Then from the recurrence formula we obtain $\Gamma(2)$, $\Gamma(3)$, . . . , $\Gamma(n)$ successively as follows:

$$\Gamma(2) = (1)\Gamma(1) = 1 \qquad \Gamma(3) = (2)\Gamma(2) = 2 \times 1$$
$$\Gamma(4) = (3)\Gamma(3) = 3 \times 2 \times 1 \qquad \text{etc.}$$

and thus

$$\Gamma(n) = (n-1)(n-2)\cdots 3 \times 2 \times 1 = (n-1)! \qquad (n = 1, 2, 3, \ldots)$$

where by definition $0! = 1$.

For any positive value of n, we may interpret the gamma function as the area under the curve $y = x^{n-1}e^{-x}$ from $x = 0$ to $x = \infty$. A plot of these curves for various n's is shown in Fig. 1-1. The areas under these curves are given in Fig. 1-2 and thus show the plot of $\Gamma(n)$ as a function of n.

An important point in Fig. 1-2 corresponds to $n = \frac{1}{2}$. To find its value, consider

$$\Gamma(\tfrac{1}{2}) = 2\int_0^\infty e^{-x^2}\,dx \qquad \text{or} \qquad \Gamma(\tfrac{1}{2}) = 2\int_0^\infty e^{-y^2}\,dy$$

where the definition (1-2) for the gamma function is being utilized. By multiplying these two values of $\Gamma(\frac{1}{2})$ together, we obtain

$$[\Gamma(\tfrac{1}{2})]^2 = \left(2\int_0^\infty e^{-x^2}\,dx\right)\left(2\int_0^\infty e^{-y^2}\,dy\right)$$
$$= 4\int_0^\infty dx \int_0^\infty e^{-(x^2+y^2)}\,dy$$

This last expression may be considered as a double integral to be evaluated over the first quadrant in the XOY plane. The above procedure is permitted since both sets of limits are constant and both integrals as well as the product or double integral converge. If polar coordinates are now introduced, we have, since $dx\,dy = r\,d\theta\,dr$,

$$[\Gamma(\tfrac{1}{2})]^2 = 4\int_0^{\pi/2} d\theta \int_0^\infty e^{-r^2}r\,dr = 4\,\frac{\pi}{2}\left[\frac{e^{-r^2}}{-2}\right]_0^\infty = \pi$$

where the limits are such that the integral is still evaluated over the first quadrant. Therefore $\Gamma(\tfrac{1}{2}) = \sqrt{\pi}$.

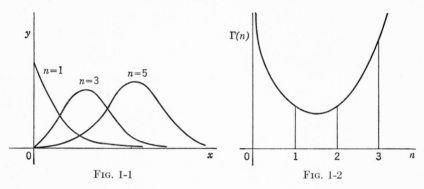

FIG. 1-1   FIG. 1-2

Many definite integrals can be evaluated by means of the gamma function either because they are of the gamma form or because they can be transformed into that form. A few illustrations follow with the appropriate transformation:

$$\int_0^\infty x^{4/5}e^{-x}\,dx = \Gamma(\tfrac{9}{5}) \tag{1-3}$$

$$\int_0^\infty x^2e^{-2x}\,dx = \tfrac{1}{8}\int_0^\infty y^2e^{-y}\,dy = \tfrac{1}{8}\Gamma(3) = \tfrac{1}{4} \qquad (2x = y) \tag{1-4}$$

$$\int_0^\infty x^9e^{-x^3}\,dx = \tfrac{1}{3}\int_0^\infty y^{7/3}e^{-y}\,dy = \tfrac{1}{3}\Gamma(1\tfrac{9}{3}) = 2\tfrac{8}{27}\Gamma(4\tfrac{1}{3})$$
$$(x^3 = y) \tag{1-5}$$

$$-\int_0^1 (\ln x)^{1/5}\,dx = -\int_\infty^0 y^{1/5}e^{-y}\,dy = \int_0^\infty y^{1/5}e^{-y}\,dy = \Gamma(\tfrac{6}{5})$$
$$(\ln x = -y) \tag{1-6}$$

1-4. Beta Functions. A second useful type of integral in the field of operations research and statistics involves two parameters and is called the *beta function*. It can be defined as follows:

$$\beta(m,n) = \int_0^1 x^{m-1}(1 - x)^{n-1}\,dx \qquad (m > 0, n > 0) \tag{1-7}$$

$$\beta(m,n) = 2\int_0^{\pi/2} \sin^{2m-1}\theta \cos^{2n-1}\theta\,d\theta \qquad (m > 0, n > 0) \tag{1-8}$$

The integral has a specific value for any given choice of m and n, provided these quantities are greater than zero; otherwise the integral diverges. Equation (1-7) is transformed into Eq. (1-8) by the change of variable $x = \sin^2 \theta$.

It turns out that the beta function is related to the gamma function. Consider the following integrals:

$$\Gamma(m) = 2 \int_0^\infty y^{2m-1} e^{-y^2}\, dy \qquad \Gamma(n) = 2 \int_0^\infty x^{2n-1} e^{-x^2}\, dx$$

If these two integrals defining gamma functions of m and n are multiplied together, we have—since the appropriate conditions are satisfied—

$$\Gamma(m)\Gamma(n) = 4 \int_0^\infty dx \int_0^\infty x^{2n-1} y^{2m-1} e^{-(x^2+y^2)}\, dy$$

As before, we may introduce polar coordinates and again evaluate the integral over the first quadrant as

$$\Gamma(m)\Gamma(n) = \left(2 \int_0^{\pi/2} \cos^{2n-1} \theta \sin^{2m-1} \theta\, d\theta \right)\left(2 \int_0^\infty r^{2(m+n)-1} e^{-r^2}\, dr \right)$$

Utilizing our definition of both beta and gamma functions,

$$\Gamma(m)\Gamma(n) = \beta(m,n)\Gamma(m + n)$$

and therefore
$$\beta(m,n) = \frac{\Gamma(m)\Gamma(n)}{\Gamma(m + n)} \qquad (1\text{-}9)$$

From this it is obvious that the beta function is symmetrical in the parameters m and n, that is,

$$\beta(m,n) = \beta(n,m)$$

The beta function is the area under the curve $y = x^{m-1}(1 - x)^{n-1}$ between the values of $x = 0$ and $x = 1$. Not only is this total area known, but tables are available for the percentage area included between 0 and x where $0 < x < 1$, and these computational aids make the curves very useful for the representation of simple mathematical models considered in later chapters. The effect of the parameters m and n on the shapes of these curves may be studied by dividing the ordinates by $\beta(m,n)$, thus making the total area equal to unity in all cases. The order of contact of the curves to the x axis at 0 and 1 is determined by the value of m and n and increases with increasing values of these parameters. When m and n are equal, the curves are symmetrical about $x = \frac{1}{2}$. The effect of assigning a value of m between 0 and 1 is to cause the curve to rise to infinity with $x = 0$ as an asymptote, although the area under the curve is still finite. A similar situation exists at $x = 1$ if n is allowed to take on a value between 0 and 1. Some of these effects are shown in Fig. 1-3a and b, where m and n are varied for purposes of illustration, but the total area is kept equal to unity in each case. A wide variety of shapes can thus be obtained with these curves, provided only one maximum is desired. When two or more maxima are required by the mathematical models being considered, several of these curves can be added together in some predetermined proportion in order to give the desired effect.

It should be observed from the following illustrative examples that the range for x from 0 to 1 is not essential, since a simple linear transformation changes the origin and the scale in such a manner that the curve will

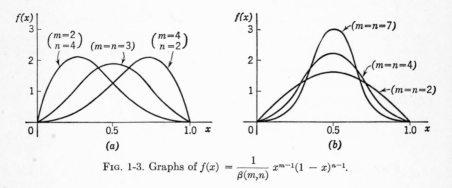

FIG. 1-3. Graphs of $f(x) = \dfrac{1}{\beta(m,n)} x^{m-1}(1 - x)^{n-1}$.

vanish at any other two points in lieu of 0 and 1. The following examples illustrate the use of the beta function in evaluating definite integrals. Where substitutions are needed, they are shown in parentheses.

$$\int_0^1 x^3(1 - x)^4 \, dx = \beta(4,5) = \frac{\Gamma(4)\Gamma(5)}{\Gamma(9)} = \frac{1}{280} \tag{1-10}$$

$$\int_0^{\pi/2} \tan^{1/2} x \, dx = \int_0^{\pi/2} \sin^{1/2} x \cos^{-1/2} x \, dx = \frac{1}{2}\beta(\tfrac{3}{4},\tfrac{1}{4})$$

$$= \frac{1}{2} \frac{\Gamma(\tfrac{3}{4})\Gamma(\tfrac{1}{4})}{\Gamma(1)} = \frac{8}{3} \Gamma(\tfrac{7}{4})\Gamma(\tfrac{5}{4}) \tag{1-11}$$

$$\int_0^1 \frac{x^2 \, dx}{\sqrt{1 - x^4}} = \frac{1}{4} \int_0^1 y^{-1/4}(1 - y)^{-1/2} \, dy \qquad (x^4 = y)$$

$$= \frac{1}{4}\beta(\tfrac{3}{4},\tfrac{1}{2}) = \frac{1}{4} \frac{\Gamma(\tfrac{3}{4})\Gamma(\tfrac{1}{2})}{\Gamma(\tfrac{5}{4})} = \frac{\sqrt{\pi}}{3} \frac{\Gamma(\tfrac{7}{4})}{\Gamma(\tfrac{5}{4})} \tag{1-12}$$

$$\int_{-2}^3 (2 + x)^2(x - 3)^3 \, dx = \int_0^5 u^2(u - 5)^3 \, du \qquad (u = 2 + x)$$

$$= 5^6 \int_0^1 y^2(y - 1)^3 \, dy \qquad (u = 5y)$$

$$= -5^6\beta(3,4) = \frac{-5^6}{60} = \frac{-15,625}{60} \approx -260.4$$

$$\tag{1-13}$$

1-5. Permutations and Combinations. Permutations and combinations relate to the possible subgroups and arrangements which can be formed from a stated collection of objects. A *permutation* is a particular sequence of a given set of objects, whereas a *combination* is the *set itself without reference to order*. Thus ABC, ACB, BAC, BCA, CAB, CBA are all different permutations but the same combination.

The relevant question in most applications is simply how many different permutations or combinations exist under the conditions assumed. An obvious but fundamental principle upon which the answer to this question rests is the so-called *mn* rule.

mn Rule. If an event A can take place in m different ways and afterward an event B can take place in n different ways for *each* instance in which A occurs, then the sequence AB can take place in mn different ways. The following three formulas are in constant use. In all cases the phrase "*r at a time*" means that the permutation or combination must contain exactly r objects.

1. Let $Pm(n,r)$ denote the number of different permutations which can be formed from n distinct objects taken r at a time. Then

$$Pm(n,r) = n(n-1)(n-2) \cdots (n-r+1) = \frac{n!}{(n-r)!} \quad (1\text{-}14)$$

There are n objects with which the first position can be filled; when any one of these is definitely chosen, there are $n-1$ objects left from which the second position can be filled; thus the first two positions, by the *mn* rule, can be filled in $n(n-1)$ ways. Having fixed the first two positions, we can fill the third with any one of the $n-2$ objects which remain; thus the first three positions can be filled in $n(n-1)(n-2)$ ways. In general, after k positions have been filled, the next position can be filled in $n-k$ ways; hence by successive use of the *mn* rule, the total number of permutations is the continued product $n(n-1)(n-2) \cdots (n-r+1)$. In case $r = n$, this product becomes equal to $n!$. If $r < n$, the factors missing from $n!$ are $n-r$, $n-r-1$, $\ldots$, 3, 2, 1, and their product exactly equals $(n-r)!$. Therefore, we may obtain the correct result in all cases if we divide $n!$ by $(n-r)!$, remembering that $0! = 1$ by definition.

2. Let $C(n,r)$ denote the number of different combinations which can be formed from n distinct objects taken r at a time. Then

$$C(n,r) = \frac{Pm(n,r)}{r!} = \frac{n!}{r!(n-r)!} \quad (1\text{-}15)$$

Since the formula $Pm(r,r)$ reduces to $r!$, it follows that every distinct combination of r objects yields $r!$ distinct permutations. Hence there are $r!$ times as many permutations as combinations, and so $C(n,r) = Pm(n,r)/r!$. The quantity $C(n,r)$ is often called a *binomial coefficient*, inasmuch as the binomial expansion of $(a + b)^n$ is given by

$$(a + b)^n = \sum_{r=0}^{n} C(n,r)a^{n-r}b^r \qquad (1\text{-}16)$$

Sometimes groups of objects having a common characteristic can be regarded as conceptually identical for the purposes at hand, and there arises a problem as to how many effectively different arrangements exist. When the n objects are not all distinct, the foregoing formulas do not hold. Suppose there are n_1 objects of type 1, n_2 objects of type 2, . . . , n_k objects of type k, where $n_1 + n_2 + \cdots + n_k = n$. In this case, we cannot give simple formulas for the number of permutations or combinations for an arbitrary number of objects r; but it so happens that the only question ordinarily considered concerns the number of different permutations of all n objects at once, and for this a simple formula can be given.

3. Let $Pm(n;n_1,n_2, \ldots ,n_k)$ denote the number of different permutations of n objects taken n at a time, given that n_i are of type i, where $i = 1, 2, \ldots , k$ and $\Sigma n_i = n$. Then

$$Pm(n;n_1,n_2, \ldots ,n_k) = \frac{n!}{n_1!n_2! \cdots n_k!} \qquad (1\text{-}17)$$

If all objects were distinguishable, there would be $n!$ different permutations. For the sake of argument, imagine the separate objects of each type tagged so as to be distinguishable as individual entities but still having the relevant characteristic in common, and consider the total number of permutations which are identical as to the order of all individuals of types 2, 3, . . . , k but different as to the particular objects of type 1 which occupy the remaining positions. Since there are $n_1!$ possible orders of all n_1 objects of type 1, there must be $n_1!$ permutations which are identical with respect to types 2, 3, . . . , k. Therefore, when the objects of type 1 are rendered indistinguishable, this group of permutations is reduced to a single pattern, and the total number of different permutations is then divided by $n_1!$. The same argument applies to all other types, and so the total divisor is the product $n_1!n_2! \cdots n_k!$.

We conclude with a few typical applications of the foregoing formulas on permutations and combinations.

Example 1-1. How many different sequences of three notes can be formed from an eight-note scale if no note is repeated? Since the order is relevant, the answer is given by the number of permutations of eight things taken three at a time:

$$Pm(8,3) = \frac{8!}{5!} = 8 \times 7 \times 6 = 336$$

Example 1-2. How many different 5-card hands can be made up from a deck of 52 cards? Here the order is immaterial, and so the answer is given by the number of combinations of 52 things taken 5 at a time:

$$C(52,5) = \frac{52!}{5!47!} = \frac{52 \times 51 \times 50 \times 49 \times 48}{5 \times 4 \times 3 \times 2 \times 1} = 2{,}598{,}960$$

Example 1-3. A light panel has six bulbs in a horizontal row. How many different signals, each showing six lights simultaneously, can be formed from three red lights, two green, and one yellow? In this case the answer is given by the number of permutations of six things taken six at a time, with three of one type, two of another, and one of still another type:

$$Pm(6;3,2,1) = \frac{6!}{3!2!1!} = \frac{6 \times 5 \times 4 \times 3 \times 2 \times 1}{3 \times 2 \times 1 \times 2 \times 1 \times 1} = 60$$

Using three colors, how should six lights be divided among them in order to obtain the maximum number of signals of the type considered? Here the object is to choose three integers x, y, z with $x + y + z = 6$, and such that $Pm(6;x,y,z)$ is greatest. Clearly the maximum is obtained by choosing $x = y = z = 2$, for if any number is taken less than 2, another must be made larger, and since the total number of factors multiplied together in the denominator of the fraction is constant (6, in this case), an increase in the size of any number will replace a smaller factor by a larger one. With two lights of each color, the number of possible signals is

$$Pm(6;2,2,2) = \frac{6!}{2!2!2!} = \frac{6 \times 5 \times 4 \times 3 \times 2 \times 1}{2 \times 1 \times 2 \times 1 \times 2 \times 1} = 90$$

EXERCISES

Find the derivatives with respect to α of the following integrals, utilizing the formula and then checking:

1. $\int_0^{\alpha x} \cos (x + \alpha) \, dx.$ **2.** $\int_0^{\sqrt{\alpha}} x \, dx.$

3. $\int_0^x \sin^{-1} \frac{x}{\alpha} \, dx.$ **4.** $\int_{\alpha^2}^{\alpha^3} (x^2 + \alpha^2) \, dx.$

By differentiating first with respect to α, find the values of the following integrals:

5. $\int_0^\pi \ln (1 + \alpha \cos x) \, dx \qquad (-1 < \alpha < 1).$ *Ans.* $\pi \ln \dfrac{1 + \sqrt{1 - \alpha^2}}{2}.$

6. $\int_0^1 \frac{(x^\alpha - 1)}{\ln x} \, dx \qquad (\alpha > -1).$ *Ans.* $\ln (\alpha + 1).$

7. By successive differentiations of $\int_0^1 x^n \, dx = 1/(n + 1)$ show that

$$\int_0^1 x^n (\ln x)^m \, dx = (-1)^m \frac{m!}{(n + 1)^{m+1}}$$

8. By successive differentiation of $\int_0^\infty dx/(x^2 + \alpha) = \pi/2 \sqrt{\alpha}$ show that

$$\int_0^\infty \frac{dx}{(x^2 + \alpha)^{n+1}} = \frac{\pi}{2} \frac{1 \times 3 \times \cdots \times (2n - 1)}{2 \times 4 \times \cdots \times 2n \alpha^{n+\frac{1}{2}}}$$

turn in

9. Find c, such that $\int_0^\infty |x - c| e^{-ax} dx$ is a minimum.   *Ans. $c = (\ln 2)/a$.*

Evaluate each of the following integrals:

10. $\int_0^\infty x^{5/2} e^{-2x} dx.$ *Ans. $\dfrac{\Gamma(\frac{7}{2})}{2^{7/2}}$.*

11. $\int_0^\infty x^4 e^{-5x^2} dx.$ *Ans. $\dfrac{\Gamma(\frac{5}{2})}{50 \sqrt{5}}$.*

12. $\int_0^1 x^{-1/5}(1 - x)^{-2/5} dx.$ *Ans. $\beta(.8,.6) = 1.95$.*

13. $\int_0^\infty x^n e^{-bx} dx.$ *Ans. $\dfrac{n!}{b^{n+1}}$.*

14. $\int_0^\infty e^{-x^3} dx.$ $y = x^3$ *Ans. $\Gamma(\frac{4}{3})$.*

15. $\int_0^1 \dfrac{dx}{\sqrt{1 - x^3}}.$ *Ans. $\dfrac{\sqrt{\pi}\,\Gamma(\frac{1}{3})}{3\Gamma(\frac{5}{6})}$.*

16. $\int_0^2 x^2(2 - x)^{13} dx.$ *Ans. $\dfrac{4{,}096}{105}$.*

17. $\int_0^1 \dfrac{dx}{\sqrt{1 - x^4}}.$ *Ans. $\dfrac{\sqrt{\pi}\,\Gamma(\frac{1}{4})}{4\Gamma(\frac{3}{4})}$.*

18. $\int_0^1 \dfrac{x^6\,dx}{\sqrt[3]{1 - x^5}}.$ *Ans. $\dfrac{9}{32}\dfrac{\Gamma(\frac{7}{5})\Gamma(\frac{5}{3})}{\Gamma(\frac{16}{15})}$.*

19. $\int_2^4 (x - 2)^{-1/6}(4 - x)^{-5/6} dx.$ *Ans. $\Gamma(\frac{5}{6})\Gamma(\frac{1}{6})$.*

20. $\int_1^4 (x - 1)^{-1/4}(4 - x)^{-3/4} dx.$ *Ans. $\Gamma(\frac{3}{4},\frac{1}{4})$.*

21. $\int_0^{\pi/2} \sqrt{\dfrac{\sin^5 x}{\cos x}}\, dx.$ *Ans. $\frac{3}{8}\Gamma(\frac{1}{4})\Gamma(\frac{3}{4})$.*

22. $\int_0^{\pi/2} \cot^{2/3} x\, dx.$ *Ans. $\frac{1}{2}\Gamma(\frac{5}{6})\Gamma(\frac{1}{6})$.*

23. $30 \int_0^\infty \dfrac{x^k\,dx}{(1 + x)^6}$ for $k = 0, 1, 2, 3, 4$ $\left(\text{substitute } x = \dfrac{y}{1 - y}\right).$

     Ans. $6, \frac{3}{2}, 1, \frac{3}{2}, 6$.

24. $\int_0^1 x^2 \left(\ln \dfrac{1}{x}\right)^3 dx$ (substitute $y = -\ln x$).   *Ans. $\frac{2}{27}$.*

25. $\int_0^\infty \dfrac{dx}{1 + x^4} \left(\text{let } x^4 = \dfrac{y}{1 - y}\right).$ *Ans. $\frac{1}{4}\Gamma(\frac{1}{4})\Gamma(\frac{3}{4})$.*

26. $\int_0^\infty \dfrac{x\,dx}{1 + x^6}.$ *Ans. $\frac{1}{6}\Gamma(\frac{1}{3})\Gamma(\frac{2}{3})$.*

27. A combination lock is opened by making three (or more) turns to the right, stopping at digit A, then two turns to the left, stopping at digit B, and finally one more turn to the right, stopping at digit C, where A, B, C are not necessarily different. How many different combinations are possible if the three digits are selected from the single numerals $0, 1, \ldots, 9$?   *Ans. 1,000.*

28. In experiments to improve the quality of a certain manufactured material, it is decided to try three different temperature levels, three different reagents, and two alternative methods of hardening. How many distinct trials are necessary if one temperature level, one reagent, and one method of hardening must be chosen in each case? *Ans.* 18.

29. How many three-digit numbers can be formed from the integers 1, 2, 3, 4, 5 if there are no restrictions on the number of repetitions of any integer? If no integer may occur more than twice in a particular number? If no repetitions are allowed? *Ans.* 125, 120, 60.

30. In how many different orders can four tires be placed on four wheels if (as is normally the case) all tires are interchangeable? If two of them are snow tires, which must be put on the rear wheels? *Ans.* 24, 4.

31. Five brands of cigarettes A, B, C, D, E are ranked in order of preference by individual smokers. How many distinct rankings (ruling out ties) are possible? In what per cent of these is brand A ranked best? *Ans.* 120, 20 per cent.

32. A man regularly drives five children to school, two in the front seat and three in back. Each child wants a turn at the front seat, and the window positions are preferred, both front and back. As a minimum, how many trips will it take before each child has occupied all possible places exactly once? What is the smallest number of trips needed for each child to occupy each place at least once if two of the children insist on sitting side by side? *Ans.* 5, 7.

33. From ten employees, a skeleton force of four must be chosen each week to work on Saturday. Each force must include one supervisor, a job for which only three of the people qualify. If none of the latter group ever serve in a nonsupervisory capacity on Saturdays, how many different selections of the skeleton force are possible? How does a supervisor compare with a regular worker as to the relative number of Saturdays each has to work? *Ans.* 105, ⅞.

34. A joint committee of four members is formed by choosing two members each from the executive boards (each made up of six people) of two organizations. Once formed, the committee chooses one of its members as chairman. Regarding committees with different chairmen as distinct, how many different committees are possible? *Ans.* 900.

35. In how many ways can a committee of five be formed from five women and seven men if the committee must be made up of two women and three men? Of at least two men and at least one woman? *Ans.* 350, 735.

36. Show that $C(n,r) = C(n-1, r) + C(n-1, r-1)$.

37. By considering the expansion of $(1 + x)^n$ for appropriate values of x show that

$$C(n,1) + C(n,2) + \cdots + C(n,n) = 2^n - 1$$

and $\qquad C(n,0) - C(n,1) + C(n,2) - \cdots (-1)^n C(n,n) = 0$

38. Suppose that by some method of forecasting it could be determined that the weather in store for the next week would be three fair, two cloudy, and two rainy days. How many different seven-day sequences answering to this description are possible? *Ans.* 210.

CHAPTER 2

PROBABILITY CONCEPTS

2-1. Introduction. A common type of phenomenon observed in many areas of human experience is characterized by the production of a series of events which are rather definitely fixed as to their possible distinct forms but haphazard as to the order in which one form follows upon another, or alternatively, by the generation of a quantitative variable having a fairly well-defined range of possible values but no consistent rule of progression. Despite the absence of any discernible law of serial order, there usually exists a striking similarity between the proportionate compositions of any pair of long records of the same phenomenon. The observed regularity of proportion in random series is the empirical basis for the so-called *laws of chance*, which are the subject matter of the *theory of probability*.

Controversies over the philosophical foundation of the theory of probability have been going on for many years. Points of view have ranged from the consideration of probability as a mathematical property of an abstract system to the definition of it as a measure of credibility or as an aspect of human psychology. Notwithstanding this diversity of thought as to the philosophical foundation, there has been almost universal agreement as to the mathematical superstructure.

The essential mathematical properties which probability must possess (and about which there is no argument) suffice to establish the theory of probability on an axiomatic basis as a rigorous branch of pure mathematics. Like the axioms of Euclidean geometry, those of probability represent idealizations of practical experience, or extensions of elementary principles of logic. Since the axioms appear arbitrary when stated without reference to their rational background, we shall indicate something of their conceptual origin by sketching two earlier approaches to the subject. Thus, the reader should not assume from the following discussions that the approaches to probability followed are the only ones possible, since many of the objections to the following definitions have been clarified in more recent axiomatic approaches.

The two earlier approaches to probability which we shall consider here are usually known as the *classical theory* and the *relative-frequency theory*, although in a sense both involve relative frequency. The crucial distinction between the two is that the classical theory presupposes a priori

12

knowledge, while the relative-frequency theory is developed in terms of observational data. Both of them have some appeal to the intuition.

We shall use the term *experiment* to denote any clearly defined procedure which is to be carried out (such as the tossing of a coin), while the term *trial* will be used to denote a single carrying out of the experiment. An *event* will be a possible result of a single trial. The following definitions of probability will involve the probability of the occurrence of a specific event. Denoting a specific event by the symbol E, we shall use the notation $\bar{E}$ for the absence of E or the failure of E to occur. The events E and $\bar{E}$ are said to be *complementary*, inasmuch as either one or the other is bound to occur; they are also *mutually exclusive*, for they cannot coexist. The symbol $P(E)$ is used to denote the probability of the occurrence of E and $P(\bar{E})$ to denote the probability of the nonoccurrence of E.

2-2. The Classical Theory. The classical theory of probability is founded upon the indefinable concept of *equally likely* events. Suppose that the possible outcomes of an experiment, reduced to their simplest cases, are $c_1, c_2, \ldots, c_n$—these being mutually exclusive and exhaustive (no other possibilities exist). Then, under the classical theory, the statement that these cases are equally likely is understood to mean that

$$P(c_1) = P(c_2) = \cdots = P(c_n) = \frac{1}{n}$$

A subgroup of these cases is called *favorable* to an event E if E occurs when and only when any one of this subgroup occurs. By this device, the definition of probability is extended beyond equally likely events: if a of the equally likely cases $c_1, c_2, \ldots, c_n$ are favorable to E, then $P(E)$ is defined as a/n. As the number a varies from its mathematical minimum of zero to its maximum of n, we thus see that the mathematically possible range of values of $P(E)$ is 0 to 1. If a of the c's are favorable to E, then $n - a$ must be unfavorable; hence, by definition, the same $n - a$ cases are favorable to $\bar{E}$, and $P(\bar{E}) = (n - a)/n$. Therefore

$$P(E) + P(\bar{E}) = 1$$

As an example of the classical approach, consider the probability that a five will be turned up on the toss of a single die. The six faces of the die constitute six mutually exclusive, exhaustive cases; thus, assuming these to be equally likely, we have $P(5) = \frac{1}{6}$. What is the probability of turning up an odd number? Representing this event by E, we see that there are three favorable cases: one, three, and five. Hence $P(E) = \frac{3}{6} = \frac{1}{2}$.

The assumption that the faces are equally likely is physically justified only to the extent that the balance of the die and the method of throwing do not favor one face more than another. The practical impossibility of manufacturing a perfect die or of making an unbiased throw is ignored. On the other hand, when the die and the tossing are idealized, equal likelihood is the only reasonable assumption, and in a real situation the effect of imperfections may be negligible.

Because the classical theory defines probability in terms of equally probable events, it may be assailed on the grounds of circular reasoning. This objection, however, loses its force when the classical definition is interpreted as the assertion of the existence of a basic concept which cannot be reduced to simpler ideas but is definable only in terms of its properties. Irreducibility is the distinctive characteristic of any fundamental concept, element, or unit, and it is so recognized in all branches of science.

A strong practical objection to the classical theory is its complete dependence upon a priori analysis. The theory can be applied only when one is able to set up a mathematical model which incorporates all possibilities and leads to the correct identification of equally likely events. In simple situations this can be done; but as a rule, a priori knowledge is insufficient to determine the probabilities of various possible events, and it is necessary to estimate them empirically. In the past, certain notable exponents of the classical theory attempted to make up for deficiencies in a priori knowledge by assigning arbitrary values (usually one-half) to any unknown probabilities. The conclusions arrived at in this fashion were often absurd and, even when plausible, had no essential bearing on the truth. Just as area, volume, and mass are objective properties of physical bodies under fixed conditions, so probability is an objective property of a system of events under fixed conditions, and assumptions having no factual basis are out of place.

As an example of the difficulty that one meets in applying the classical theory, let us consider a hypothetical experiment in which a very large number of people are asked to draw a chord at random inside a circle of given radius R. After the chords are drawn, an equilateral triangle is inscribed in the circle, and the problem is to deduce from probability considerations what percentage of the chords may be expected to be longer than the side of the triangle. From different a priori assumptions as to what events are equally likely, the classical theory can give a variety of answers, two of which can be obtained by the following arguments. In any case, the expected percentage is simply 100 times the corresponding probability.

Represent the chord as AB (Fig. 2-1a). In our first analysis, we construct the tangent CD at the point A and let ϕ denote the angle which the chord makes with the tangent. Measuring ϕ in the conventional counterclockwise direction, let us make the assumption that all values of ϕ from 0 to 180° inclusive are equally likely. Now to determine the condi-

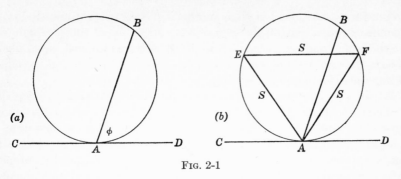

Fig. 2-1

tions under which the length of AB exceeds the length S of the inscribed equilateral triangle, let us construct the triangle so that A is one of the vertices. Then, referring to Fig. 2-1b, we know from plane geometry that side AF makes an angle of 60° with CD and that side AE makes an angle of 120° with CD. Hence the length of AB will exceed S provided that ϕ lies between 60 and 120°. Since this favorable range is one-third the total range, the probability in question is $\frac{1}{3}$. For the reader who wonders what effect the exclusion of the end points 60 and 120° of the favorable range has on the probability, we state here that because of continuity, this exclusion is immaterial; the general principle will be expounded in Chap. 4.

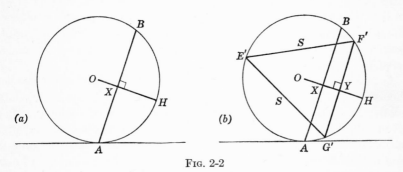

Fig. 2-2

In our second analysis, we bisect the chord AB by the radius OH (length R) and let X denote the point of intersection (Fig. 2-2a). Then the distance $\overline{OX}$ can range from zero to R, and we shall now assume that all of these values are equally likely. This time, to compare the length of AB to S, we locate the triangle $E'F'G'$ so that one side $F'G'$ is bisected by OH, the point of intersection being Y. From Fig. 2-2b it is clear that the length of AB exceeds S when $\overline{OX}$ is less than $\overline{OY}$. From plane geometry it is easy to show that OH and $F'G'$ are perpendicular bisectors of each other, whence $\overline{OY} = R/2$. Consequently, the chord length exceeds S for half of the possible range of values of $\overline{OX}$. By this second analysis, therefore, the probability in question is $\frac{1}{2}$.

The fact that these two answers are different implies that the initial assumptions are incompatible. That is, if the values of ϕ are equally likely, then the values of $\overline{OX}$ cannot be equally likely, and vice versa. We shall consider this question of functional dependence further in Chap. 6.

2-3. The Relative-frequency Theory. The relative-frequency theory of probability is founded upon an observational concept. A record is kept of the number of times (say n_1) that a certain event E occurs in n trials of an appropriate experiment. The ratio n_1/n is called the *relative frequency* of the event E, and the complementary ratio $(n - n_1)/n$, the relative frequency of $\bar{E}$. Denoting the two relative frequencies by $R(E)$ and $R(\bar{E})$ respectively, we see that each has a mathematically possible range of 0 to 1 and that $R(E) + R(\bar{E}) \equiv 1$. We have previously made a point of the regularity of proportion in random series. By this we mean the tendency of relative frequencies to stabilize at definite values as the number of trials increases. This tendency has been verified experimentally on numerous occasions and seems to be inherent in the nature of random phenomena. Therefore, the *existence of a limiting value is postulated*, and the probability $P(E)$ of the event E is defined as the limit approached by the relative frequency as the number of trials increases indefinitely:

$$P(E) \equiv \lim_{n \to \infty} \frac{n_1}{n} \equiv \lim_{n \to \infty} R(E)$$

Similarly

$$P(\bar{E}) \equiv \lim_{n \to \infty} \frac{n - n_1}{n} \equiv \lim_{n \to \infty} R(\bar{E}) \quad \text{and} \quad P(E) + P(\bar{E}) = 1$$

A definition of this type is known as an *operational definition*, so called because the term defined by it is the result of a prescribed operation or series of operations. Such definitions have proved very useful in ridding experimental science of a great deal of ambiguity and confusion. From the mathematical standpoint, however, an operational definition is decidedly awkward, because mathematical rigor requires immutable classifications. Therefore, an axiomatic development is more appropriate for the mathematical theory, although empirical estimates of probability are obtained from relative frequencies. A limit in the ordinary sense of mathematics would be more satisfactory as the basis of a mathematical theory, but an operational limit does not have the same rigorous definition as a mathematical one. This difference between mathematical convergence and the convergence described here as operational will become increasingly clear as subsequent material is developed.

As an illustration of the relative-frequency definition of probability, consider a blood-typing survey conducted in Massachusetts by Mac-Cready and Manin in 1951. Out of 150,064 persons tested, 125,055 were found to possess the type of blood classified as Rh D-positive. Hence, the relative frequency of Rh D-positive is approximately .833. In so far as the people tested constituted a representative cross section of all human beings, we may regard the stated relative frequency as an estimate of the probability of Rh D-positive in the entire human race, or more specifically, as an estimate of the probability of Rh D-positive among the residents of Massachusetts. The true probability only exists for an instantaneous point in time because of deaths and births, but it can be estimated to greater accuracy by taking larger samples at that single instant of time. Strictly speaking, when samples must be taken over a period of time, one is not estimating a quantity which is actually the limit of n_1/n as $n \to \infty$. This limit is, of course, essential to the definition, and this example illustrates one of the practical difficulties in empirical estimates of probability. However, empirical estimates are necessary, and we have to accept their inherent limitations.

2-4. Properties of Relative Frequencies. Although fundamentally different in concept, the classical theory and the relative-frequency theory agree in defining probability as a ratio. As a consequence, both theories yield the same basic laws of probability, because these are derived from the algebraic properties of ratios. Let us therefore examine some of these properties.

Property 1. For a single event E we have already noted that $R(E)$ is a real number lying somewhere in the range 0 to 1 and such that $R(E) + R(\bar{E}) = 1$.

Now consider two events A and B, which may exist simultaneously. All possible results of a given experiment may be classified under some one of four mutually exclusive categories: (A,B), $(A,\bar{B})$, $(\bar{A},B)$, $(\bar{A},\bar{B})$—representing the simultaneous occurrence of A and B, the simultaneous occurrence of A and $\bar{B}$, etc. Denoting the respective numbers of occurrences by n_1, n_2, n_3, n_4, and the total by n, we may summarize the results as shown in Table 2-1. The total number of occurrences of A is $n_1 + n_2$,

TABLE 2-1

Category	(A,B)	$(A,\bar{B})$	$(\bar{A},B)$	$(\bar{A},\bar{B})$	Total
Number of occurrences	n_1	n_2	n_3	n_4	n

and the total number of occurrences of B is $n_1 + n_3$. Hence the corresponding relative frequencies are

$$R(A) = \frac{n_1 + n_2}{n} \qquad R(B) = \frac{n_1 + n_3}{n}$$

It often happens that a sufficient condition for the occurrence of some contingent result is the single or simultaneous occurrence of two events A, B. The composite event defined by the occurrence of either A or B alone or both together is denoted by the symbol $A + B$. (As an analogy, a joint meeting of two organizations is open to all who belong to either one, including, of course, all who belong to both.) Since the definition of $A + B$ is satisfied by each of the categories (A,B), $(A,\bar{B})$, $(\bar{A},B)$, the relative frequency of $A + B$ is

$$R(A + B) = \frac{n_1 + n_2 + n_3}{n} = \frac{n_1 + n_2}{n} + \frac{n_1 + n_3}{n} - \frac{n_1}{n}$$

Hence,

Property 2

$$R(A + B) = R(A) + R(B) - R(A,B)$$

If the separate quantities n_1, n_2, etc., were known, the most direct method of calculating $R(A + B)$ would, of course, be simply that which follows from the definition, namely $(n_1 + n_2 + n_3)/n$. The point of introducing the formula stated in Property 2 is that most mathematical problems entail the expression of one variable in terms of others, and the relative frequencies $R(A)$, $R(B)$, $R(A,B)$ are usually the ones most readily available from either direct observation or theoretical considerations.

We now introduce the idea of *conditional relative* frequencies. In the theory of probability, the word *conditional* signifies restriction to a special class as distinguished from the *unconditional* inclusion of all possibilities. An event E occurring under condition C is denoted by the symbol $E|C$, read "E given C." A conditional relative frequency is calculated in the same manner as an ordinary (unconditional) relative frequency except that the calculation is confined to those events which satisfy the prescribed criterion (condition). The conditional relative frequency of A given B, denoted by $R(A|B)$, is simply the proportionate number of occurrences of A among all occurrences of B, hence the ratio of the number of simultaneous occurrences of A and B to the total number of occurrences of B:

$$R(A|B) = \frac{n_1}{n_1 + n_3} = \frac{n_1/n}{(n_1 + n_3)/n} = \frac{R(A,B)}{R(B)}$$

By a similar argument we obtain the conditional relative frequency of B given A as

$$R(B|A) = \frac{n_1}{n_1 + n_2} \equiv \frac{R(A,B)}{R(A)}$$

Combining these statements into one chain of relationships, we arrive at

Property 3

$$R(A,B) \equiv R(A)R(B|A) \equiv R(B)R(A|B)$$

The object of expressing Property 3 in the form of a double identity is that the unknown quantity in a problem varies according to the circumstances; hence it is convenient to bring out all of the relationships at once.

2-5. Laws of Probability. A system of axioms for a subject can be formulated in more than one way and yet have the same logical consequences. Couched in the technical terms of modern mathematical analysis, a complete set of axioms for the theory of probability is intelligible only to readers with considerably more background than we wish to presuppose or supply. However, the following three properties, suggested by the behavior of relative frequencies, suffice for most purposes as an axiomatic basis of probability. We call them properties rather than axioms because, aside from formality of statement, a system of axioms should be reduced to the fewest possible assertions, whereas we have chosen an extended form of expression of Property 3 in the interest of convenience.

Property 1 (General Character of Probability). The probability $P(E)$ of an event E is a real number in the range of 0 to 1. The probability of an impossible event is 0, that of an event certain to occur is 1, and in general $P(E) + P(\bar{E}) = 1$.

Property 2 (Law of Total Probability)

$$P(A + B) = P(A) + P(B) - P(A,B)$$

Property 3 (Law of Compound or Joint Probability). If neither $P(A)$ nor $P(B)$ is zero

$$P(A,B) = P(A)P(B|A) = P(B)P(A|B)$$

If either $P(A)$ or $P(B)$ is zero,

$$P(A,B) = 0$$

In a more advanced treatment of this subject, the counterpart of the number of occurrences of an event is a well-defined mathematical quantity known as *measure*. In connection with continuous variables, it is usually possible to interpret measure geometrically as area or volume. One of the paradoxes of an infinite number of possibilities, however, is that a probability of zero does not necessarily imply impossibility, nor does a probability of unity necessarily imply certainty. This may be understood by noting that a relative frequency will approach zero if the numerator remains finite while the denominator approaches infinity, or even if the numerator increases at too slow a rate in comparison with the denominator. Again, from the geometrical point of view, a rectangle may be shrunk to a line, which has zero area but nevertheless the locus exists.

2-6. Fundamental Theorems. The quantity $P(A + B)$ is called the *total probability* of A and B. If two events A, B are *mutually exclusive*, their simultaneous occurrence is impossible, and $P(A,B) = 0$. In that case Property 2 yields $P(A + B) = P(A) + P(B)$. This result can be generalized to any finite number of mutually exclusive events. For let A, B, C be mutually exclusive and set $S = A + B$. Then

$$A + B + C \equiv S + C$$

and

$$P(S + C) = P(S) + P(C) = P(A) + P(B) + P(C)$$

a result which can be extended by induction to any finite number of mutually exclusive events. Hence the following theorem:

THEOREM 2-1 (Law of Total Probability for Mutually Exclusive Events). If A, B, . . . , N are mutually exclusive events, then

$$P(A + B + \cdots + N) = P(A) + P(B) + \cdots + P(N)$$

With regard to an infinite number of events the extension is reasonable but not rigorously demonstrable. Hence one of the axioms in a technically complete set asserts that the extension does hold for an infinite number of mutually exclusive events. We shall take this extension for granted.

From Property 2 we may also deduce a more general theorem applicable to any finite number of events, whether mutually exclusive or not. Let A, B, C be any three events, which need not be mutually exclusive, and as before, set $S = A + B$. Then

$$P(A + B + C) \equiv P(S + C) = P(S) + P(C) - P(S,C)$$
$$= P(A) + P(B) - P(A,B) + P(C) - P(S,C)$$

Now the symbol (S,C) means that C occurs in conjunction with A or B or both and has the same logical import as the expression $(A,C) + (B,C)$ since the simultaneous occurrence of (A,C) and (B,C) implies nothing more nor less than the simultaneous occurrence of A, B, C. Accordingly,

$$P(S,C) \equiv P[(A,C) + (B,C)] = P(A,C) + P(B,C) - P(A,B,C)$$

Therefore

$$P(A + B + C) = P(A) + P(B) + P(C)$$
$$- P(A,B) - P(A,C) - P(B,C) + P(A,B,C)$$

When this result is extended by induction, the following theorem is obtained.

THEOREM 2-2 (General Law of Total Probability). The probability $P(A + B + \cdots + N)$ equals the algebraic sum of the probabilities of the events in all possible distinct combinations: singles, pairs, triples,

. . . , N-tuples. The sign is plus for the odd combinations (singles, triples, etc.) and minus for the even combinations (pairs, quadruples, etc.).

The probability of the simultaneous occurrence of two or more events is called the *compound probability*, or synonymously, the *joint probability*, of the events. The relations stated by Property 3 can be generalized to any finite number of events. Thus, considering the simultaneous occurrence of three events A, B, C, let X denote the simultaneous occurrence of A and B. Then

$$(A,B,C) \equiv (X,C)$$

and $\quad P(A,B,C) = P(X)P(C|X) = P(A)P(B|A)P(C|A,B)$

Since all permutations of the letters A, B, C have the same meaning as regards the simultaneous occurrence of the three events, there are six equivalent expressions of the foregoing type. For example, we also have

$$P(A,B,C) \equiv P(B,C,A) = P(B)P(C|B)P(A|B,C)$$

Continuing in the same vein, we may express the joint probability of any finite number N of events A, B, C, . . . , M, N as the product of N factors, the first of which is the unconditional probability of any particular one of the events chosen arbitrarily, the second, the conditional probability of any particular one of the remaining events given the occurrence of the one first selected, and the general term, the conditional probability of any particular one of the remaining events given the occurrence of those already chosen. In all there are $N!$ equivalent expressions for this same joint probability. Putting this rule in the form of a theorem, we have:

THEOREM 2-3 (General Law of Compound Probability)

$$P(A,B,C, \ldots ,M,N) = P(A)P(B|A)P(C|A,B) \cdots$$
$$P(N|A,B,C, \ldots ,M)$$

A special case of great importance arises when the events are *independent*. In the probability sense, two events A,B are said to be independent when and only when neither one affects the probability of the occurrence of the other. The formal definition of independence is that

$$P(B|A) = P(B) \qquad P(A|B) = P(A)$$

It turns out that each one of these equations implies the other, for if either holds, the joint probability assumes the symmetrical form

$$P(A,B) = P(A)P(B)$$

from which the other equation can be deduced. Consequently, a sufficient *definition of independence* of two events is that their joint probability equals the product of their respective unconditional probabilities. An advantage of this form of definition is that it does not break down when one of the events has zero probability. The reader's attention is called to the fact that *mutually exclusive* events are not independent unless the probability of one of them is zero, for by definition the probability of the simultaneous occurrence of mutually exclusive events is necessarily zero. In general, N events are independent if the probability of each event is unaffected by the occurrence or nonoccurrence of any of the others, either singly or in combination. A formal definition is as follows:

Definition of Independence. The events $A, B, C, \ldots, N$ are mutually independent as a system if the probability of every N-fold combination which can be formed from these events or their complements in any proportion (as $ABC \cdots N; \bar{A}BC \cdots N; A\bar{B}C \cdots N; \ldots; \bar{A}\bar{B}C \cdots N; \ldots; \bar{A}\bar{B}\bar{C} \cdots \bar{N}$) factors into the product of the probabilities of the N components of the combination.

This definition is, of course, both the necessary and sufficient condition for the events to be independent. If, however, the events *are* independent it follows that the joint probability is equal to the product of the individual probabilities. Hence,

THEOREM 2-4 (Law of Compound Probability for Independent Events)

$$P(A,B,C, \ldots,N) = P(A)P(B)P(C) \cdots P(N)$$

Since the 2^N possible N-fold combinations of $A, B, C, \ldots, N$ and $\bar{A}, \bar{B}, \bar{C}, \ldots, \bar{N}$ represent a complete system of mutually exclusive categories, their total probability is necessarily equal to unity. Moreover, the factorization of their probabilities in the case of independence guarantees the analogous probability factorization of all possible combinations of any subset of the initial N events and hence the independence of any subset. (This fact may be established by applying the law of total probability to a typical subset.) On the other hand, the independence of subsets does not suffice for the independence of the entire system.

The definition of independence for a system of events is illustrated by the following example, in which the dependence or independence of three events A, B, C is determined under four different hypothetical situations, each giving rise to its own set of compound probabilities, as shown in Table 2-2. Under the first three situations, $P(A) = P(B) = P(C) = \frac{1}{2}$.

Under situation I, some of the compound probabilities factor just as they would for independent events—in particular, the triple combination ABC for

$$P(A,B,C) = \frac{1}{8} = P(A)P(B)P(C)$$

and the same is true of three others: $A\bar{B}C$, $\bar{A}BC$, $\bar{A}\bar{B}C$. Furthermore, the two events A, C are independent as a pair, for

$$P(A,C) = P(A,B,C) + P(A,\bar{B},C)$$
$$= \tfrac{1}{8} + \tfrac{1}{8} = \tfrac{1}{4} = P(A)P(C)$$

Nevertheless the three events A, B, C are not mutually independent as a system, because not all of the compound probabilities yield the requisite

TABLE 2-2. COMPOUND PROBABILITIES OF THREE EVENTS UNDER
FOUR HYPOTHETICAL SITUATIONS

Joint event	Situation I	Situation II	Situation III	Situation IV
ABC	$\tfrac{1}{8}$	$\tfrac{1}{4}$	$\tfrac{1}{8}$	$\alpha\beta\gamma + \epsilon$
$AB\bar{C}$	0	0	$\tfrac{1}{8}$	$\alpha\beta(1 - \gamma) - \epsilon$
$A\bar{B}C$	$\tfrac{1}{8}$	0	$\tfrac{1}{8}$	$\alpha(1 - \beta)\gamma - \epsilon$
$A\bar{B}\bar{C}$	$\tfrac{1}{4}$	$\tfrac{1}{4}$	$\tfrac{1}{8}$	$\alpha(1 - \beta)(1 - \gamma) + \epsilon$
$\bar{A}BC$	$\tfrac{1}{4}$	0	$\tfrac{1}{8}$	$(1 - \alpha)\beta\gamma - \epsilon$
$\bar{A}B\bar{C}$	$\tfrac{1}{8}$	$\tfrac{1}{4}$	$\tfrac{1}{8}$	$(1 - \alpha)\beta(1 - \gamma) + \epsilon$
$\bar{A}\bar{B}C$	0	$\tfrac{1}{4}$	$\tfrac{1}{8}$	$(1 - \alpha)(1 - \beta)\gamma + \epsilon$
$\bar{A}\bar{B}\bar{C}$	$\tfrac{1}{8}$	0	$\tfrac{1}{8}$	$(1 - \alpha)(1 - \beta)(1 - \gamma) - \epsilon$

factorization. This failure is evident in the case of the four remaining triple combinations $(AB\bar{C}, A\bar{B}\bar{C}, \bar{A}BC, \bar{A}\bar{B}C)$, and it also occurs in the two pairs of events A, B and B, C for

$$P(A,B) = \tfrac{1}{8} \neq P(A)P(B)$$
$$P(B,C) = \tfrac{3}{8} \neq P(B)P(C)$$

Under situation II, the events A, B, C are clearly dependent, for none of the triple combinations yields the factorization required for independence. Nevertheless, all of the pairs meet this criterion, for

$$P(A,B) = \tfrac{1}{4} = P(A)P(B)$$
$$P(A,C) = \tfrac{1}{4} = P(A)P(C)$$
$$P(B,C) = \tfrac{1}{4} = P(B)P(C)$$

Thus the events are pairwise independent and yet dependent as a whole system.

Under situation III, the events are independent.

Situation IV was constructed by setting $P(A) = \alpha$, $P(B) = \beta$, $P(C) = \gamma$ and requiring the events to be pairwise independent, as in situation II. If, in addition, we require that $P(A,B,C) = P(A)P(B)P(C) = \alpha\beta\gamma$, we have $\epsilon = 0$, and the events become independent, as shown by the factorization of the probabilities of all triple combinations. With N events instead of three, we could have independent subsets of all orders less than N and still have the N-fold system dependent.

2-7. General Comments. Since the outcome of a contemplated action is often in doubt prior to its performance, the major use of probability

lies in making judicious guesses, for probability represents the summary
and generalization of experience.   A considered decision to pursue a
stated course of action is usually reached by weighing the odds associated
with various possible outcomes, in so far as these eventualities can be fore-
seen.   In several contexts, but conspicuously in this one, certain loosely
phrased expressions have become so much a part of the accepted terminology of probability that they have acquired special idiomatic significance of their own.   After the fact, the outcome of a particular action is
uniquely determined; therefore, with reference to a single situation the
probability of any designated event is either one or zero, depending upon
whether it does or does not correspond to the actual result.   Understood
as a ratio, probability has only this trivial interpretation as applied to
unique happenings, and we agree not to use the term probability in this
sense.   Hence, when we say that A has a probability p of succeeding in a
proposed enterprise, what we really mean is that according to available
records on comparable cases, the relative frequency of successes is p.
How pertinent the records themselves are may be open to question, but
improving the estimate of probability by sharpening the classification is
a project for research.

Practical applications of the theory of probability call for an intelligent
combination of empirical knowledge and mathematical deduction.   The
basic probabilities are estimated by computing the appropriate relative
frequencies from observational data, or in sufficiently clear-cut situations,
they are inferred from a priori considerations according to the classical
tradition.   The probabilities of various composite events are then derived
by applying the laws of probability to the component events, single or
joint.   Separate estimates are needed for joint probabilities unless the
assumption of independence is justified.   Incidentally, the use of the
classical model in practical research is intended merely as a short cut to,
and idealization of, results potentially obtainable from relative frequencies.   When it is necessary to keep track of the chronological order
of events, the natural procedure of setting up chronological classifications
or of introducing time as an explicit variable is sometimes analytically
inconvenient.   By exercising proper care in the definition of terms, it is
nearly always possible to regard any particular sequence of events as a
simultaneous occurrence in the logical present.

2-8. Illustrations of General Principles.   The ideas thus far developed
equip us to solve a wide variety of problems.   The following simple examples are presented in order to put the definitions to work and demonstrate
the application of general principles.

Example 2-1.   Alta and Webster City are two weather stations in Iowa.   Letting
A and W denote the occurrence of rain at Alta and Webster City respectively during
any 24-hr period in the month of June, it is found that $P(A) = P(W) = .40$ and

$P(A,W) = .28$. Determine the two conditional probabilities $P(A|W)$ and $P(W|A)$ as well as the total probability $P(A + W)$. Are A and W independent? The conditional probabilities are found by using Property 3. Here,

$$P(A|W) = \frac{P(A,W)}{P(W)} = \frac{.28}{.40} = .70$$

$$P(W|A) = \frac{P(A,W)}{P(A)} = \frac{.28}{.40} = .70$$

The total probability is found by using Property 2.

$$P(A + W) = P(A) + P(W) - P(A,W)$$
$$= .40 + .40 - .28 = .52$$

The two events are not independent since $P(A|W) \neq P(A)$ or equivalently, $P(A,B) \neq P(A)P(B)$.

Example 2-2. Given $P(A) = \alpha$, $P(B) = \beta$, and $P(A,B) = \alpha\beta$, prove that $P(A,\bar{B})$, $P(\bar{A},B)$, and $P(\bar{A},\bar{B})$ factor as they should in accordance with the general definition of independence. By Property 1 we have $P(\bar{A}) = 1 - P(A) = 1 - \alpha$ and $P(\bar{B}) = 1 - P(B) = 1 - \beta$. Now there are two exhaustive mutually exclusive ways in which event A can occur; namely, in conjunction with B or in conjunction with $\bar{B}$. Therefore, by Theorem 2-1 (Total Probability for Mutually Exclusive Events),

$$P(A) = P(A,B) + P(A,\bar{B})$$

whence, by substitution,
$$\alpha = \alpha\beta + P(A,\bar{B})$$
$$P(A,\bar{B}) = \alpha - \alpha\beta = \alpha(1 - \beta) = P(A)P(\bar{B})$$
Similarly,
$$P(B) = P(A,B) + P(\bar{A},B)$$
$$\beta = \alpha\beta + P(\bar{A},B)$$
$$P(\bar{A},B) = (1 - \alpha)\beta = P(\bar{A})P(B)$$

Finally, since the four pairs of events (A,B), $(A,\bar{B})$, $(\bar{A},B)$, $(\bar{A},\bar{B})$ are exhaustive, their total probability is unity by Property 1, and since they are mutually exclusive, we may apply Theorem 2-1 to obtain

$$P(A,B) + P(A,\bar{B}) + P(\bar{A},B) + P(\bar{A},\bar{B}) = 1$$

By substitution, therefore,

$$P(\bar{A},\bar{B}) = 1 - \alpha\beta - \alpha(1 - \beta) - (1 - \alpha)\beta$$
$$= 1 - \alpha(\beta + 1 - \beta) - (1 - \alpha)\beta$$
$$= (1 - \alpha)(1 - \beta) = P(\bar{A})P(\bar{B})$$

Alternatively, this last result can be obtained in the same manner as the first two. Thus

$$P(\bar{A}) = P(\bar{A},B) + P(\bar{A},\bar{B})$$
$$1 - \alpha = (1 - \alpha)\beta + P(\bar{A},\bar{B})$$
$$P(\bar{A},\bar{B}) = (1 - \alpha)(1 - \beta) = P(\bar{A})P(\bar{B})$$

Therefore, the requirement of factorization is satisfied in all cases, and the simple definition of independence as given for two events agrees with the general definition, as of course it should.

Example 2-3. An electrical mechanism containing four switches will fail to operate unless all of them are closed. In the probability sense, the switches are independent with regard to proper closing or failure to close, and for each switch the probability of failure is .1. Find the probability of failure of the whole mechanism, neglecting all sources of failure except switches. Letting F denote failure and $\bar{F}$ the complementary event that the mechanism operates, we apply Property 1 and write

$$P(F) = 1 - P(\bar{F})$$

Letting S_1 denote the event that switch 1 is closed and $\bar{S}_1$ the complementary event that it is open, we are given that $P(\bar{S}_1) = .1$, whence

$$P(S_1) = 1 - P(\bar{S}_1) = .9$$

and similarly for the other switches. Now the mechanism operates only when all switches are closed, and this corresponds to the compound event (S_1,S_2,S_3,S_4), whence

$$P(\bar{F}) = P(S_1,S_2,S_3,S_4)$$

Applying Theorem 2-4, the Law of Compound Probability for Independent Events, we have

$$P(S_1,S_2,S_3,S_4) = P(S_1)P(S_2)P(S_3)P(S_4)$$
$$= (.9)(.9)(.9)(.9) = (.9^4) = .6561$$

Hence $P(\bar{F}) = .6561$ and

$$P(F) = 1 - .6561 = .3439$$

This is the simplest way of solving the problem, but it is instructive to solve it in another way using Theorem 2-2. Since the mechanism will fail whenever one or more of the switches fail to close, the event F is equivalent to the composite event $(\bar{S}_1 + \bar{S}_2 + \bar{S}_3 + \bar{S}_4)$. We have to use the general law of total probability, because the events are independent and, therefore, certainly not mutually exclusive. By Theorem 2-2, then,

$$P(F) = P(\bar{S}_1 + \bar{S}_2 + \bar{S}_3 + \bar{S}_4) = P(\bar{S}_1) + P(\bar{S}_2) + P(\bar{S}_3) + P(\bar{S}_4) - P(\bar{S}_1,\bar{S}_2)$$
$$- P(\bar{S}_1,\bar{S}_3) - P(\bar{S}_1,\bar{S}_4) - P(\bar{S}_2,\bar{S}_3) - P(\bar{S}_2,\bar{S}_4) - P(\bar{S}_3,\bar{S}_4) + P(\bar{S}_1,\bar{S}_2,\bar{S}_3)$$
$$+ P(\bar{S}_1,\bar{S}_2,\bar{S}_4) + P(\bar{S}_1,\bar{S}_3,\bar{S}_4) + P(\bar{S}_2,\bar{S}_3,\bar{S}_4) - P(\bar{S}_1,\bar{S}_2,\bar{S}_3,\bar{S}_4)$$

By inspection we note that there are four single events, six pairs, four triples, and one quadruple. Since the events are independent, the compound probabilities equal the products of the corresponding single probabilities, and since these are uniform we may collect terms of like degree as follows:

$$P(F) = 4(.1) - 6(.1^2) + 4(.1^3) - (.1^4)$$
$$= .4 - .06 + .004 - .0001$$
$$= .3439$$

Accordingly, although this alternative method of solution is far more complicated than the first and not to be recommended in a situation to which that one applies, it yields the correct answer and illustrates the general fact that all methods employing appropriate mathematical principles in valid ways will lead to the same results.

Example 2-4. Sixty orders are to be filled in a warehouse, and it is known that five of them are for a certain item A. If these 60 orders are filled at random, what is the probability that the first and fourth orders are for item A and that simultaneously the second and third are not? What is the probability that at least two orders of item A are in the first four orders to be filled?

Let A denote the event that a particular order being filled is for item A and let $\bar{A}$ denote the complementary event that it is not for item A. Since the probability that a particular order falls in a specified class (whether A or $\bar{A}$) is affected by the number of orders of the same class already filled, this problem illustrates the General Law of

Compound Probability (Theorem 2-3). A good way to attack the problem is to imagine a deck of 60 cards, all alike except that 5 of them are marked A and 55 marked $\bar{A}$. The random filling of orders may be thought of as dealing the cards from a thoroughly shuffled deck, so that all cards available on a given trial have equal chances of being picked. The event that the first and fourth orders are for item A and the second and third are not corresponds to dealing the card sequence $A, \bar{A}, \bar{A}, A$. Since there are 5 cards marked A, the probability that the first card will be an A is $5/60$. On the second trial, there are 59 cards in the deck, and 55 are marked $\bar{A}$. Hence the conditional probability that the second card will be an $\bar{A}$ is $55/59$. On the third trial, there are 58 cards, 54 of which are marked $\bar{A}$; consequently, the conditional probability that the third card is an $\bar{A}$ is $54/58$. Finally, on the fourth trial, there remain 57 cards, 4 of which are marked A, and so the conditional probability that the fourth card is an A is $4/57$. Therefore, multiplying these together in accordance with Theorem 2-3, we get

$$P(A,\bar{A},\bar{A},A) = (5/60)(55/59)(54/58)(4/57) = \frac{59{,}400}{11{,}703{,}240} = .0051$$

The probability of the event E that at least two orders of item A are among the first four to be filled is equal to $1 - P(\bar{E})$ where $\bar{E}$ denotes the event that the first four orders contain less than two A's, hence zero or one. Now the probability of no A is given by

$$P(0) = P(\bar{A},\bar{A},\bar{A},\bar{A}) = (55/60)(54/59)(53/58)(52/57) = \frac{8{,}185{,}320}{11{,}703{,}240} = .6994$$

Since one A can occur in four mutually exclusive ways, its total probability is

$$P(1) = P(A,\bar{A},\bar{A},\bar{A}) + P(\bar{A},A,\bar{A},\bar{A}) + P(\bar{A},\bar{A},A,\bar{A}) + P(\bar{A},\bar{A},\bar{A},A)$$
$$= (5/60)(55/59)(54/58)(53/57) + (55/60)(5/59)(54/58)(53/57)$$
$$+ (55/60)(54/59)(5/58)(53/57) + (55/60)(54/59)(53/58)(5/57)$$

Noticing that the denominators are the same in all cases and that the numerators differ only as to the order in which the numbers appear, we conclude that all of these probabilities are equal and that

$$P(1) = \frac{4(787{,}050)}{11{,}703{,}240} = \frac{3{,}148{,}200}{11{,}703{,}240} = .2690$$

Therefore, $P(\bar{E}) = P(0) + P(1) = .9684$

and the required probability is

$$P(E) = 1 - P(\bar{E}) = .0316$$

Example 2-5. A batch of N items contains k defective ones, although the majority $N - k$ are up to specification. If n items are picked out at random, what is the probability that the first c of them $(c < k)$ are defective while the remaining $n - c$ items are not? What is the total probability that exactly c out of n items picked at random will be defective? The principles involved in this problem are much the same as those in Example 2-4. From Theorem 2-3, the probability $P(E)$ of obtaining a sequence of c defective items followed by $n - c$ standard items is given by the product of fractions, such that each numerator equals the available number of items in the stated class at the commencement of the trial represented, and each denominator equals the corresponding total number of all items. Hence

$$P(E) = \frac{k}{N} \frac{k-1}{N-1} \cdots \frac{k+1-c}{N+1-c} \frac{N-k}{N-c} \frac{N-k-1}{N-c-1} \cdots \frac{N-k+1-n+c}{N+1-n}$$

We may express this result more compactly if we multiply and divide it by the quantity

$$\frac{(k - c)!(N - k - n + c)!}{(N - n)!}$$

which we then incorporate with the original expression to obtain

$$P(E) = \frac{k!(N - k)!(N - n)!}{N!(k - c)!(N - k - n + c)!} \tag{2-1}$$

The probability of any other sequence with c defectives in n trials would be computed in the same fashion. As we observed in Example 2-4, the numerator factors, though occurring in a different order, would involve the same set of numbers and thus yield the same product as before, while the denominator factors, being unaltered, would also yield the same product as before. Hence all sequences with c defectives in n trials have the same probability, given by Eq. (2-1). Students are often surprised by this fact, because they erroneously attach special significance to the pattern itself.

The number S of distinct sequences containing exactly c defective items in a total of n is equal to the number of permutations $Pm(n; c, n - c)$ of n things taken n at a time with c being of one type and the rest of another type; that is,

$$S = Pm(n; c, n - c) = \frac{n!}{c!(n - c)!} = C(n,c) \tag{2-2}$$

The total probability, say $P(c)$, of exactly c defectives in n trials is equal to the number of sequences S times their common probability $P(E)$:

$$P(c) = SP(E) = \frac{n!k!(N - k)!(N - n)!}{c!(n - c)!N!(k - c)!(N - k - n + c)!}$$

For algebraic elegance, we regroup these terms, obtaining the formula

$$P(c) = \frac{C(k,c)C(N - k, n - c)}{C(N,n)} \tag{2-3}$$

This is known as the *hypergeometric law of probability*.

In the solution of this problem, we have visualized the sampling process as the drawing of items in sequence, one by one. That this serial concept can sometimes be avoided through an appropriate model is demonstrated by the following alternative method of solving the second part. Fixing our attention on a whole sample of n items, we note that out of a batch of N items there are $C(N,n)$ possible samples which are distinct, one from another, in the sense of differing by at least one individual item. From k defects, we can choose c individuals in $C(k,c)$ different ways, and for each way we must make up the deficit $n - c$ by drawing from the store of $N - k$ standard items. This we can do in $C(N - k, n - c)$ different ways, and so (by the mn rule) there exist $C(k,c)$ times $C(N - k, n - c)$ different samples of n items containing exactly c defectives. Therefore, assuming that all possible distinct samples are equally likely, the required probability is

$$P(c) = \frac{C(k,c)C(N - k, n - c)}{C(N,n)}$$

which agrees with Eq. (2-3).

Example 2-6. An experiment can yield k possible mutually exclusive results $R_1, R_2, \ldots, R_k$, the respective probabilities of which are $p_1, p_2, \ldots, p_k$, and their total probability is unity, that is, $p_1 + p_2 + \cdots + p_k = 1$. In N independent trials of the experiment, what is the total probability of obtaining exactly n_1 results of the first type, n_2 of the second, . . . , and n_k of the kth, where $n_1 + n_2 + \cdots + n_k = N$? Since the trials are independent, the probability of obtaining any particular result R_i on a given trial is wholly unaffected by the results of other trials. Therefore the probability P_s of any stated sequence of results is equal to the product of their separate unconditional probabilities, and so

$$P_s = p_1{}^{n_1} p_2{}^{n_2} \cdots p_k{}^{n_k}$$

The number S of distinct sequences yielding the stated number of results of each kind is equal to $Pm(N;n_1,n_2, \ldots ,n_k)$, and the total probability, say $P(n_1,n_2, \ldots ,n_k)$, is given by the product SP_s; whence

$$P(n_1,n_2, \ldots ,n_k) = \frac{N!}{n_1!n_2! \cdots n_k!} p_1{}^{n_1} p_2{}^{n_2} \cdots p_k{}^{n_k} \tag{2-4}$$

This is known as the *multinomial law of probability*. The name is derived from the fact that the general term of the expansion of the multinomial $(x_1 + x_2 + \cdots + x_k)^N$ is given by an expression of the same form as Eq. (2-4) except that the powers of $p_1, p_2, \ldots , p_k$ in the latter are replaced by corresponding powers of $x_1, x_2, \ldots , x_k$.

The special case with $k = 2$, corresponding to two alternatives $(E, \bar{E})$, is known as the *binomial law of probability*. Noting that $n_2 = N - n_1$ and $p_2 = 1 - p_1$, we have

$$P(n_1,n_2) = \frac{N!}{n_1!(N - n_1)!} p_1{}^{n_1} (1 - p_1)^{N-n_1} \tag{2-5}$$

Since the permutation formula $Pm(N;n_1,n_2)$ for two alternatives reduces to the combination formula $C(N,n_1)$, we may write the binomial law of probability as

$$P(n_1,n_2) = C(N,n_1) p_1{}^{n_1} (1 - p_1)^{N-n_1} \tag{2-6}$$

Example 2-7. An engineer's report on the causes of failure of hot water heaters for home use revealed that 90 per cent of the failures could be ascribed to one of three defects: leaking seams, leaking connections, or pin-point corrosion—the respective probabilities being .4, .3, .2. Neglecting the remote possibility of simultaneous defects and assuming independent trials, what is the probability that a random sample of five failures would contain two instances of leaking seams, two of leaking connections, one of pin-point corrosion, and none due to miscellaneous causes? Under the hypothesis that simultaneous defects are negligible, we may regard the different types of failure as mutually exclusive events, and by including the miscellaneous category, we obtain an exhaustive system. Hence the multinomial law of probability directly applies, and the answer is given by

$$P(2,2,1,0) = \frac{5!}{2!2!1!0!} (.4^2)(.3^2)(.2^1)(.1^0)$$
$$= (30)(.00288) = .0864$$

Example 2-8. The probability of a salesman's making a sale on a single call is $\frac{1}{6}$. What is the probability that he will make at least one sale in the next five calls? What is the probability that he will make four or more sales in these same five calls? Assuming that one call does not affect another (which, of course, may not be strictly true), we apply the binomial law of probability. Letting $P(S,R)$ denote the probability of exactly S sales and R refusals in $S + R$ calls, the probability $P(E)$ of the event that the salesman makes at least one sale is equal to $1 - P(\bar{E})$ where $\bar{E}$ denotes the complementary event that no sales are made.   Here $S + R = 5$ and $\bar{E}$ is equivalent to $(0,5)$ whence

$$P(\bar{E}) = P(0,5) = \frac{5!}{0!5!} (\tfrac{1}{6})^0 (\tfrac{5}{6})^5 = .402$$

and the probability of making at least one sale is

$$P(E) = 1 - P(\bar{E}) = .598$$

The event E' of making four or more sales can occur in two mutually exclusive ways, namely, by making exactly four sales or by making exactly five sales.   Hence

$$\begin{aligned} P(E') &= P(4,1) + P(5,0) \\ &= C(5,4)(\tfrac{1}{6})^4(\tfrac{5}{6})^1 + C(5,5)(\tfrac{1}{6})^5(\tfrac{5}{6})^0 \\ &= .0032 + .0001 = .0033 \end{aligned}$$

Example 2-9.   In matching pennies three people A, B, C flip one coin each at a given signal and then compare results.   If one coin shows a different side from the other two, the "odd man" wins; if all three are alike the toss is repeated until one is different. A "match" is defined as any situation with one coin different from the other two. Assuming fair play with unbiased coins, show that all players have equal chances of winning.   Find the probability that in a series of six such matches, C would lose at least five times.   Indicating the side of a coin by H or T and listing results in the order of players A, B, C we may exhibit the possible match situations and designate the winners as follows:

$$\begin{array}{lll} (H,H,T;C) & (H,T,H;B) & (T,H,H;A) \\ (T,T,H;C) & (T,H,T;B) & (H,T,T;A) \end{array}$$

Since there are six equally likely match situations and each player wins in two of them, all players have equal chances of winning, namely $\tfrac{1}{3}$.   Letting (W,L) signify that player C wins exactly W times and loses exactly L times in $W + L$ trials, the event E of his losing at least five out of six matches can occur in two mutually exclusive ways, $(1,5)$ and $(0,6)$, the respective probabilities of which are given by the binomial law. Therefore,

$$\begin{aligned} P(E) &= P(1,5) + P(0,6) \\ &= C(6,1)(\tfrac{1}{3})^1(\tfrac{2}{3})^5 + C(6,0)(\tfrac{1}{3})^0(\tfrac{2}{3})^6 \\ &= 6(.0439) + 1(.0878) = .351 \end{aligned}$$

2-9. Bayes' Theorem.   Given a set of mutually exclusive events B_1, B_2, $\ldots$, B_n, let us assume that the occurrence of one or another of them is a necessary condition for the occurrence of an event A.   Depending on the circumstances, the B's may precede A in time or may occur simultaneously with A.   From the viewpoint of the logical present, both types of association may be regarded as constituting joint events, and we shall denote the corresponding probabilities by the same symbol $P(B_i,A)$, where B_i is a specific one of the B's.

From Property 3 we have

$$P(B_i,A) = P(B_i)P(A|B_i) = P(A)P(B_i|A)$$

Therefore, the conditional probability of B_i given A is

$$P(B_i|A) = \frac{P(B_i)P(A|B_i)}{P(A)}$$

This conditional probability is understood to mean (in elementary terms) the proportionate number of times that the antecedent (or concomitant) of A is B_i. In connection with the use of probability in deciding upon a course of action, we have previously noted an idiomatic contraction of the precise formulation of the probability statement, and a similar idiom is used in this context. Thus, the following type of question is often propounded: Having observed A on a particular trial, what is the probability that the antecedent was B_i? Taken literally, this question refers to a unique situation and has only the trivial answer of one or zero, as the case may be; but it is really meant to refer (as it were) to the relative frequency of B_i among all situations characterized by the occurrence of A.

While the probability $P(A)$ could be estimated directly as a relative frequency if records were available, it is often more feasible to depend upon mathematical synthesis. For instance, one might have access to a large amount of data on the relative frequencies of the B's but comparatively little data on A. This would be the case if A were a new development in the economic world or perhaps a newly discovered symptom in medical research. Under such circumstances it might be possible to deduce the conditional probabilities $P(A|B_i)(i = 1, 2, \ldots, n)$ from theoretical considerations (typically true of kinematic problems) or to design small-scale experiments by which the conditional probabilities could be estimated. When this is possible, $P(A)$ can be computed from the other information. Since the B's are mutually exclusive, the event A is logically equivalent to the following sum of mutually exclusive events:

$$(B_1, A) + (B_2, A) + \cdots + (B_n, A)$$

Hence, by Theorem 2-1,

$$P(A) = P(B_1, A) + P(B_2, A) + \cdots + P(B_n, A)$$

which, by Property 3, may be expressed as

$$P(A) = P(B_1)P(A|B_1) + P(B_2)P(A|B_2) + \cdots + P(B_n)P(A|B_n)$$

Therefore, substituting this result in the denominator of the expression for $P(B_i|A)$, we obtain what is known as *Bayes' theorem*:

$$P(B_i|A) = \frac{P(B_i)P(A|B_i)}{P(B_1)P(A|B_1) + P(B_2)P(A|B_2) + \cdots + P(B_n)P(A|B_n)}$$

Although Bayes' theorem can be developed rigorously from the basic laws of probability, it is one of the most controversial topics in all probability theory.   One point of attack is the uniqueness of a particular event. However, this point is not peculiar to Bayes' theorem and is wholly avoidable by exercising care in the precise phrasing of statements.   Another criticism, which applies only to inappropriate uses of Bayes' theorem, is that under some conditions a multiplicity of possible antecedents does not exist; there is one and only one B, but its nature is unknown.   This criticism was occasioned by misguided attempts to estimate certain numerical constants as though they were variables instead of fixed quantities.   For this purpose, the use of Bayes' theorem is admittedly fallacious. Again, the theorem has been put in an unfavorable light because many writers on the classical theory have been prone to make gratuitous assumptions as to the probabilities of the respective B's—generally that they were equally likely.   This, of course, is no fault of the theorem itself. These objections notwithstanding, if there does exist a variety of possible antecedents for the event A, and if the component probabilities are properly estimated from data or inferred from legitimate hypotheses, then the use of Bayes' theorem is perfectly sound.

Example 2-10.   Three urns, U_1, U_2, U_3, contain white balls, black balls, and red balls, in different proportions. U_1 contains one white, two black, and three red balls; U_2 contains two white, one black, and one red ball; and U_3 contains four white, five black, and three red balls.   We reach into one urn and draw out two balls, without knowing which urn was sampled.   If it turns out that one ball is white and the other is red, find the respective probabilities that the urn sampled was U_1, that it was U_2, that it was U_3.   Since it is reasonable, in this case, to assume that all three urns are equally likely to have been chosen, we have $P(U_i) = \frac{1}{3}$ ($i = 1, 2, 3$).   The conditional probabilities for the event A are now easily computed on the basis of the knowledge of what is actually present in each urn, so that $P(A|U_1) = \frac{1}{5}$, $P(A|U_2) = \frac{1}{3}$, and $P(A|U_3) = \frac{2}{11}$.   Substituting these values in Bayes' formula we obtain the respective probabilities, which, of course, add up to unity.

$$P(U_1|A) = \frac{(\frac{1}{3})(\frac{1}{5})}{(\frac{1}{3})(\frac{1}{5}) + (\frac{1}{3})(\frac{1}{3}) + (\frac{1}{3})(\frac{2}{11})} = \frac{33}{118}$$

$$P(U_2|A) = \frac{(\frac{1}{3})(\frac{1}{3})}{(\frac{1}{3})(\frac{1}{5}) + (\frac{1}{3})(\frac{1}{3}) + (\frac{1}{3})(\frac{2}{11})} = \frac{55}{118}$$

$$P(U_3|A) = \frac{(\frac{1}{3})(\frac{2}{11})}{(\frac{1}{3})(\frac{1}{5}) + (\frac{1}{3})(\frac{1}{3}) + (\frac{1}{3})(\frac{2}{11})} = \frac{30}{118}$$

Example 2-11.   In the experience of a certain insurance company, customers who have sufficient funds in their checking accounts postdate a check by mistake once in 1,000 times, while customers who write checks on insufficient funds invariably postdate them.   The latter group constitutes 1 per cent of the total.   A cashier receives a postdated check from a customer.   What is the probability that such a customer has insufficient funds?   There are two possible antecedents to this postdated check; namely, the client came from the population of customers with sufficient funds (B_1) where $P(B_1) = .99$ or alternately from the group of customers with insufficient funds (B_2) where $P(B_2) = .01$.   The two conditional probabilities for the event A are now given by the statement of the problem as $P(A|B_1) = .001$ and $P(A|B_2) = 1.00$. Therefore using Bayes' theorem

$$P(B_1|A) = \frac{(.99)(.001)}{(.99)(.001) + (.01)(1.00)} = .09$$

and
$$P(B_2|A) = \frac{(.01)(1.00)}{(.99)(.001) + (.01)(1.00)} = .91$$

Thus the probability that the customer has insufficient funds in his account is .91.

Example 2-12. An unbiased coin is tossed, and if it comes up heads, a black ball is placed in an urn, but if tails, a white ball. This is done four times. Another person now samples the urn by drawing out two balls simultaneously, which turn out to be black. What is the probability that there were two black and two white balls in the urn? Because of the method used in filling the urn, there exist five possibilities for the final color distribution of the four balls, and the probability of the occurrence of each color combination can be computed. They are as follows:

Four white (B_1): $P(B_1) = \frac{1}{16}$
Three white and one black (B_2): $P(B_2) = \frac{4}{16}$
Two white and two black (B_3): $P(B_3) = \frac{6}{16}$
One white and three black (B_4): $P(B_4) = \frac{4}{16}$
Four black (B_5): $P(B_5) = \frac{1}{16}$

Since in this case the event (A) cannot occur with antecedents B_1 and B_2, the conditional probabilities $P(A|B_i)$ $(i = 1, 2)$ must equal zero. The other three conditional probabilities are computed as

$$P(A|B_3) = \frac{1}{C(4,2)} = \frac{1}{6} \qquad P(A|B_4) = \frac{C(3,2)}{C(4,2)} = \frac{1}{2} \qquad P(A|B_5) = 1$$

and therefore the required probability is given by Bayes' formula:

$$P(B_3|A) = \frac{(\frac{6}{16})(\frac{1}{6})}{(\frac{6}{16})(\frac{1}{6}) + (\frac{4}{16})(\frac{1}{2}) + (\frac{1}{16})(1)} = \frac{6}{6 + 12 + 6} = \frac{1}{4}$$

2-10. Geometrical Probability. Many problems of a probability nature present facets which can be solved geometrically. For this reason, we shall now discuss a few simple examples of geometrical probability. This subject introduces in a natural way a broader concept of probability which goes beyond the elementary notion of the number of occurrences of discrete events.

In the nature of geometrical probability, all points under consideration lie within prescribed boundaries, and the probability measure is so defined that the total probability of the admissible region is unity, while that of all exterior space is zero. Since any finite portion of space, no matter how small, contains an infinite number of points, probability cannot be defined in terms of the number of points included. Instead, it is defined in terms of the geometrical measure appropriate to the dimensionality of the admissible region: in one dimension, length; in two dimensions, area; in three dimensions, volume. Although it is perfectly possible to define probability as a variable function of position, in geometrical problems it is usually assumed that the probability measure of any subdivision of the admissible region is directly proportional to the size of the subdivision.   Thus, in one dimension, if the admissible region is a line segment of length R, the probability measure of any included segment of length r is r/R, that of an infinitesimal segment of length dr is dr/R, and that of the whole segment is $R/R = 1$.   The statement "a point is chosen at random" is a conventional expression for the fact that the chosen point can be any point within the region designated, and the probability of its falling within any stated portion of that region is equal to the probability measure of the portion itself.

Example 2-13.   On a straight line segment AB, a point C somewhere between A and B is so located that the distance $a = AC$ is greater than the distance $b = CB$.   Let us choose a point X at random in the segment AC and a point Y at random in segment CB.   What is the probability that the lengths AX, XY, and YB could form a triangle?   Referring to Fig. 2-3, let x be the distance from A to X, and y the distance

FIG. 2-3

from Y to B.   Without regard to whether or not the specified segments could form a triangle, all possible values of x must lie in the range 0 to a, while all possible values of y must lie in the range 0 to b.   We shall call the possible ranges of these two variables the *admissible region*, and by choosing two rectangular coordinates, as shown in Fig. 2-4, we may represent this admissible region by a rectangle of base a and height b.

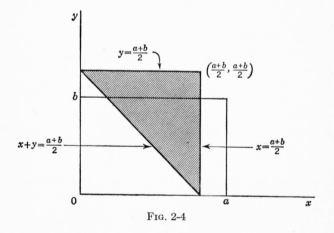

FIG. 2-4

The problem is to determine that portion of the admissible region which includes all points such that the segments may form a triangle.   If the area of this portion is r, then the required probability is r/ab, since the total area of the admissible region is ab.

In order that the three lengths may correspond to the sides of a triangle, it is necessary and sufficient that each length will be less than the sum of the other two lengths. This fact leads to three conditions:

Condition 1:

$$x < (a + b - x - y) + y \qquad \text{that is, } x < \frac{a+b}{2}$$

Condition 2:

$$(a + b - x - y) < x + y \qquad \text{that is, } x + y > \frac{a+b}{2}$$

Condition 3:

$$y < (a + b - x - y) + x \qquad \text{that is, } y < \frac{a+b}{2}$$

Since these three conditions have to be satisfied simultaneously, it is obvious that x must be taken to the left of the straight line $x = (a + b)/2$, that y must be chosen below the straight line $y = (a + b)/2$, and at the same time x and y simultaneously must lie above the straight line $x + y = (a + b)/2$. All of this can be seen geometrically by reference to Fig. 2-4, where the shaded area represents the points which satisfy the three inequalities. Only that portion of the shaded area which overlaps the rectangle will include all points which satisfy all conditions of the problem. Since the area of overlap is $b^2/2$, the probability of the event is

$$P(E) = \frac{b^2/2}{ab} = \frac{b}{2a}$$

Example 2-14. Consider a set of ruled lines infinite in extent and infinite in number. They are parallel, and the distance from one to the next is d. A needle of length a (where a is less than d) is tossed randomly on the set of ruled lines. What is the probability that the needle will intersect one of the ruled lines? This is known as the *Buffon needle problem.* Referring to Fig. 2-5, let the variable x be the perpendicular

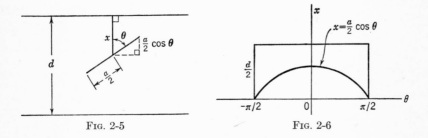

Fig. 2-5   Fig. 2-6

distance from the mid-point of the needle to the nearest line, and let the angle θ be that angle which the needle makes with the perpendicular. Thus x takes on a value at random somewhere between 0 and $d/2$ and the angle θ assumes a value at random somewhere between $-\pi/2$ and $+\pi/2$. From Fig. 2-5, it is apparent that if x is less than $(a/2) \cos \theta$ the needle will intersect one of the straight lines, and if x is greater than that amount, it will fail to intersect. Therefore, the curve $x = (a/2) \cos \theta$ is the boundary between the regions of intersection and nonintersection. Referring to Fig. 2-6, we now have a rectangle of height $d/2$ and base π whose area represents the total field of possible values of x and θ, while the area under the cosine curve is that portion of the admissible region for which the needle intersects the straight lines. Therefore the probability is

$$P(E) = \frac{\int_{-\pi/2}^{\pi/2} (a/2) \cos \theta \, d\theta}{(d/2)\pi} = \frac{2a}{\pi d}$$

Example 2-15. The base x and altitude y of a triangle are obtained by picking points X and Y at random on two line segments of length a and b respectively (see Fig. 2-7). What is the probability that the area of the triangle with base x and altitude y is less than $ab/4$? Since the area of the triangle is given by $xy/2$, this quantity is required to be less than $ab/4$. Now the hyperbola $xy = ab/2$ divides the admissible area, which is a rectangle with base a and altitude b, into parts I and II (see Fig. 2-8).

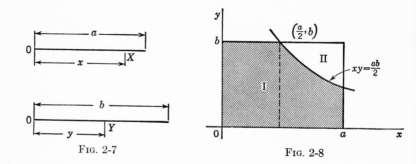

Fig. 2-7   Fig. 2-8

Pairs of values for x and y which fall in area I will determine triangles with area less than $ab/4$ and, of course, those points in II will determine triangles with areas greater than $ab/4$. Therefore, the desired probability is

$$P = \frac{ab/2 + \int_{a/2}^{a} (ab/2x) \, dx}{ab} = \tfrac{1}{2}(1 + \ln 2) = .85$$

Example 2-16. A triangle is cut from a piece of thin sheet metal. This triangle is to be tossed at random upon a ruled board as in Buffon's needle problem. The distance between rulings d is greater than any side of the triangle. What is the probability that the triangular figure will cover any portion of any line? Let the sides of the triangle be denoted by A, B, and C, and their actual lengths by a, b, and c respectively. If a ruled line cuts through the boundary of the triangle it must cut two and only two of the sides. Therefore if it intersects at all, it cuts either A and B, or A and C, or B and C. Let $P(A,B)$, $P(A,C)$, and $P(B,C)$ be the respective probabilities of these happenings. Then the total probability of intersection will be

$$P = P(A,B) + P(A,C) + P(B,C)$$

But the respective probabilities $P(A)$, $P(B)$, $P(C)$ that it intersects any particular one of the sides A, B, C can also be expressed as follows from the law of total probability:

$$P(A) = P(A,B) + P(A,C)$$
$$P(B) = P(A,B) + P(B,C)$$
$$P(C) = P(A,C) + P(B,C)$$

If these three equations are added together, we obtain

$$P(A) + P(B) + P(C) = 2P(A,B) + 2P(A,C) + 2P(B,C) = 2P$$

and therefore
$$P = \frac{P(A) + P(B) + P(C)}{2}$$

The result of the Buffon needle problem can now be applied to the evaluation of $P(A)$, $P(B)$ and $P(C)$ since these probabilities depend on the lengths of the sides. Consequently,

$$P = \frac{2a/\pi d + 2b/\pi d + 2c/\pi d}{2} = \frac{a + b + c}{\pi d} = \frac{\text{perimeter}}{\pi d}$$

EXERCISES

1. The individual cards in a special deck of 20 are marked as follows:

$$\bar{A}\bar{B}, \; AB, \; \bar{A}\bar{B}, \; \bar{A}B, \; A\bar{B}, \; \bar{A}\bar{B}, \; AB, \; \bar{A}B, \; \bar{A}\bar{B}, \; A\bar{B}$$
$$AB, \; \bar{A}B, \; A\bar{B}, \; \bar{A}\bar{B}, \; \bar{A}B, \; AB, \; \bar{A}\bar{B}, \; A\bar{B}, \; \bar{A}B, \; AB$$

Assuming all cards equally likely, find $p(A)$, $p(B)$, $p(A,B)$, $p(A + B)$, $p(A|B)$, $p(B|A)$, by count of favorable cases. By substitution, verify the laws of total and compound probability, and state whether or not A and B are independent.

Ans. By direct count, $p(A) = {}^{10}\!/_{20} = .5 = p(B)$; $p(A,B) = {}^{5}\!/_{20} = .25$; $p(A + B) = {}^{15}\!/_{20} = .75$; $p(A|B) = {}^{5}\!/_{10} = .5 = p(B|A)$. By substitution, $p(A + B) = p(A) + p(B) - p(A,B) = .5 + .5 - .25 = .75$ which checks; $p(A,B) = p(A)p(B|A) = (.5)(.5) = .25$ which also checks; A and B are independent, inasmuch as $p(A,B) = p(A)p(B)$.

2. Referring to Example 2-9, explain why the figure $\frac{1}{3}$ given for the probability that a particular player wins is actually a conditional probability. What is the unconditional probability that a particular player wins? In three independent trials, what is the probability of at least one match?

Ans. There are eight possible outcomes of a toss, and by considering the results of individual coins as independent events, we find that all outcomes are equally likely, since each has a probability of $\frac{1}{8}$. The match situations exclude the two possible ties, (H,H,H) and (T,T,T), the total probability of which is $\frac{1}{4}$. Hence the probability of winning, being computed under the condition that a match exists, is a conditional probability. The unconditional probability that a particular player wins is $\frac{2}{8} = \frac{1}{4}$. The probability of at least one match in three trials is the complement of the probability of three ties, hence equal to $1 - (\frac{1}{4})^3 = .9844$.

3. The 2^N relations implied by the general definition of independence of N events are not all independent. Show that three events A, B, C, are mutually independent as a system if the following four relations are satisfied: $p(A,B) = p(A)p(B)$; $p(A,C) = p(A)p(C)$; $p(B,C) = p(B)p(C)$; $p(A,B,C) = p(A)p(B)p(C)$.

4. If a perfectly balanced die is rolled, what is the probability that the number of spots on the face turned up is greater than 2? Divisible by 3? *Ans.* $\frac{2}{3}$, $\frac{1}{3}$.

5. The three letters of the word "cat" are permuted in all possible distinct ways and then one permutation is picked at random. What is the probability that it spells a recognized word in the English language? *Ans.* $\frac{1}{3}$.

6. Three people A, B, C, who live in the same neighborhood, work in different parts of the city but utilize the same bus line. They aim to leave their offices regularly at 5 P.M. and each takes the first bus that comes along. In the rush hour, the buses leave at five-minute intervals. Random variations of travel time to the bus terminal work out in such a way that each person has a probability of $\frac{1}{4}$ of making the 5:10 bus, a probability of $\frac{1}{2}$ of making the 5:15, and a probability of $\frac{1}{4}$ of having to wait for the 5:20. Assuming independence, what is the probability that they will all take the same bus home?

Ans. $\frac{19}{64}$.

7. A bag contains three white, six red, and three black balls of equal size. Three are drawn at random. What is the probability that all will be of the same color?

Ans. $\frac{1}{10}$.

8. Out of a random group of four people, what is the probability that two or more shall have been born on the same day of the week? Assume all seven days equally likely.

Ans. $1 - \frac{120}{343} \approx .65$.

9. An industrial inspection rule reads: "Draw a random sample of four pieces. Test each for breaking strength. Accept the entire lot if all four pieces break above 1,200 lb." A lot comes along with 20 per cent of its contents below 1,200 lb. breaking strength. What is the probability that such a lot will be accepted under the given inspection procedure? Consider the lot size so large that we may ignore the effect of such a small depletion on the probability that an individual piece will fail the test.

Ans. .4096.

10. If two perfect dice are rolled, what is the probability that the total number of spots is equal to 7? Divisible by 4?

Ans. $\frac{1}{6}$, $\frac{1}{4}$.

11. Among ten students eligible to serve on a certain committee, two are sophomores, four juniors, and four seniors. If a committee of four is chosen by lot, what is the probability that it will consist of two juniors and two seniors? One sophomore, two juniors, and one senior? All seniors?

Ans. $\frac{6}{35}$, $\frac{8}{35}$, $\frac{1}{210}$.

12. Cards are drawn one by one without replacement from an initially full deck without jokers. What is the probability that the first and fourth will be a king with any other card except a king in the second and third draw? What is the probability of obtaining at least one king in the first two draws?

Ans. .00417, .149.

13. A bag contains N balls of equal size but different colors, and B of them are black. Two balls are drawn out one at a time without replacement. Show that the total probability that the second ball is black is B/N.

14. Assuming the probability of male birth to be $\frac{7}{12}$ and that of female $\frac{5}{12}$, what is the probability that a family of five children will have two girls and three boys?

Ans. .345.

15. Forty light bulbs are on display in a supermarket, and three are bad. If a customer picks out five at random what is the probability that all will be good? That two will be bad?

Ans. .662, .035.

16. Department A has four employees, department B, five, and department C, six. Three people are absent on Monday morning. Find the probability that no person is absent from C. Two are absent from C. All are absent from the same department.

Ans. .185, .297, .075.

17. A bag contains five white, three red, and four black balls. Three are drawn at random without replacement. Find the probability that no ball is red. Exactly one is red. At least one is red. All are of the same color. No two are of the same color.

Ans. $\frac{21}{55}$, $\frac{27}{55}$, $\frac{34}{55}$, $\frac{3}{44}$, $\frac{3}{11}$.

18. Referring to Example 2-9 in the light of Exercise 2, what is the probability that in four independent trials each player will win once and there will be one tie?

Ans. $\frac{3}{32}$.

19. From a standard deck of 52 playing cards five individual drawings are made such that the card withdrawn is replaced and the deck shuffled before the next card is picked. What is the probability of drawing one heart, two diamonds, one spade, and one club? Two cards of any suit and one of each of the others? *Ans.* $\frac{15}{256}$, $\frac{15}{64}$.

20. Two players A, B toss coins and compare results; B pays A a fixed amount if both coins show the same side, but A pays B the same amount if the sides are different. Suppose that A is allowed to choose whichever side he wishes but that B is required to determine his side at random by fair flipping of the coin, which we assume is unbiased. Show that no system which A might employe can give him an advantage over B.

/ **21.** In a straight poker hand (five cards, no jokers), what is the probability of getting exactly (a) one pair, (b) two pairs, (c) three of a kind?

Ans. This problem can be analyzed in several ways, but perhaps the most nearly foolproof method is to consider the number of ways of selecting the possible denominations and then the number of ways of obtaining suits within denominations. Thus for (a) we may select the denomination of the pair in $C(13,1)$ ways, and for any denomination we may choose two cards in $C(4,2)$ ways. This done, we may select three other denominations in $C(12,3)$ ways and choose a card from each of these three in $C(4,1)$ ways. Now the total number of distinct five-card hands is equal to $C(52,5)$. Hence, the required probability is

$$(a) \qquad P = \frac{C(13,1)C(4,2)C(12,3)[C(4,1)]^3}{C(52,5)} = .4226$$

Similarly, for (b) we can select the two denominations of the pairs in $C(13,2)$ ways and for both denominations choose suits in $C(4,2)$ ways. This done we may select one more denomination in $C(11,1)$ ways and choose the particular card from it in $C(4,1)$ ways. Thus

$$(b) \qquad P = \frac{C(13,2)[C(4,2)]^2C(11,1)C(4,1)}{C(52,5)} = .0475$$

By the same line of argument, the probability of obtaining exactly three of a kind is found to be

$$(c) \qquad P = \frac{C(13,1)C(4,3)C(12,2)[C(4,1)]^2}{C(52,5)} = .0211$$

/ **22.** In a straight poker hand what is the probability of getting (a) a flush (five cards of the same suit), (b) a full house (three of one kind and two of another kind)?

Ans.

$$(a) \qquad P = \frac{C(4,1)C(13,5)}{C(52,5)} = .0020$$

$$(b) \qquad P = \frac{C(13,1)C(4,3)C(12,1)C(4,2)}{C(52,5)} = .0014$$

/ **23.** What is the probability of throwing a "four" before a "seven" with two dice?
$$\text{\emph{Ans.} } \tfrac{1}{3} \text{ [Hint: Sum infinite geometric series.]}$$

/ **24.** The probability of winning on a single toss of the dice is p. A starts, and if he fails, he passes the dice to B, who then attempts to win on his toss. They continue passing the dice back and forth until one of them wins. What are their respective probabilities of winning? *Ans.* $p/(1 - q^2)$, $pq/(1 - q^2)$.

/ **25.** The probability of winning on a single toss of the dice is p. There are n contestants. The first one tries and if he fails he passes the dice to the second contestant. The second contestant also tries to win on a single toss and if he fails he passes the dice on to the third, etc. This procedure continues until somebody wins. If all n contestants fail on the first try, the dice again return to the first contestant and the procedure is continued. What is the probability of the kth contestant winning? What is the limiting value of this probability?
$$\text{\emph{Ans.} } q^{k-1}p/(1 - q^n); \text{ limit as } p \to 0 \text{ is } 1/n.$$

26. Two urns U_1 and U_2 contain white and black balls in different proportions. U_1 contains two white balls and one black, while U_2 contains one white ball and five black balls. One ball is transferred from U_1 to U_2 and then one ball is drawn from the latter. It happens to be white. What is the probability that the transferred ball was white?

Ans. $\frac{4}{5}$.

27. Three urns contain the following proportions of white and red balls respectively: $1W,\ 2R;\ 2W,\ 1R;\ 2W,\ 2R$. One urn is selected at random and one ball drawn out, which happens to be white. What is the probability that one of the first two urns was chosen?

Ans. $\frac{2}{3}$.

28. Stores A, B, and C under single directorship have 50, 75, 100 employees and respectively 50 per cent, 60 per cent and 70 per cent of these are women. Resignations are equally likely among all employees, regardless of sex. One employee resigns, and this is a woman. What is the probability that she works in store C? *Ans.* $\frac{1}{2}$.

29. A line AB with middle point O and total length a is given. A point X is chosen at random on the line. What is the probability that AX, BX, and AO can form a triangle?

Ans. $\frac{1}{2}$.

30. Three points are chosen at random on the circumference of a circle. Assuming all arcs are equally likely, what is the probability that they lie on the same semicircle?

Ans. $\frac{3}{4}$.

31. Three points X_1, X_2, and X_3 are taken at random on AB. What is the probability that X_3 lies between X_1 and X_2? *Ans.* $\frac{1}{3}$.

32. Given $ax + b = 0$. The coefficient a is chosen at random between 1 and 2 and the coefficient b at random between -1 and $+1$, all possible values being equally likely. What is the probability that the solution of the equation will be greater than .25?

Ans. $\frac{5}{16}$.

33. In the triangle of Fig. 2-9, the length of side AB is fixed and is equal to two units. Side AC has variable length x determined by picking a point at random on a line segment of four units length so that all values of x from 0 to 4 inclusive are equally likely. The angle O is also determined by a random process, and all values from 0 to π inclusive are equally likely. From geometrical considerations what is the probability that the area of triangle ABC is less than two square units? *Ans.* .753.

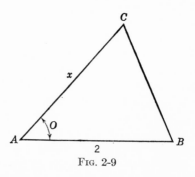

FIG. 2-9

34. Solve Buffon's needle problem when the length a of the needle is greater than the distance d between two consecutive lines.

Ans. The probability of intersecting at least one line is $(2a/\pi d)(1 - \sin \phi) + 2\phi/\pi$ where $\cos \phi = d/a$.

CHAPTER 3

DISCRETE RANDOM VARIABLES

3-1. Introduction. Basic concepts of probability were developed in Chap. 2 in terms of events. While these were defined as the possible outcomes of an experiment and were interpreted as numerical quantities in some instances (geometrical probability, in particular), the main emphasis was upon events of a qualitative nature. In this chapter and most of those to follow, the emphasis will be placed upon quantitative material, because a great many applications of probability theory concern the numerical values of appropriate variables rather than qualitative events, such as "heads or tails," "standard or defective," "fair, cloudy, or rainy," etc. Very often, the variable under consideration will be capable of taking on any one of an infinite number of possible values. Nevertheless, provided that probability can be defined at all for the results of a given type of experiment, the total probability of all possible results will necessarily be unity, because one result or another will be certain to occur. Our study from now on will deal with whole systems of numerical quantities, such as the set of possible numbers of times certain events may occur in a fixed number of trials, or the entire range of values which a physical measurement or observation can yield.

On an abstract level, ordinary mathematics is concerned with independent variables, the values of which may be chosen arbitrarily, and dependent variables, which are determined by the values assigned to the former. In the concrete domain, science aims at the discovery of laws whereby natural phenomena are interrelated, and the value of a particular variable can be determined when pertinent conditions are prescribed. Nevertheless, there exist enormous areas of objective reality characterized by changes which do not seem to follow any definite pattern or have any connection with recognizable antecedents. We do not mean to suggest an absence of causality. However, from the viewpoint of an observer who cannot look behind the scenes, a variable produced by the interplay of a complex system of causes exhibits irregular (though not necessarily discontinuous) variations which are, to all intents and purposes, random. Broadly speaking, a variable which eludes predictability in assuming its different possible values is called a *random variable*, or synonymously a *variate*. More precisely, a random variable must have a specific range or

41

set of possible values and a definable probability associated with each value.

A few examples of random variables are:

1. The number of points scored by a basketball team from game to game
2. The daily number of absentees from an office
3. The weekly grocery bill of a family
4. The daily or weekly volume of gasoline used by an individual driver
5. The amount of time spent daily (or weekly, or monthly, etc.) by one person (or any group of people) in commuting

A random variable is said to be *discrete* if it is capable of assuming only a finite (or denumerably infinite) number of distinct values, whereas it is said to be *continuous* in a given range if it can assume any value lying in that range. In the examples cited, the first three variates are discrete, and the last two are continuous.

3-2. Distributions. The *distribution* of a random variable is the definition of its mathematical behavior, that is, the specification of its possible values together with their respective probabilities. In this chapter, we shall confine our attention to discrete variates. Here the specification of admissible values is accomplished by simple enumeration, and the probability attached to each value is given by a mathematical formula or table. A discrete variate having a finite number of distinct values, say $x_1, x_2, \ldots, x_n$, entails nothing essentially new, for by regarding the occurrence of each possible value x_i as constituting an event E_i, we may apply the theory already developed for qualitative events. If the distinct values are unlimited in number, we may consider a corresponding infinite system of events and postulate the extension of the laws of probability to infinite sets. Continuous variates, however, are more subtle, because their admissible values are so dense that they cannot be placed in one-to-one correspondence with any denumerable series of events, not even an infinite series. Nevertheless, we shall find in Chap. 4 that by a fairly simple device, continuous variables also can be brought within the scope of probability.

3-3. Probability Functions. In connection with random variables, we are usually interested in numerical relationships such as $x \geq a$ or $b < x < c$, and we accommodate our probability notation accordingly. Thus the symbols

$$P(x \geq a) \qquad P(b < x < c)$$

are read, respectively, as "the probability that x equals or exceeds a," and "the probability that x lies between b and c."

For convenience, we shall adopt a shortened notation $f(x_i)$ for the probability $P(x = x_i)$ that a variate x assumes a given one of its possible values, x_i. Ordinarily $f(x_i)$ will turn out to be merely a particular case of a general mathematical formula which holds for all of the admissible values of x, and for this reason, we shall denote the general formula by $f(x)$. With reference to a discrete variate, therefore, the function $f(x)$, which we shall call the *probability function* of x, yields the probability that the variate in question takes on any given one of its admissible values. The *distribution* of x is then defined simply by stating the equation for $f(x)$ and indicating the allowable values which x may assume.

Example 3-1. As a simple example of a discrete variate having only a small number of admissible values, consider the toss of an unbiased die and let the occurrence of an ace or a six be considered a success. If the die is tossed three times (or if three different dice are tossed once), the number of successes can assume any one of four values: 0, 1, 2, 3. From the classical theory, the probability of success on a single trial is $\frac{2}{6} = \frac{1}{3}$, while that of failure is $\frac{2}{3}$. The numbers of distinct sequences of successes and failures which yield 0, 1, 2, 3 successes, respectively, in three tosses are 1, 3, 3, 1. Therefore, if x denotes the number of successes, the total probabilities (assuming independence) are

$$f(0) = P(x = 0) = (\tfrac{2}{3})^3 = \tfrac{8}{27} \qquad f(1) = P(x = 1) = (3)(\tfrac{2}{3})^2(\tfrac{1}{3}) = \tfrac{12}{27}$$
$$f(2) = P(x = 2) = (3)(\tfrac{2}{3})(\tfrac{1}{3})^2 = \tfrac{6}{27} \qquad f(3) = P(x = 3) = (\tfrac{1}{3})^3 = \tfrac{1}{27}$$

and
$$f(0) + f(1) + f(2) + f(3) = \tfrac{27}{27} = 1$$

showing (as must always be the case) that the sum of the probabilities of all admissible values is unity. Referring to Example 2-6, Eq. (2-6), we note that all of these probabilities may be obtained from a single formula by using the binomial law of probability. Accordingly, we may express the distribution of x as follows:

$$f(x) = C(3,x)(\tfrac{1}{3})^x(\tfrac{2}{3})^{3-x} \qquad (x = 0, 1, 2, 3)$$

The graph of this function is shown in Fig. 3-1. We shall call this kind of graph a *line diagram*.

FIG. 3-1. The probability function $f(x)$ of the discrete variate x considered in Example 3-1.

3-4. Distribution Functions.   Besides the probability that x is equal to a particular one of its possible values, we often have occasion to use the probability that x exceeds a stated value, or the complementary probability that x is equal to or less than a stated value.   The probability $P(x \leq x_i)$ that x is less than or equal to x_i is denoted by the symbol $F(x_i)$. By definition, then,

$$F(x_i) = P(x \leq x_i) \tag{3-1}$$

More generally, the function $F(x)$, which we shall call the *distribution function* of x, will yield the probability that the variate in question takes on any value less than or equal to the stated value x.   Instead of using the probability function to define the distribution of a discrete random variable, the distribution function, together with a statement of the admissible values of x, may be employed.   Although this alternative is

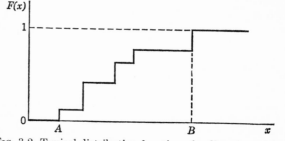

Fig. 3-2. Typical distribution function of a discrete variate.

not very appealing where discrete variates are concerned, the distribution function is actually the more powerful tool; in fact, by means of it we are able to unify the theory of discrete and continuous variates as well as combinations of both.   We shall elaborate further in Chap. 4, but for the present we shall merely point out a few general features of distribution functions.   If the least possible value which a certain random variable x can assume is denoted by A and the greatest possible value by B, then it is evident that the graph of $F(x)$ will coincide with the x axis for all values of x less than A and will coincide with the horizontal line $F = 1$ for all values of x greater than or equal to B.   Discrete variates necessarily yield distribution functions of the discontinuous type (step function) shown in Fig. 3-2.   The reason is that values of x which cannot occur in actuality add nothing to the probability that a random value of the variate will lie in a stated range; consequently the graph of $F(x)$ is horizontal between admissible values but takes a finite step at each point on the x axis which corresponds to an admissible value.   Since $F(x)$ is discontinuous in this case, its value at an admissible value of x is not defined explicitly.   For convenience $F(x)$ is everywhere defined so that it is always continuous *on the right*, that is, $F(x + 0) = F(x)$.

TABLE 3-1. CORRESPONDING VALUES OF $f(x)$ AND $F(x)$ IN EXAMPLE 3-1

x	0	1	2	3
$f(x)$	$\frac{8}{27}$	$\frac{12}{27}$	$\frac{6}{27}$	$\frac{1}{27}$
$F(x)$	$\frac{8}{27}$	$\frac{20}{27}$	$\frac{26}{27}$	$\frac{27}{27}$

For the variate considered in Example 3-1, corresponding values of the probability function $f(x)$ and the distribution function $F(x)$ are given in Table 3-1. The graph of the distribution function is shown in Fig. 3-3.

FIG. 3-3. The distribution function $F(x)$ of the discrete variate x considered in Example 3-1.

3-5. Random Sampling. Already in the course of this book we have touched upon the subject of random sampling without making explicit reference to the distribution of a random variable, but we are now prepared for a more detailed statement.

The concept of random sampling is the operational link between the abstract theory of probability and its practical application to observable phenomena. From the sampling viewpoint, an observation yields a particular value of a random variable, which has a distribution of potential values. Sampling is said to be *independent* when one observation does not affect another in a probability sense. Typically, observations are made on individual physical objects belonging to a definite set or collection of objects, technically termed a *population* or *universe*, and it often happens that the act of taking the observation involves the withdrawal of the object observed. If the withdrawal of an object disturbs the probability distribution in the remainder of the population from which it is taken (as in a deck of cards), then in order to keep the probabilities constant, the observed item must be put back before another drawing is made. With an infinite population, we may disregard sampling depletions, but in sampling from a finite population we have to take them into account. When replacement in the initial finite population is ruled out by the conditions of the problem (as in dealing card hands), we may imagine a synthetic population of all possible distinct samples, and then regard the process as one of drawing at random from that synthetic population. Thus the effect of depletion can be overcome through an appropriate model.

One basic postulate of random sampling is that the empirical distribution function of a sequence of independent observations will tend toward a fixed form as the number of observations increases without limit. We *postulate* the *existence* of an *observational process* having the properties of independence and convergence toward a fixed form of distribution, and we *name* the process *random sampling*. Conceivably, some observational process could yield a fixed limiting form in a systematic way. For instance, we could deal one card at a time from the top of a deck and return it to the bottom, thus picking 52 different cards in a fixed order, and the cycle could be repeated indefinitely. A random process has no preassigned order of individual values, nor is the order definable in any way except by complete enumeration of the series, term by term. Random sampling is a process of obtaining observations in such a way that one observation has the same chance as another of taking on (or in the case of a continuous variate, falling in the neighborhood of) any value which the variate sampled is capable of assuming; and the limiting relative frequency of any class of values empirically realized in an infinite sequence is identically equal to the probability of the same class in the idealized distribution of potential values. The logical role of the distribution of potential values is to provide a foundation for an axiomatic treatment of probability; this is necessary for mathematical rigor, inasmuch as mathematics is essentially deductive. Since all observations are governed independently by the same distribution, all can be identified with (in the sense of being particular values of) independent, identically distributed random variables.

3-6. Significance Tests. A significance test is a mathematical procedure applied to empirical data for deciding, on grounds of probability, whether or not a suitably formulated hypothesis is tenable. An observational result is said to be *significant*, and the hypothesis in question is *rejected*, when the obtained result belongs to an objectively specified unfavorable class having a fixed, small probability of occurrence in random samples from the hypothesized population. Two key words here are *random* and *class*. Probability is trivial or meaningless unless there is some element of randomness involved; hence, within the framework of observational conditions (either natural or controlled), there must be freedom for the "chips to fall as they may." This means that the sample must be random as far as the variable (usually called the test variate) used to test the hypothesis is concerned, although the raw data need not be wholly random. The notion of a class is needed, because in almost any population containing a large number of distinct values or types, the probability of drawing any *prescribed* value or type by random selection is extremely small. For example, when 13 playing cards are dealt from a standard deck without jokers, it is certain that the outcome will be a legitimate hand of bridge. Now, the probability of obtaining any pre-assigned hand as a random draw from the deck is less than 1 in 600 billion (the number of distinct hands being about 6.35×10^{11}), and if the hand were specified in advance, the event of drawing it would be overwhelmingly significant of skill. Unforeseen in its particular composition, however, the same hand would signify nothing more or less than the fact that some combination or other is bound to occur, and that the number of distinct combinations is extremely large. A continuous variate presents this situation in its logical ultimate. Significance, therefore, involves not

FIG. 3-4. Possible critical regions of probability .05 for use in significance tests.

only the principle of small probability, but also the issue of logical interpretation with reference to the essential import of the hypothesis. Such interpretation is made by dividing all possible values of the test variate (each one being a random draw from the hypothesized population) into two classes: the *acceptance region* and the *critical region*, also called the *rejection region*. The boundaries of the classes are set in such a way that the total probability (unity) is appropriately divided between them, say .95, .05, or .99, .01. Subject to this arbitrary division, the acceptance region is then defined as the class of all results which are construed as favorable to the hypothesis, while the critical region or rejection region is the complementary class of all results which are construed as unfavorable. The probability assigned to the critical region, commonly either .05 or .01, is called the *significance level*. Although other values than these two are sometimes used, depending upon the problem itself, the significance level should always be chosen before the experiment is conducted. The critical region ordinarily includes the more extreme values of a variate. Depending on what is logically relevant to the hypothesis, the critical region might include only the highest bracket of values, or only the lowest bracket; or it might be divided in a suitable manner (usually in equal amounts as to probability) between the highest and lowest brackets. Typical situations are illustrated graphically in Fig. 3-4, wherein, for the sake of simplicity, the probability function $f(x)$ has been represented as a smooth curve.

Although the typical working hypothesis cannot be subjected to a direct probabilistic examination, the same end can be achieved indirectly. The equivalent of establishing a given hypothesis is to discredit its logical alternative. In place of a working hypothesis that a certain tendency exists, we may examine the contrary proposition that the alleged tendency is absent. From the latter viewpoint, all possible empirical results are regarded as occurring at random within a definite framework. This assumption lends itself to precise expression in terms of a probability distribution, and because of its negative character, it is commonly called the *null hypothesis*. It is essential, however, that the variable actually used in the significance test be such that its probability distribution would be known if the null hypothesis were true.

3-7. The Binomial Distribution. The remainder of this chapter is devoted mainly to the introduction of certain discrete distributions, which are important enough from the standpoint of general use to be regarded as basic equipment for practical applications of probability theory. The first of these is the *binomial distribution*.[1]

Assuming that the occurrence of an event E is subject to chance, the number x of occurrences in n independent trials is a discrete random variable, the possible values of which are $0, 1, 2, \ldots, n$. If the probability p of the occurrence of E on an individual trial is constant, then x is called a binomial variate, and its distribution is known as the binomial distribution. Since the failure of E to occur on a given trial automatically implies the occurrence of the complementary event $\bar{E}$, the probability of which is $q = 1 - p$, any possible sequence of n trials is necessarily made up of x instances of E ("successes") and $n - x$ instances of $\bar{E}$ ("failures"), where x may take on any one of its admissible values $0, 1, 2, \ldots, n$. Applying the binomial law of probability (Example 2-6, Eq. 2-6), we may write down the binomial distribution at once:

$$f(x) = C(n,x)p^x q^{n-x} \qquad (x = 0, 1, 2, \ldots, n; q = 1 - p) \quad (3\text{-}2)$$
$$\text{Binomial Distribution}$$

The binomial distribution with $n = 3$, $p = \frac{1}{3}$ has already been presented in Example 3-1. Different selections of n and p give rise to various geometric shapes. Adjustable constants, such as n and p in the binomial distribution, are called *parameters*, and empirical estimates of parameters are called *statistics*. In Fig. 3-5, the parameter n is held constant ($n = 9$) and the parameter p is allowed to vary ($p = .2, .5, .8$), while in Fig. 3-6, p is held constant and n is allowed to vary ($n = 9, 16, 25$).

Figure 3-5 illustrates the fact that the binomial distribution is symmetrical if $p = .5$ but nonsymmetrical otherwise. A nonsymmetrical

---

[1] This is also called the Bernoulli distribution after J. Bernoulli (1654–1705), who was one of the pioneers in the theory of probability.

distribution is said to be *skewed* in the direction toward which it trails off; thus the distribution with $p = .2$ is skewed toward the right, while that with $p = .8$ is skewed toward the left. Incidentally, the interchange of p and q in any binomial distribution yields its mirror image, as demonstrated by the first and third graphs of this figure. Figure 3-6 bears out the general fact that given p, the skewness of the binomial distribution becomes less pronounced as n increases.

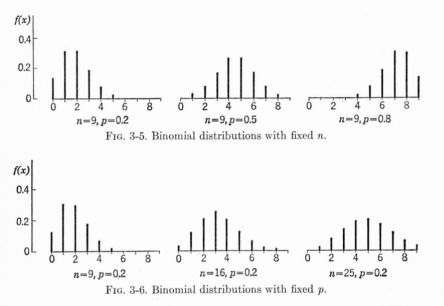

FIG. 3-5. Binomial distributions with fixed n.

FIG. 3-6. Binomial distributions with fixed p.

The probability functions and distribution functions of these binomial variates are exhibited numerically in Tables 3-2 and 3-3 to four decimals. We shall refer to these later on. The successive values of the F's are given by the corresponding progressive sums of the f's except where rounding errors in the latter figures violate the logical requirements that $F(x) < 1$ when $x < n$, and $F(n) = 1$.

Any probability distribution must yield unit total probability for the entire set of admissible values of the variate, and this fact serves as a check on the validity of alleged distributions. We may ascertain that $\sum_x f(x) = 1$ for the binomial distribution by applying the binomial theorem. Thus

$$\sum_{x=0}^{n} f(x) = q^n + nq^{n-1}p + \cdots + nqp^{n-1} + p^n = (q + p)^n = 1^n = 1$$

TABLE 3-2. PROBABILITY AND DISTRIBUTION FUNCTIONS OF
CERTAIN BINOMIAL VARIATES WITH FIXED n ($n = 9$)

x	$p = .2$		$p = .5$		$p = .8$	
	$f(x)$	$F(x)$	$f(x)$	$F(x)$	$f(x)$	$F(x)$
0	.1342	.1342	.0020	.0020	.0000	.0000
1	.3020	.4362	.0176	.0196	.0000	.0000
2	.3020	.7382	.0703	.0899	.0003	.0003
3	.1762	.9144	.1641	.2540	.0028	.0031
4	.0661	.9805	.2461	.5001	.0165	.0196
5	.0165	.9970	.2461	.7462	.0661	.0857
6	.0028	.9998	.1641	.9103	.1762	.2619
7	.0003	1.0000	.0703	.9806	.3020	.5639
8	.0000	1.0000	.0176	.9982	.3020	.8659
9	.0000	1.0000	.0020	1.0000	.1342	1.0000

TABLE 3-3. PROBABILITY AND DISTRIBUTION FUNCTIONS OF
CERTAIN BINOMIAL VARIATES WITH FIXED p ($p = .2$)

x	$n = 9$		$n = 16$		$n = 25$	
	$f(x)$	$F(x)$	$f(x)$	$F(x)$	$f(x)$	$F(x)$
0	.1342	.1342	.0281	.0281	.0038	.0038
1	.3020	.4362	.1126	.1407	.0236	.0274
2	.3020	.7382	.2111	.3518	.0708	.0982
3	.1762	.9144	.2463	.5981	.1358	.2340
4	.0661	.9805	.2001	.7982	.1867	.4207
5	.0165	.9970	.1201	.9183	.1960	.6167
6	.0028	.9998	.0550	.9733	.1633	.7800
7	.0003	1.0000	.0197	.9930	.1108	.8908
8	.0000	......	.0055	.9985	.0623	.9531
9	.0000	......	.0012	.9997	.0294	.9825
10	.....	......	.0002	.9999	.0118	.9943
11	.....	......	.0000	.9999	.0040	.9983
12	.....	......	.0000	.9999	.0012	.9995
13	.....	......	.....	.9999	.0003	.9998
14	.....	......	.....	.9999	.0001	.9999
15	.....	......	.....	.9999	.0000	.9999
16	.....	......	.....	1.0000	.0000	.9999
..	.....	......	.....	......	.....	.9999
..	.....	......	.....	......	.....	.9999
..	.....	......	.....	......	.....	.9999
25	.0000	1.0000	.0000	1.0000	.0000	1.0000

Example 3-2. The green light at an intersection is on for 15 sec at a time, the yellow for 5, and the red for 55. Assuming that traffic conditions induce random variations in arrival times, so that "making the green light" is a chance event, let us find the distribution of successes in respectively 5 and 25 independent trials. Here we have a problem in geometric probability in the time domain. Letting G, Y, R stand for green, yellow, red, the complete cycle of lights is G, Y, R; and if T denotes the total length of a cycle, we have $T = 15 + 5 + 55 = 75$ sec. Hence the probability p that a random point of time will fall in the interval G is

$$p = \frac{G}{T} = \frac{15}{75} = .2$$

and $q = 1 - p = .8$. For any number n of independent trials, the number x of successes has the binomial distribution with $p = .2$. The distribution of successes for 5 independent trials is given to four places of decimals in Table 3-4. The distribution for 25 independent trials was previously given in Table 3-3 and was displayed graphically in Fig. 3-6.

TABLE 3-4. DISTRIBUTION OF SUCCESSES IN FIVE INDEPENDENT TRIALS
WITH $p = .2$

x	0	1	2	3	4	5
$f(x)$	.3277	.4096	.2048	.0512	.0064	.0003
$F(x)$	.3277	.7373	.9421	.9933	.9997	1.0000

In both cases ($n = 5$, $n = 25$) let us find the probability that the relative frequency of successes in n trials will be greater than twice the probability p of success on a single trial. Since the relative frequency is x/n and $2p = .4$, the required condition is that $x/n > .4$, whence $x > (.4)n$. When $n = 5$ this means that $x > 2$, and the corresponding probability is

$$P(x > 2) = 1 - F(2) = 1 - .942 = .058$$

When $n = 25$, we have $x > 10$ and

$$p(x > 10) = 1 - F(10) = 1 - .994 = .006$$

Therefore, with the larger number of trials, the chances are much smaller that the relative frequency obtained experimentally will deviate greatly from the true probability of success.

Example 3-3. Supposing that in the manufacture of stationery, a defective sheet of paper occurs at random with probability $p = \frac{1}{500}$, let us consider the distribution of the number x of defects in a ream of 500 sheets. This distribution, which is binomial with $n = 500$ and $p = \frac{1}{500}$, is presented numerically (to three places of decimals) in Table 3-5 and graphically in Fig. 3-7. From these exhibits, we see that reams with no defects or only one defect are fairly common, that on the average fewer than one in five reams would have two defects, and that not more than five reams in one thousand would have more than four defects, if we computed the relative frequency over a long series of trials.

TABLE 3-5. DISTRIBUTION OF THE NUMBER x OF DEFECTIVE SHEETS IN A
REAM OF 500 WHERE $p = \frac{1}{500}$

x	0	1	2	3	4	5	6	7†
$f(x)$	.367	.368	.184	.061	.015	.003	.001	.000
$F(x)$	.367	.735	.919	.980	.995	.998	.999	.999

† $P(x > 7) < .00006$.

The computation of $f(x)$ and $F(x)$ for the binomial distribution is laborious if n is at all large. Excellent tables giving p at intervals of .01 and n up to 49 were published in 1950 by the National Bureau of Standards under the title "Tables of the Binomial Probability Distribution." Many of the binomial exhibits of this chapter were prepared with their aid. These tables, in turn, were adapted from the well-known "Tables of the

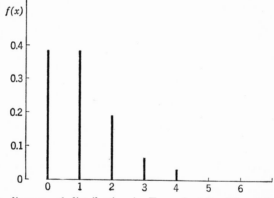

FIG. 3-7. Line diagram of distribution in Example 3-3. Binomial with $n = 500$ $p = \frac{1}{500}$.

Incomplete Beta-function," which were published in 1934 by the Biometric Laboratory, then under the direction of Karl Pearson. Although the evaluation of binomial probabilities is only one of many uses of the incomplete beta function $I_p(u,v)$, it is indeed a remarkable property of the binomial distribution that partial sums of $f(x)$ (which, of course, are sums of discrete terms) are exactly given by integrals of a continuous variable. Using integration by parts, the student may verify the following equation:

$$1 - F(k - 1) = \sum_{x=k}^{n} C(n,x)p^x q^{n-x} = \frac{\int_0^p y^{k-1}(1 - y)^{n-k}\, dy}{\int_0^1 y^{k-1}(1 - y)^{n-k}\, dy} \quad (3\text{-}3)$$

In Pearson's notation, the latter ratio is denoted by $I_p(k, n - k + 1)$.

Outside of the range of available tables, it is usually sufficient in practice to approximate the binomial distribution by either (depending on the circumstances) the Poisson distribution or the normal distribution, both of which will be discussed later on. If, despite tables and approximations, there should arise an occasion for the computation of binomial probabilities, the arithmetic can be shortened by the following recurrence formulas, which the reader is invited to verify by substitution.

$$f(x + 1) = \frac{(n - x)p}{(x + 1)q} f(x) \qquad f(x - 1) = \frac{xq}{(n - x + 1)p} f(x) \quad (3\text{-}4)$$

For large n, it is advisable to choose a value of x in the neighborhood of np, and after evaluating $f(x)$ at this point by logarithms (or logarithms of factorials) to apply Eq. (3-4) on either side of the chosen value of x. This technique was used in Example 3-3 and also in the following example.

Example 3-4. When we discuss the approximation of the binomial distribution by the Poisson distribution or the normal, we shall want the exact values for purposes of comparison. For future reference, we present in Table 3-6 a portion of the binomial distribution with $n = 2,500$, $p = .02$. From Fig. 3-8, we see that the distribution is nearly symmetrical, on account of the large value of n, even though p is small.

FIG. 3-8. Line diagram of binomial distribution with $n = 2,500$, $p = .02$.

Example 3-5. A paint manufacturer has favorable laboratory reports on an ingredient purported to improve the wearing quality of shellac. Desiring a limited field trial, he arranges with the owners of six buildings to allow experimental tests on their property. Each building has a much-used wooden staircase with three flights of 12 steps each. Half of the 36 steps are to be coated with regular shellac and the other half with fortified shellac. Possible extraneous factors are neutralized and independence of the observations ensured by a technique of randomization.

The odd-numbered steps are treated with one finish or another, depending (let us say) upon the toss of a balanced coin, and the next even-numbered step is given the alternative treatment. In this way, both treatments are used the same number of times, and both have equal chances of exposure to any outside influences that might be operative. As a measure of wear after three months of use, the damaged area for each treatment is recorded as a percentage of the total area covered, and separate figures are reported for each of the six buildings. It will be proved in Example 5-9, although it is intuitively obvious, that if any two continuous variates y_1, y_2 have the same distribution function, then the probability is $\frac{1}{2}$ that a random observation of y_1 will exceed a random observation of y_2. Under the null hypothesis, the two wear-

TABLE 3-6. PORTION OF BINOMIAL DISTRIBUTION WITH $n = 2,500$, $p = .02$

x	$f(x)$	$F(x)$	x	$f(x)$	$F(x)$
(0–25)	.0000	.0001†	52	.0536	.6469
26	.0001	.0002	53	.0505	.6974
27	.0001	.0003	54	.0467	.7441
28	.0002	.0005	55	.0424	.7865
29	.0004	.0009	56	.0378	.8243
30	.0006	.0015	57	.0331	.8574
31	.0010	.0025	58	.0284	.8858
32	.0016	.0041	59	.0240	.9098
33	.0025	.0066	60	.0199	.9297
34	.0036	.0102	61	.0163	.9460
35	.0052	.0154	62	.0131	.9591
36	.0073	.0227	63	.0103	.9694
37	.0099	.0326	64	.0080	.9774
38	.0131	.0457	65	.0061	.9835
39	.0169	.0626	66	.0046	.9881
40	.0212	.0838	67	.0034	.9915
41	.0260	.1098	68	.0025	.9940
42	.0311	.1409	69	.0018	.9958
43	.0363	.1772	70	.0013	.9971
44	.0413	.2185	71	.0009	.9980
45	.0460	.2645	72	.0006	.9986
46	.0501	.3146	73	.0004	.9990
47	.0534	.3680	74	.0003	.9993
48	.0557	.4237	75	.0002	.9995
49	.0569	.4806	76	.0001	.9996
50	.0569	.5375	77	.0001	.9997
51	.0558	.5933	78	.0000	.9997

† Although the values of $f(x)$ in this range are zero to four decimals, their sum rounds to .0001.

percentages in the same building are random observations from the same population. Thus a possible test variate x would be the number of positive differences. Besides the hypothesis that positive and negative differences are equally likely, there is the tacit assumption that the six differences are mutually independent. Using this hypothesis and a critical region of .05 situated on the right-hand tail of the distribution, would one accept or reject this hypothesis on the basis of the experimental results shown in Table 3-7?

Here the distribution of the test variate, under the null hypothesis, is

$$f(x) = \frac{C(6,x)}{2^6} = \frac{C(6,x)}{64} \qquad (x = 0, 1, \ldots, 6)$$

For the reader's convenience, this distribution is exhibited in Table 3-8.

TABLE 3-7. PERCENTAGE DAMAGE AFTER THREE MONTHS

Building	Regular Shellac	Fortified Shellac	Difference reg. − fort.
1	5	2	3
2	11	7	4
3	4	5	−1
4	14	8	6
5	9	4	5
6	12	11	1

Since we have chosen a one-sided critical region and .05 as the level of significance, the boundary of this region will be determined by starting with the largest value of x and working downward until the total probability is as close as possible to .05 without exceeding it. Here we find that the only admissible value is $x = 6$, since the next lower value 5 would bring the total probability up to .11. The results shown in Table 3-7 yield five positive differences and one negative difference; hence $x = 5$, and this value does not fall in the critical region which we preassigned before the experiment was conducted. Therefore we accept the null hypothesis and conclude that this test does not indicate a significant difference between the wearing qualities of fortified and regular shellac. In other words, the possibility of obtaining five or more positive differences by chance alone is such that one would not admit that the result was due to the difference in the shellacs. From the practical point of view this means that if a difference does exist more observations or else a more sensitive test would be necessary in order to demonstrate it.

TABLE 3-8. DISTRIBUTION OF THE NUMBER OF POSITIVE DIFFERENCES UNDER THE NULL HYPOTHESIS

x	0	1	2	3	4	5	6	Sum
$f(x)$	.016	.094	.234	.312	.234	.094	.016	1.000

Example 3-6. Sometimes it is possible to construct from the sample itself a synthetic population to use as the basis of a test of significance. This is illustrated below using the observations in Table 3-7. The sign test takes no account of the magnitude of the differences. If we have any way of knowing the probability distribution of the differences under the assumption of no improvement, we could apply a more sensitive test by incorporating this information. In default of such knowledge, we can construct a population of differences based upon the observations themselves. The idea here is that the two quantities in each pair might just as well have been interchanged. Thus the synthetic population consists of six possible pairs of differences: $(3, -3)$; $(4, -4)$; $(1, -1)$; $(6, -6)$; $(5, -5)$; $(1, -1)$. And by hypothesis, we are drawing a random sample of six numbers—one from each pair. This implies that the population of distinct samples consists of 64 possibilities, ranging from one extreme with all signs negative to the other, with all signs positive. These are shown in Table 3-9. This time, as our test variate we choose the sum of the six differences. For our immediate purpose, it is not necessary to construct the entire distribution of x, but for the sake of clarity we have done so, with the results shown in Table 3-10. The nearest we can come to the significance level .05 is to set the boundary of the critical region at $x = 18$, which yields $P(x \geq 18) = \frac{3}{64} \approx .047$. With the test variate selected, the actual

TABLE 3-9. SYNTHETIC POPULATION

Serial number	Sample	Sum	Serial number	Sample	Sum
1	−3, −4, −1, −6, −5, −1	−20	33	+3, −4, −1, −6, −5, −1	−14
2	−3, −4, −1, −6, −5, +1	−18	34	+3, −4, −1, −6, −5, +1	−12
3	−3, −4, −1, −6, +5, −1	−10	35	+3, −4, −1, −6, +5, −1	−4
4	−3, −4, −1, −6, +5, +1	−8	36	+3, −4, −1, −6, +5, +1	−2
5	−3, −4, −1, +6, −5, −1	−8	37	+3, −4, −1, +6, −5, −1	−2
6	−3, −4, −1, +6, −5, +1	−6	38	+3, −4, −1, +6, −5, +1	0
7	−3, −4, −1, +6, +5, −1	+2	39	+3, −4, −1, +6, +5, −1	+8
8	−3, −4, −1, +6, +5, +1	+4	40	+3, −4, −1, +6, +5, +1	+10
9	−3, −4, +1, −6, −5, −1	−18	41	+3, −4, +1, −6, −5, −1	−12
10	−3, −4, +1, −6, −5, +1	−16	42	+3, −4, +1, −6, −5, +1	−10
11	−3, −4, +1, −6, +5, −1	−8	43	+3, −4, +1, −6, +5, −1	−2
12	−3, −4, +1, −6, +5, +1	−6	44	+3, −4, +1, −6, +5, +1	0
13	−3, −4, +1, +6, −5, −1	−6	45	+3, −4, +1, +6, −5, −1	0
14	−3, −4, +1, +6, −5, +1	−4	46	+3, −4, +1, +6, −5, +1	+2
15	−3, −4, +1, +6, +5, −1	+4	47	+3, −4, +1, +6, +5, −1	+10
16	−3, −4, +1, +6, +5, +1	+6	48	+3, −4, +1, +6, +5, +1	+12
17	−3, +4, −1, −6, −5, −1	−12	49	+3, +4, −1, −6, −5, −1	−6
18	−3, +4, −1, −6, −5, +1	−10	50	+3, +4, −1, −6, −5, +1	−4
19	−3, +4, −1, −6, +5, −1	−2	51	+3, +4, −1, −6, +5, −1	+4
20	−3, +4, −1, −6, +5, +1	0	52	+3, +4, −1, −6, +5, +1	+6
21	−3, +4, −1, +6, −5, −1	0	53	+3, +4, −1, +6, −5, −1	+6
22	−3, +4, −1, +6, −5, +1	+2	54	+3, +4, −1, +6, −5, +1	+8
23	−3, +4, −1, +6, +5, −1	+10	55	+3, +4, −1, +6, +5, −1	+16
24	−3, +4, −1, +6, +5, +1	+12	56	+3, +4, −1, +6, +5, +1	+18
25	−3, +4, +1, −6, −5, −1	−10	57	+3, +4, +1, −6, −5, −1	−4
26	−3, +4, +1, −6, −5, +1	−8	58	+3, +4, +1, −6, −5, +1	−2
27	−3, +4, +1, −6, +5, −1	0	59	+3, +4, +1, −6, +5, −1	+6
28	−3, +4, +1, −6, +5, +1	+2	60	+3, +4, +1, −6, +5, +1	+8
29	−3, +4, +1, +6, −5, −1	+2	61	+3, +4, +1, +6, −5, −1	+8
30	−3, +4, +1, +6, −5, +1	+4	62	+3, +4, +1, +6, −5, +1	+10
31	−3, +4, +1, +6, +5, −1	+12	63	+3, +4, +1, +6, +5, −1	+18
32	−3, +4, +1, +6, +5, +1	+14	64	+3, +4, +1, +6, +5, +1	+20

sample value is $x = 18$, which falls within the critical region. Thus we reject the null hypothesis at the .047 level of significance and infer that the added ingredient *does* improve the wearing quality of shellac. This procedure is sometimes referred to as the *magnitude test*.

Most of the computational labor of this analysis can be avoided by constructing

TABLE 3-10. DISTRIBUTION OF SAMPLE SUMS

x	$f(x)$	x	$f(x)$	x	$f(x)$
-20	$\frac{1}{64}$	-6	$\frac{4}{64}$	8	$\frac{4}{64}$
-18	$\frac{2}{64}$	-4	$\frac{4}{64}$	10	$\frac{4}{64}$
-16	$\frac{1}{64}$	-2	$\frac{5}{64}$	12	$\frac{3}{64}$
-14	$\frac{1}{64}$	0	$\frac{6}{64}$	14	$\frac{1}{64}$
-12	$\frac{3}{64}$	2	$\frac{5}{64}$	16	$\frac{1}{64}$
-10	$\frac{4}{64}$	4	$\frac{4}{64}$	18	$\frac{2}{64}$
-8	$\frac{4}{64}$	6	$\frac{4}{64}$	20	$\frac{1}{64}$

the critical region directly. The largest sample sum is obtained when all signs are positive, which can happen in just one way. The next largest sum is obtained when the smallest difference is negative. The smallest difference is unity, and there are two instances of this magnitude. Therefore, there are two possible samples having a sum equal to 18 and one sample having a sum of 20, making a total of three samples with a sum of 18 or greater. With only 64 distinct possibilities, we cannot enlarge the critical region by even one more element without exceeding .05. Hence, the critical region is $x = 18, 20$ and the actual significance level is $\frac{3}{64}$.

3-8. The Multinomial Distribution. Whereas the binomial distribution pertains to two alternative results E, $\bar{E}$ of an experiment, the *multinomial distribution* applies to any exhaustive set of mutually exclusive results R_1, R_2, . . . , R_k. If n independent trials are made, and the probability of R_i on a single trial is p_i (where $p_1 + p_2 \cdots + p_k = 1$), the multinomial distribution is the compound or joint distribution of the numbers of results of each type, say x_1 instances of R_1, x_2 of R_2, . . . , x_k of R_k, where $x_1 + x_2 + \cdots + x_k = n$. This distribution is obtained immediately from the multinomial law of probability (Example 2-6, Eq. 2-4). Hence,

$$f(x_1, x_2, \ldots , x_k) = \frac{n!}{x_1! x_2! \cdots x_k!} \, p_1{}^{x_1} p_2{}^{x_2} \cdots p_k{}^{x_k} \qquad (3\text{-}5)$$

Multinomial Distribution

where

$$p_1 + p_2 + \cdots + p_k = 1 \qquad x_1 + x_2 + \cdots + x_k = n$$
$$x_i = 0, 1, 2, \ldots$$

Inasmuch as the x's have a fixed total, any one of them can be eliminated and replaced by the expression n minus the sum of the others; similarly any one of the p's can be expressed as unity minus the sum of the others. Hence, we may regard the multinomial distribution as a joint distribution of $k - 1$ discrete variates and containing k independent parameters. However, the symmetrical form used in Eq. (3-5) is the simplest algebraic statement. The fact that the sum of $f(x_1, x_2, \ldots , x_k)$ taken over all admissible values of the x's is unity is established by noticing that

58   PROBABILITY AND RANDOM VARIABLES

$f(x_1,x_2, \ldots ,x_k)$ is simply the general term of the multinomial expansion of $(p_1 + p_2 + \cdots + p_k)^n$ and the latter expression reduces to 1^n or 1.

Example 3-7. Competitors A, B, C control respectively 50 per cent, 30 per cent, and 20 per cent of the market for a certain commodity. In a random sample of four independent buyers, what is the distribution of trade division among the three companies? This is an example of the multinomial distribution with $n = 4$, $p_1 = .5$, $p_2 = .3$, $p_3 = .2$. Letting x_1, x_2, x_3 denote the respective numbers of customers of A, B, C, the distribution is

$$f(x_1,x_2,x_3) = \frac{4!}{x_1!x_2!x_3!} (.5)^{x_1}(.3)^{x_2}(.2)^{x_3} \qquad (x_1 + x_2 + x_3 = 4; x_i = 0, 1, \ldots , 4)$$

The numerical values of this joint-probability function are given in Table 3-11.

TABLE 3-11. MULTINOMIAL DISTRIBUTION WITH $n = 4$, $p_1 = .5$, $p_2 = .3$, $p_3 = .2$; JOINT-PROBABILITY FUNCTION OF EXAMPLE 3-7

(x_1,x_2,x_3)	$f(x_1,x_2,x_3)$	(x_1,x_2,x_3)	$f(x_1,x_2,x_3)$	(x_1,x_2,x_3)	$f(x_1,x_2,x_3)$
4,0,0	.0625	2,0,2	.0600	0,4,0	.0081
3,1,0	.1500	1,3,0	.0540	0,3,1	.0216
3,0,1	.1000	1,2,1	.1080	0,2,2	.0216
2,2,0	.1350	1,1,2	.0720	0,1,3	.0096
2,1,1	.1800	1,0,3	.0160	0,0,4	.0016

Over-all sum: 1.0000

Example 3-8. Show that the respective total probabilities of the various values of one of the x's in the multinomial distribution follow the binomial distribution. This fact is intuitively obvious, since the total probability of a stated value of a particular x is obtained by adding the probabilities of all distinct ways in which that value can occur, and this amounts to consolidating these ways into one composite alternative. However, it is instructive to work out an analytic proof. Holding the value of x_1 fixed, let us put $m = n - x_1$ and write $p_2' = p_2/(1 - p_1)$, $p_3' = p_3/(1 - p_1)$, $\ldots$, $p_k' = p_k/(1 - p_1)$. Then $p_2' + p_3' + \cdots + p_k' = 1$ because $p_2 + p_3 + \cdots + p_k = 1 - p_1$; also $x_2 + x_3 + \cdots + x_k = m$. If we divide and multiply by $(n - x_1)! = m!$ we may revamp the joint-probability function as follows:

$$f(x_1,x_2, \ldots ,x_k) = f_1(x_1)g(x_2,x_3, \ldots ,x_k) \tag{3-6}$$

where
$$f_1(x_1) = \frac{n!}{x_1!(n - x_1)!} p_1^{x_1}(1 - p_1)^{n-x_1} \tag{3-7}$$

$$g(x_2,x_3, \ldots ,x_k) = \frac{m!}{x_2!x_3! \ldots x_k!} p_2'^{x_2}p_3'^{x_3} \ldots p_k'^{x_k} \tag{3-8}$$

Now the function $g(x_2,x_3, \ldots ,x_k)$ satisfies all the conditions for the multinomial distribution with parameters m, p_2', $\ldots$, p_k'. Hence, the sum of g over all admissible values of x_2, x_3, $\ldots$, x_k is unity, and so the corresponding sum of $f(x_1,x_2, \ldots ,x_k)$ reduces to $f_1(x_1)$, as was to be proved. As we shall explain in Chap. 5, the resultant distribution $f_1(x_1)$ is known as the *marginal distribution* of x_1, and we have proved that this marginal distribution of x_1 is binomial with parameters n, p_1. By the same token, the function $g(x_2,x_3, \ldots ,x_k)$ constitutes the *conditional* joint-probability function of x_2, x_3, $\ldots$, x_k for a given value of x_1, and we have found that the conditional distribution of these variates is multinomial with parameters $m = n - x_1$, $p_2' = p_2/(1 - p_1), \ldots, p_k' = p_k/(1 - p_1)$. By mere change of notation, corresponding propositions can be established for each of the other variates $x_2, x_3, \ldots, x_k$ in turn.

3-9. The Hypergeometric Distribution.

The independence of successive trials, assumed in deriving the binomial and multinomial distributions, is realizable in an infinite population, but in the case of a finite population, it necessitates the continual replacement of each unit withdrawn. The *hypergeometric distribution* applies to sampling from a finite population without replacement. Consider a population of N objects and let a denote the number of these which are of type A. Suppose that the sampling process is random to the extent that all objects which are still available after any number of removals are equally likely to be chosen on the next drawing; we shall describe this sampling situation as *conditionally random*. Now if such a conditionally random sample of n objects is withdrawn, and x denotes the number of these which are of type A, the distribution of x is called the *hypergeometric distribution*. If $n \leq a$, the admissible values of x are obviously $0, 1, 2, \ldots, n$ whereas if $n > a$, the admissible values stop short at a. By applying the hypergeometric law of probability (Example 2-5, Eq. 2-3), we may write down the distribution as follows:

$$f(x) = \frac{C(a,x)C(N - a, n - x)}{C(N,n)} \qquad (x = 0, 1, 2, \ldots, [n,a]) \quad (3\text{-}9)$$

Hypergeometric Distribution

where $[n,a]$ means the smaller of the two numbers n, a if they are different, or, of course, their common value if they are the same. In this distribution, there are three parameters N, a, n. Later on in this section, we shall show that $f(x)$ sums to unity.

Example 3-9. As the couples enter the ballroom for a college dance, each person is given a ticket bearing a number, no two of which are alike. A duplicate set of tickets is thoroughly mixed during the intermission, and 3 are drawn at random, prizes being awarded to the holders of the matching numbers. If 50 people attend the dance, what is the probability that at least 1 person out of a certain group of 3 couples wins a prize? What is the probability that this group receives 2 prizes? Here the 50 tickets constitute a population with $N = 50$, the 6 tickets which duplicate those held by the 3 couples make up objects of type A, with $a = 6$, and the three tickets drawn provide the sample, with $n = 3$. Accordingly, the questions are answered by calculating terms of the hypergeometric distribution with $N = 50$, $a = 6$, $n = 3$, the general term of which is

$$f(x) = \frac{C(6,x)C(44, 3 - x)}{C(50,3)}$$

The calculation of these terms is exhibited in Table 3-12. The probability that at least 1 person in the group wins a prize is equal to the complement of the probability that no person wins, hence

$$P(x \geq 1) = 1 - f(0) = .3243$$

The probability that this group receives two prizes is simply $f(2) = .0337$.

TABLE 3-12. CALCULATION OF TERMS OF HYPERGEOMETRIC DISTRIBUTION WITH
$N = 50, \ a = 6, \ n = 3$

x	$3 - x$	$C(6,x)$	$C(44, 3 - x)$	Product†	$f(x)$	$F(x)$
0	3	1	13,244	13,244	.6757	.6757
1	2	6	946	5,676	.2896	.9653
2	1	15	44	660	.0337	.9990
3	0	20	1	20	.0010	1.0000

† $C(50,3) = 19,600$; sum of products $= 19,600$.

Analyzing this problem from another viewpoint, we may regard the three lucky numbers as constituting the objects of type A and the numbers held by the three couples as constituting the sample. True, the numbers might not be assigned in a random order as the couples enter the ballroom, but the fact that the duplicate set of tickets has been randomized produces essentially the same effect. Thus we conclude that the probabilities in question could be obtained equally well from an alternative hypergeometric distribution with $N = 50, \ a = 3, \ n = 6$, that is,

$$f(x) = \frac{C(3,x)C(47, 6 - x)}{C(50,6)}$$

This conclusion is perfectly correct, for (as the reader may easily verify by expressing $f(x)$ in terms of factorials) the interchange of a and n in the hypergeometric distribution has no effect on the numerical value of $f(x)$. For comparison with the previous distribution, the calculation of $f(x)$ with $a = 3, \ n = 6$ is exhibited in Table 3-13. The respective terms of the two distributions are identical.

TABLE 3-13. CALCULATION OF TERMS OF HYPERGEOMETRIC DISTRIBUTION WITH
$N = 50, \ a = 3, \ n = 6$

x	$6 - x$	$C(3,x)$	$C(47, 6 - x)$	Product†	$f(x)$	$F(x)$
0	6	1	10,737,573	10,737,573	.6757	.6757
1	5	3	1,533,939	4,601,817	.2896	.9653
2	4	3	178,365	535,095	.0337	.9990
3	3	1	16,215	16,215	.0010	1.0000

† $C(50,6) = 15,890,700$; sum of products $= 15,890,700$.

Example 3-10. In the development of a vaccine to combat a certain ailment A, two groups V and C of 100 animals each are carefully selected so that as far as possible one group is a duplicate of the other. This is done by obtaining matched pairs and assigning one member to V at random (for instance, by flipping an unbiased coin) and the other to C. All animals in group V are vaccinated, but for comparative purposes no animal in group C (the "control" group) is vaccinated. All animals in both groups are then equally exposed to ailment A. It turns out that 10 animals contract the ailment and that 9 of these are in the control group. How impressive is this result with regard to the efficacy of the vaccine? This is a typical problem of experimental research, wherein the very fact that a new process or product is in the stage of development rules out a convincing demonstration of merit on the basis of established knowledge. Only the naïve accept an experimental result as final; the experienced realize how readily a favorable indication can be a stroke of luck. Therefore, it is routine policy to suspend judgment until the workings of pure chance have been investigated. To this end, we tentatively adopt the negativistic attitude that we are dealing with random phenomena (this assumption is called the *null hypothesis*) and try to formulate a mathematical model under which we can compute the probabilities of all possible experimental outcomes. In this case, we lump the two groups together, note that there are 10 animals of type A, and look into the distribution of the variate x, which represents the number of instances of type A we would obtain by chance if we selected 100 animals by lot. According to our null hypothesis, group V represents nothing more special than a random half of a deck of cards; anything not in group V automatically gets assigned to group C. The distribution of x is hypergeometric with $N = 200$, $a = 10$, $n = 100$. Hence

$$f(x) = \frac{C(10,x)C(190, 100 - x)}{C(200,100)} \qquad (x = 0, 1, \ldots, 10)$$

This distribution is shown in Table 3-14. From the fact that $F(1) = .0093$, we see

TABLE 3-14. HYPERGEOMETRIC DISTRIBUTION WITH $N = 200$, $a = 10$, $n = 100$

x	0	1	2	3	4	5	6	7	8	9	10
$f(x)$	.0008	.0085	.0410	.1153	.2082	.2525	.2082	.1153	.0410	.0085	.0008
$F(x)$	.0008	.0093	.0503	.1656	.3738	.6263	.8345	.9498	.9908	.9993	1.0000

that the probability is less than .01 that as few as one ailing animal would have been included in group V on a chance basis. Having thus found that the comparative freedom from attack in the vaccinated group is not reasonably attributed to chance, we are prepared to say that the evidence in favor of efficacy is strong. We shall make further use of this kind of reasoning in Sec. 3-10.

Example 3-11. A certain number a out of a pack of N cards, which are otherwise alike, are marked with the letter A. The pack is then thoroughly shuffled, and b of the cards are marked with the letter B, without reference to whether or not a particular card was previously marked A. Letting x denote the number of cards bearing the double mark A, B, what is the distribution of x? From N cards we can choose b cards to be marked with the letter B in $C(N,b)$ distinct ways. Any such assortment which contains x cards already marked A will now have x double-marked cards, and the rest, $b - x$, will bear the single mark B. Now there are $C(a,x)$ distinct ways of selecting x of the A cards to be used in this assortment, and for any given selection of A cards, there are $C(N - a, b - x)$ ways of choosing the remaining $b - x$ cards from the $N - a$ unmarked cards. Therefore the number of distinct ways of obtaining x double-marked cards is given by the product $C(a,x)C(N - a, b - x)$, and the distribution of x is

$$f(x) = \frac{C(a,x)C(N - a, b - x)}{C(N,b)} \qquad (x = 0, 1, 2, \ldots, [b,a])$$

which is hypergeometric with parameters N, a, b. The logical equivalence of a and b, which is evident in this context, points once again to the fact that the distribution would not be altered if these two parameters were interchanged.

For large values of N, the computation of the terms of the hypergeometric distribution becomes laborious, and because there are three parameters, convenient tables have not been compiled. However, the work is shortened considerably by means of the following recursion formulas, which are derived by simple division.

$$f(x + 1) = \frac{(n - x)(a - x)}{(x + 1)(N - a - n + 1 + x)} f(x)$$

$$f(x - 1) = \frac{x(N - a - n + x)}{(n + 1 - x)(a + 1 - x)} f(x)$$

(3-10)

In addition we also have

$$f(0) = \frac{C(N - a, n)}{C(N, n)}$$

(3-11)

which can be expressed either as the quotient of two products of n factors or as the quotient of two products of a factors, whichever is easier. This idea was used in computing Table 3-14.

One may readily surmise that the hypergeometric distribution approaches the binomial as N and a become sufficiently large, for sampling depletion can be considered negligible if n is small compared to a (and a fortiori small compared to N). In that case, we may divide both numerator and denominator of the quotient $(a - x)/(N - a - n + 1 + x)$ by N, obtaining, in the limit, the quotient p/q where $p = a/N$, $q = (N - a)/N$. Therefore,

$$f(x + 1) \rightarrow \frac{(n - x)}{(x + 1)} \frac{p}{q} f(x)$$

in agreement with the binomial recursion formula. Moreover,

$$f(0) = \frac{(N - a)(N - a - 1) \cdots (N - a + 1 - n)}{(N)(N - 1) \cdots (N + 1 - n)}$$

and under the conditions stated, $f(0) \rightarrow q^n$. Consequently, it follows by induction that the successive terms of the hypergeometric distribution approach the corresponding terms of the binomial for very large values of the parameters N, a and comparatively small values of n.

We have yet to prove that the terms $f(x)$ of the hypergeometric probability function sum to unity. This fact may be established by employing the identity

$$(1 + u)^N \equiv (1 + u)^a (1 + u)^{N-a}$$

(3-12)

Expanding both sides of (3-12) by the binomial theorem we have

$$\sum_{n=0}^{N} C(N,n)u^n \equiv \left[\sum_{r=0}^{a} C(a,r)u^r \right] \left[\sum_{s=0}^{N-a} C(N-a, s)u^s \right] \quad (3\text{-}13)$$

Now multiplying the two sums on the right side of Eq. (3-13) together and collecting terms of degree n in u, we find that the result is

$$u^n[C(a,0)C(N-a, n) + C(a,1)C(N-a, n-1) + \cdots$$
$$+ C(a,n)C(N-a, 0)]$$

Therefore, equating coefficients of u^n on both sides of Eq. (3-13) we get

$$C(N,n) = \sum_{x=0}^{n} C(a,x)C(N-a, n-x) \quad (3\text{-}14)$$

whence, as was to be proved,

$$\sum_{x} f(x) = 1$$

In this proof we have taken it for granted that $n \le a$, but this can be done without loss of generality, because these two parameters are interchangeable.

3-10. The Hypergeometric Test for the Difference between Two Percentages. Having pursued research aimed at altering the relative frequency of some attribute A in the population considered, the investigator sets up an experiment to test the efficacy of the proposed procedure. For test purposes, two equivalent groups of individuals are secured. One of these, conventionally designated as the experimental group, will receive the treatment in question, while the other, designated as the control group, will not. After the treatment has had time to take its supposed effect, the two samples will be compared as to their relative frequencies of attribute A. For a *fixed* total sample size, maximum precision will be achieved by dividing the two groups equally. On the other hand, recruiting difficulties or the expense of treatment may restrict the size of the experimental group without appreciably affecting the size of the control group. In this situation, the total sample size is not definitely prescribed, and provided that comparability can be maintained, the control group should be as large as practicable; for consistent with any stipulated conditions, statistical precision increases with total sample size. Since the object of research here has been to produce a change in a stated direction, either increase or decrease as the case may be, the critical region should generally be one-sided. The statistical question to be decided is whether or not the two relative frequencies are significantly different, in the sense that they could not be reasonably considered as random specimens of the same population.

In the first sample, let us say, there are N_1 observations, and of these, a number a_1 exhibit the attribute A, while the remaining $N_1 - a_1$ observations do not. In the second sample, having N_2 observations, a number a_2 exhibit attribute A, while the remaining $N_2 - a_2$ observations do not. These facts are represented schematically in Table 3-15, wherein $N \equiv N_1 + N_2$ and $a \equiv a_1 + a_2$.

TABLE 3-15. CONTINGENCY TABLE

Designation	A	Not A	Total
Sample 1..........	a_1	$N_1 - a_1$	N_1
Sample 2..........	a_2	$N_2 - a_2$	N_2
Total............	a	$N - a$	N

If both samples were drawn at random from the same infinite population, the common probability of attribute A would be some definite quantity p, but since its value is unknown, we resort to constructing a population in which the probability of A is a weighted average of the percentages observed in the two samples. That is, we simply combine the data, thereby obtaining a finite population consisting of $N = N_1 + N_2$ elements, of which the number $a = a_1 + a_2$ exhibit A. Imagine now, the population of all distinct pairs of samples that could be formed from the combined data by arbitrarily allocating N_1 observations to the first sample and the remaining N_2 observations to the second. By construction, both samples are now being drawn from the same finite population of N observations, in the sense that initially all individuals have equal chances of being included in a particular sample. The population, of course, is exhausted by the two samples; nevertheless, it is intuitively plausible that in the long run, if an unlimited number of independent trials could be made, the probability of A would be the same in both. The truth of this conjecture can be established by a simple argument, based on mathematical expectation; but until this topic has been discussed (Chap. 7), the student may accept the following statements without proof. In the first sample, the mean number of A's is $N_1 a/N$ and in the second, $N_2 a/N$. In each, therefore, the mean relative frequency is a/N.

In any selection, let x denote the number of type A elements assigned to sample 1. Then there are $a - x$ elements of type A in sample 2, and the percentages are x/N_1 and $(a - x)/N_2$ respectively. As a test variate, we should naturally consider employing the difference between the sample percentages, say

$$d = \frac{x}{N_1} - \frac{a - x}{N_2}$$

However, it is evident that d is uniquely determined by x, and since the latter is more convenient to use, we shall choose x as our test variate. By simplifying, we readily obtain

$$d = \frac{Nx - aN_1}{N_1 N_2} = \frac{N}{N_1 N_2}\left(x - \frac{aN_1}{N}\right)$$

whence it is clear that the two percentages will be equal $(d = 0)$ when $x = aN_1/N$.

Depending on the working hypothesis, critical regions will be constructed (as indicated in Sec. 3-6) with the desired significance level. Since x is a hypergeometric variate, its distribution is

$$f(x) = \frac{C(a,x)C(N - a, N_1 - x)}{C(N,N_1)} \qquad (x = 0, 1, \ldots , [a,N_1]) \quad (3\text{-}15)$$

Like many other contributions to statistics, the hypergeometric test is due to R. A. Fisher. The following example was based on a real experiment, but we have simplified it for purposes of illustration.

Example 3-12. In a carefully controlled experiment on the value of elastic stockings in the treatment of thromboembolic diseases, case histories on 4,694 hospital patients were compiled. Half of. this group wore elastic stockings during the period of treatment, and the other half (the control group) did not. The total sample was divided into 2,347 matched pairs chosen on the basis of nearly equal proneness to or affliction with thromboembolic diseases. By random selection, one member of each pair was allocated to the stocking group, and the other member, to the control group. A great deal of additional information was gained from the experiment, but to simplify the problem, let us confine our attention to the incidence of deaths. The issue, then, is whether we are justified in concluding, on the strength of the obtained evidence, that the stockings are a significant factor in reducing mortality. The null hypothesis is that the stockings have no effect. Letting x denote the number of deaths in the stocking group, we shall use a one-sided critical region which, in view of the working hypothesis, will be built up from the lower end of the scale. Choose .05 as the level of significance.

As it turned out, eight deaths due to embolism occurred in the control group, but no deaths occurred in the stocking group. The distribution of x, under the null hypothesis, is shown in Table 3-16. The nearest we can approach .05 without over-

TABLE 3-16. DISTRIBUTION, UNDER NULL HYPOTHESIS, OF NUMBER OF DEATHS IN STOCKING GROUP

x	0	1	2	3	4	5	6	7	8
$f(x)$	.004	.031	.109	.219	.274	.219	.109	.031	.004
$F(x)$	.004	.035	.144	.363	.637	.856	.965	.996	1.000

shooting is .035, and the corresponding boundary of the critical region will be $x = 1$. Since the observed value $x = 0$ falls within the critical region, even with a more stringent level of significance than we initially planned to use, the null hypothesis is rejected, and we accept the working hypothesis that in the treatment of thrombo-embolic diseases, elastic stockings are a significant factor in reducing mortality.[1]

Once again, the numerical labor of performing the test can be reduced a great deal by confining the computation to what is actually needed. Since the critical region starts at the lower end, we need only compute $f(0)$, in this case, in order to find out whether the chosen level of significance is satisfied.

In the hypergeometric test, the magnitude test, and other tests commonly employed, the distribution obtained under the null hypothesis is actually a conditional distribution. By holding to a constant level of significance in the conditional distributions, we ensure the same level in the marginal distribution; but the boundaries of the critical regions vary from one experiment to another, whereas they would remain fixed if the marginal distribution could be used. Admittedly, it would be preferable to base the test on the marginal distribution, but requirements of experimental control or difficulties in obtaining suitable data often impose such limitations on the availability of information that it is impossible to prescribe the marginal distribution of the test variate. Therefore, the conditional distribution is accepted as the alternative to abandoning the problem entirely.

3-11. The Geometric Distribution. If a chance event E has a constant probability p of occurring on any given trial, the number of trials x needed for the first occurrence of E is a discrete random variable which can take on any one of an infinite number of positive integral values 1, 2, 3, ... The distribution of x is called the *geometric distribution* because of its mathematical form. The only way in which trial x can yield the first occurrence of E is to have an unbroken run of $x - 1$ failures in the first $x - 1$ trials, followed by a success on trial x. The compound probability of $x - 1$ failures is q^{x-1}, and so that of $x - 1$ failures followed by a success is $q^{x-1}p$. Therefore, the geometric distribution is given by

$$f(x) = q^{x-1}p = pq^{x-1} \qquad (x = 1, 2, 3, \ldots) \qquad (3\text{-}16)$$
Geometric Distribution

Thus the geometric distribution is characterized by the single parameter p, since $q = 1 - p$. From the familiar formula for the sum of an infinite geometric series, we have

$$\sum_{x=1}^{\infty} f(x) = \frac{p}{1 - q} = \frac{p}{p} = 1 \qquad (3\text{-}17)$$

By the same token, the distribution function $F(x)$ is given by

$$F(x) = \sum_{t=1}^{x} f(t) = 1 - q^x \qquad (3\text{-}18)$$

[1] Although the hypergeometric distribution is not strictly applicable (since the samples were not drawn at random), a difference which is judged significant by this

Example 3-13. What are the chances that it will take more than six tosses to throw a seven with a pair of dice? The probability of throwing a seven on any toss is $\frac{1}{6}$, and so the probability that more than six trials will be required for the first success is

$$P(x > 6) = 1 - F(6) = 1 - [1 - (\frac{5}{6})^6] = (\frac{5}{6})^6 = .3349$$

Hence the probability is greater than $\frac{1}{3}$ that it will take more than six tosses to throw a seven with a pair of dice, despite the fact that the probability of obtaining a seven on a single toss is $\frac{1}{6}$. The first ten terms of this geometric distribution are shown in Table 3-17. Here the distribution function $F(x)$ has been computed independently by Eq. (3-18).

TABLE 3-17. GEOMETRIC DISTRIBUTION WITH $p = \frac{1}{6}$

x	1	2	3	4	5	6	7	8	9	10
$f(x)$	.1667	.1389	.1157	.0965	.0804	.0670	.0558	.0465	.0388	.0323
$F(x)$	.1667	.3056	.4213	.5177	.5981	.6651	.7209	.7674	.8062	.8385

3-12. The Poisson Distribution. Many random phenomena of interest in science and industry yield a discrete variate x having an infinite number of possible integral values 0, 1, 2, 3, . . . and satisfying conditions which lead to the *Poisson distribution:*

$$f(x) = e^{-\mu} \frac{\mu^x}{x!} \qquad (\mu > 0; \ x = 0, 1, 2, 3, \ldots) \qquad (3\text{-}19)$$

Poisson Distribution

Typical examples of Poisson variates include: (1) the number of inert particles of stated type suspended per cubic centimeter in a well-mixed liquid vehicle, (2) the number of misprints per page in a large volume of comparable printed material, (3) the number of responses per day to a large number of questionnaires, (4) the number of calls per minute at a telephone switchboard, (5) the number of accidents of a given kind per

FIG. 3-9

year in a large community under stable conditions, (6) the number of α particles emitted per unit time by a radioactive element, (7) the number of rocket-bomb hits within a specified small portion of a comparatively large area under prolonged bombardment. Let us now derive this distribution on the basis of a few simple hypotheses concerning the behavior of the following physical situation.

Events appear to occur at random in time and can be thus represented as points along the time axis (see Fig 3-9). A time interval of length T is chosen with the starting point picked at random anywhere on the line.

technique has passed a more severe test as we have increased the chance of accepting the null hypothesis.

On the basis of the following four assumptions, let us find the probability of exactly n of these events occurring in the random time interval T.

1. Statistical equilibrium. This hypothesis demands that the probability of n events occurring in this period of time T is exactly the same, regardless of where the interval T commences. It is also equivalent to stating that the average number of events per unit time is the same, regardless of how the infinite number of unit lengths are chosen on the time axis in order to obtain this average. Thus, if there are λ events per unit length of time, then the average number of events in the interval T is λT.

2. The probability that *one* observation will fall in an interval dT is $\lambda\, dT$. Thus, the probability of an observation falling in length dT is proportionate to dT, and doubling dT doubles the probability. This assumption is a basic one for the Poisson distribution, and it is an important concept.

3. The probability of two or more events in dT is of higher order than dT. The consequences of this assumption are the same as those following from the hypothesis that the events are independent.

4. The differentiability with respect to T. This introduces the restriction that the probability of n events occurring in the interval of T increases or decreases continuously as T increases or decreases. Thus, the probability itself has a continuous derivative with respect to T, which exists for all values of T.

Now let $P(n,T)$ be the probability that exactly n events have occurred in the time interval T. Then (since the law of total probability holds when, as in this case, the events are mutually exclusive) n events can occur in the interval $T + dT$ in the following ways, provided assumption 1 is true:

$$P(n, T + dT) = P(n,T)P(0,dT) + P(n - 1, T)P(1,dT)$$
$$+ P(n - 2, T)P(2,dT) + \cdots \quad (3\text{-}20)$$

where the following relation must exist:

$$P(0,dT) = 1 - P(1,dT) - P(2,dT) - \cdots \quad (3\text{-}21)$$

Replacing $P(0,dT)$ from Eq. (3-21) in Eq. (3-20) and dividing by dT gives

$$\frac{P(n, T + dt) - P(n,T)}{dT} = \frac{P(1,dT)}{dT}[P(n - 1, T) - P(n,T)] + \cdots$$
$$(3\text{-}22)$$

Now by assumption 4, the left-hand side of Eq. (3-22) in the limit becomes the derivative of $P(n,T)$ with respect to the interval T. All terms but the first on the right-hand side are zero by assumption 3, and thus by replacing $P(1,dT)$ by $\lambda\, dT$, according to assumption 2, we have

$$\frac{dP(n,T)}{dT} + \lambda P(n,T) = \lambda P(n-1, T) \tag{3-23}$$

We shall define $P(-1, T) = 0$ so that by setting $n = 0$ in Eq. (3-23) there results

$$\frac{dP(0,T)}{dT} + \lambda P(0,T) = 0$$

which has the solution

$$P(0,T) = ce^{-\lambda T} \qquad \text{where } c = 1, \text{ since } P(0,0) = 1$$

Now by assuming $n = 1$ in Eq. (3-23), we have

$$\frac{dP(1,T)}{dT} + \lambda P(1,T) = \lambda e^{-\lambda T}$$

which has as the solution

$$P(1,T) = \frac{(\lambda T)e^{-\lambda T}}{1!}$$

if we assume the initial condition $P(1,0) = 0$.

Continuing to operate recursively on Eq. (3-23), we have finally

$$P(n,T) = \frac{e^{-\lambda T}(\lambda T)^n}{n!} \tag{3-24}$$

Since λT is the average number of occurrences, the parameter μ in Eq. (3-19) for the Poisson distribution may be interpreted as the average number of occurrences or successes. Thus, <u>if the average number of successes is μ, the probability of x successes is given by</u>

$$f(x) = \frac{e^{-\mu}\mu^x}{x!} \qquad \begin{array}{l} x = 0, 1, 2, \ldots \\ \mu > 0 \end{array} \tag{3-25}$$

In the above derivation the average number of events per unit time was considered a constant. In many situations, however, this is not a good assumption. For example, if the events were the arrival of customers at a

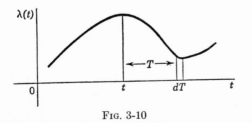

Fig. 3-10

restaurant, the rate would certainly be a function of the time of day. Let $\lambda(t)$ be the density of events per unit time at any instant t so that $\lambda(t)$ would change continuously as in Fig. 3-10. Let $P(n,T,t)$ be the probability of exactly n events occurring in a time interval T after a beginning instant t. The previous assumptions will still be made, except of course that the probability that an observation will fall in an interval dT is now $\lambda(t + T)\, dT$, so that

$$P(n,\ T + dT,\ t) = P(n,T,t)P(0,\ dT,\ t + T)$$
$$+ P(n - 1,\ T,\ t)P(1,\ dT,\ t + T) + \cdots \quad (3\text{-}26)$$

and

$$P(0,\ dT,\ t + T) = 1 - P(1,\ dT,\ t + T) - P(2,\ dT,\ t + T) \cdots \quad (3\text{-}27)$$

Since $P(1,\ dT,\ t + T) = \lambda(t + T)\, dT$, we may now substitute $P(0,\ dT,\ t + T)$ from Eq. (3-27) into Eq. (3-26) and simplify as before. Thus

$$\frac{dP(n,T,t)}{dT} + \lambda(t + T)P(n,T,t) = \lambda(t + T)P(n - 1,\ T,\ t) \quad (3\text{-}28)$$

If again we define $P(-1,T,t) = 0$ and also $\mu(t,T) = \int_0^T \lambda(t + T)\, dT$, then the successive integration of Eq. (3-28) gives

$$P(n,T,t) = \frac{\mu^n e^{-\mu}}{n!} \qquad \text{where } \mu = \int_t^{T+t} \lambda(u)\, du \qquad (3\text{-}29)$$

Thus the Poisson distribution is quite general and even can be applied to a situation where the density of events is variable.

The fact that the Poisson distribution is characterized by the single parameter μ makes it feasible to tabulate it extensively. Excellent tables have been prepared by E. C. Molina under the title "Poisson's Exponential Binomial Limit."[2] Molina's tables give $f(x)$ and $1 - F(x - 1)$ to 6 decimals (seven for very small μ) for values of μ up to 100 by varying decimal intervals of μ from .001 to 15 and unit intervals beyond 15. Figure 3-11, drawn from Molina's tables, demonstrates the Poisson distribution for $\mu = 1, 2, 3, 5, 10$. The distribution is highly skewed to the right when $\mu \leq 1$ but becomes more nearly symmetrical as μ increases.

By substituting in (3-19) it is easy to verify the fact that the Poisson probability function satisfies the following recursion formulas:

$$f(x + 1) = \frac{\mu}{x + 1}\, f(x) \qquad f(x - 1) = \frac{x}{\mu}\, f(x) \qquad (3\text{-}30)$$

In using these formulas to compute successive values of $f(x)$, it is convenient to start at $f(0)$ when μ is small, but when μ is large it is better to choose an initial value of x near μ.

[1] E. C. Molina, "Poisson's Exponential Binomial Limit," D. Van Nostrand Company, Inc., Princeton, N.J., 1942.

As suggested by some of the examples cited, and by the title of Molina's tables, the Poisson distribution is a limiting form of the binomial under certain conditions.   These conditions are that $p \to 0$ and $n \to \infty$ in such

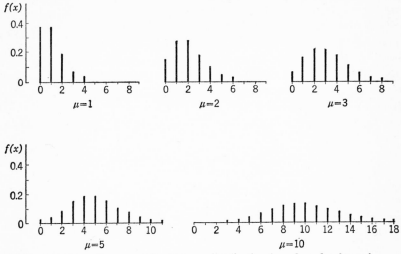

FIG. 3-11. Line diagram of the Poisson distribution for selected values of μ.

a manner that the product np remains finite and approaches a definite limit μ.   Examining the binomial recurrence formula

$$f(x + 1) = \frac{(n - x)p}{(x + 1)q} f(x) \tag{3-31}$$

under these assumptions, we observe that $(n - x)p \to np \to \mu$ while $q \to 1$ whence

$$f(x + 1) \to \frac{\mu}{x + 1} f(x) \tag{3-32}$$

in agreement with the Poisson recurrence formula (3-30).   Moreover, we have

$$f(0) = q^n = (1 - p)^n \equiv (1 + h)^{-np/h} \tag{3-33}$$

where $h = -p$.   Therefore,

$$\lim f(0) = \lim (1 + h)^{-np/h} = e^{-\mu} \tag{3-34}$$

and this fact together with (3-32) shows inductively that the binomial distribution approaches the Poisson.   For any n if p is small, the Poisson distribution with $\mu = np$ may be used to approximate the binomial.   The maximum error increases with p but is nearly independent of n.

Illustrations of the Poisson approximation to the binomial are afforded by Examples 3-3 and 3-4.   In Example 3-3, $n = 500$ and $p = \frac{1}{500}$, so

72   PROBABILITY AND RANDOM VARIABLES

that $\mu = np = 1$.   In Example 3-4, $n = 2,500$, $p = .02$, and $\mu = np = 50$. Corresponding values of $f(x)$ for the binomial and Poisson distributions are presented in Table 3-18 for Example 3-3 and in Table 3-19 for Example 3-4.   In the first comparison, the greatest difference amounts to four units in the fourth decimal place, and in the second, the greatest difference is six units in the fourth decimal place.   The important question in many applications of probability theory is whether or not the probability of a certain event is less than some prescribed critical value, for instance, .05 or .01.   Therefore, with regard to an approximation of this probability, it is ordinarily the absolute value of the error rather than the relative error which affects our decision.

TABLE 3-18. COMPARISON OF PROBABILITY FUNCTIONS $f(x)$ OF BINOMIAL DISTRIBUTION WITH $n = 500$, $p = \frac{1}{500}$ AND POISSON DISTRIBUTION WITH $\mu = np = 1$

x	Binomial	Poisson
0	.3675	.3679
1	.3682	.3679
2	.1841	.1839
3	.0612	.0613
4	.0153	.0153
5	.00303	.00307
6	.00050	.00051
7	.000071	.000073

The fact that the Poisson distribution is so widely used as an approximation to the binomial sometimes gives the false impression that it has no independent status of its own.   It should be clearly understood that the Poisson distribution is a true probability distribution, mathematically derivable from definite premises, and having properties and applications unique to itself.

3-13. A Single Waiting Line.   The concepts which are fundamental to the Poisson distribution are used many times in the development of mathematical models for industrial and scientific work.   A very simple illustration is now presented from the field of what is usually termed "waiting lines" or "queueing theory."   Let us assume that we have a single servicing station at which customers arrive in such a manner that the probability of exactly n arrivals in an interval of time T is given by Eq. (3-24).   The λ in this equation represents the average number of people who arrive at the service station per unit of time.   If a customer arrives and the servicing unit is not busy, he immediately enters the servicing unit and starts being served.   If the servicing unit is busy, he has to wait his turn, and since only one person can be served at a time, the customers

TABLE 3-19. COMPARISON OF PROBABILITY FUNCTIONS $f(x)$ OF BINOMIAL DISTRIBUTION WITH $n = 2,500$, $p = .02$ AND POISSON DISTRIBUTION WITH $\mu = np = 50$

x	Binomial	Poisson	x	Binomial	Poisson
(0–25)	.0000	.0000	52	.0536	.0531
26	.0001	.0001	53	.0505	.0501
27	.0001	.0001	54	.0467	.0464
28	.0002	.0002	55	.0424	.0422
29	.0004	.0004	56	.0378	.0376
30	.0006	.0007	57	.0331	.0330
31	.0010	.0011	58	.0284	.0285
32	.0016	.0017	59	.0240	.0241
33	.0025	.0026	60	.0199	.0201
34	.0036	.0038	61	.0163	.0165
35	.0052	.0054	62	.0131	.0133
36	.0073	.0075	63	.0103	.0105
37	.0099	.0102	64	.0080	.0082
38	.0131	.0134	65	.0061	.0063
39	.0169	.0172	66	.0046	.0048
40	.0212	.0215	67	.0034	.0036
41	.0260	.0262	68	.0025	.0026
42	.0311	.0312	69	.0018	.0019
43	.0363	.0363	70	.0013	.0014
44	.0413	.0412	71	.0009	.0010
45	.0460	.0458	72	.0006	.0007
46	.0501	.0498	73	.0004	.0005
47	.0534	.0530	74	.0003	.0003
48	.0557	.0552	75	.0002	.0002
49	.0569	.0563	76	.0001	.0001
50	.0569	.0563	77	.0001	.0001
51	.0558	.0552	78	.0000	.0001

who are waiting queue up in front of the servicing unit. Let us also assume that the servicing unit is capable of servicing an average number of customers per hour which is a constant, and that the probability that it will service exactly n customers in a time T is again given by an equation of the same form as (3-24) where λ is now the average service rate.

If P_n is the probability that there are n units in line at time t (including the customer being served), A the average arrival rate, and S the average servicing rate, then we may set up a system of differential equations relating the various states in which the system may find itself. According to the Poisson hypothesis, the probability of an arrival in time dt is $A\ dt$, and the probability of a completion of a service occurring in time dt is $S\,dt$. Also, only one event can occur in an interval of time dt which eliminates the possibility of a simultaneous occurrence of an arrival and a service completion. Thus, the change in the probability of being in state P_0 (i.e., dP_0) is made up of two mutually exclusive events. One possibility is that the system is in the state P_0 and a customer arrives. This contribution to the change is, of course, negative, since it decreases the probability of the occurrence of this state. The other possibility is that the system has one customer in service and he completes his service in this instant of time dt. This contribution to dP_0 is positive. When, however, dP_1 is considered, there are now four mutually exclusive possibilities. The system can be in state P_0 with an arrival occurring, or in state P_2 with a service completion, both of which increase the probability of P_1. If the system is in state P_1, either an arrival or a service completion changes this state and therefore contributes negatively to dP_1. We thus have the following system of equations:

$$
\begin{aligned}
dP_0 &= -AP_0\,dt + SP_1\,dt \\
dP_1 &= -AP_1\,dt - SP_1\,dt + AP_0\,dt + SP_2\,dt
\end{aligned}
\qquad (3\text{-}35)
$$

$$
\cdots\cdots\cdots\cdots\cdots\cdots\cdots\cdots
$$

$$
dP_n = [AP_{n-1} + SP_{n+1} - (S + A)P_n]\,dt
$$

$$
\cdots\cdots\cdots\cdots\cdots\cdots\cdots
$$

This system of differential equations is infinite and cannot in general be solved. However, if only the steady-state solution is desired which gives the percentage of the time that the system is in each of the states on the average, then this may be obtained by assuming that

$$
\frac{dP_0}{dt} = \frac{dP_1}{dt} = \cdots = \frac{dP_n}{dt} = \cdots = 0
\qquad (3\text{-}36)
$$

which yields

$$
-AP_0 + SP_1 = 0
$$
$$
-A_1P_1 - SP_1 + AP_0 + SP_2 = 0
\qquad (3\text{-}37)
$$
$$
\cdots\cdots\cdots\cdots\cdots\cdots
$$
$$
AP_{n-1} + SP_{n+1} - (S + A)P_n = 0
$$

If these equations are solved successively, each variable may be expressed in terms of P_0 or

$$
P_1 = \frac{A}{S}\,A_0 \qquad P_2 = \frac{A^2}{S^2}\,P_0 \qquad \cdots \qquad P_n = \frac{A^n}{S^n}\,P_0 \qquad \text{etc.} \quad (3\text{-}38)
$$

Since the sum of the probabilities must equal unity, it follows that

$$
\sum_{n=0}^{\infty} P_n = P_0\left(1 + \frac{A}{S} + \frac{A^2}{S^2} + \cdots\right) = 1
\qquad (3\text{-}39)
$$

which, if $A/S < 1$, gives

$$P_0 = 1 - \frac{A}{S} \quad \text{or} \quad P_n = \left(1 - \frac{A}{S}\right)\left(\frac{A}{S}\right)^n \qquad (3\text{-}40)$$

EXERCISES

1. For an unbiased coin, the probability of heads is $\frac{1}{2}$. Letting x denote the number of heads in five independent tosses, write an equation for the probability of any possible number of heads and indicate the values of x for which the equation is valid. Show by actual addition that the separate probabilities add up to unity.

$Ans.$ $f(x) = C(5,x)/32$ $(x = 0, 1, \ldots , 5)$.

2. Assuming that the sexes are equally likely, what is the distribution of the number of girls in a family of six children? Plot the probability function and the distribution function. What is the probability that a family of six children will have at least two girls?

$Ans.$ Binomial with $n = 6$, $p = \frac{1}{2} = q$; hence $f(x) = C(6,x)(\frac{1}{2})^6$, $(x = 0, 1, \ldots , 6)$; $P(x \geq 2) = \frac{57}{64} \approx .89$.

3. If A, B, C match pennies and odd man wins, what is the distribution of the number of times that A wins in four matches? Assume that there must be an odd man to constitute a match. Plot the probability function and distribution function. To three decimals compute the probability: (a) that A wins exactly twice, (b) that A loses at least twice, (c) that A either wins all matches or loses all matches (total probability).

$Ans.$ $f(x) = C(4,x)(\frac{1}{3})^x(\frac{2}{3})^{4-x}$ $(x = 0, 1, \ldots , 4)$; (a) .296; (b) .889; (c) .210.

4. Human blood types have been classified into four exhaustive, mutually exclusive categories O, A, B, AB. In a certain very large population, the respective probabilities of these four types are .46, .40, .11, .03. Given that the population is so large that sampling depletions may be ignored, find the probability that a random sample of five individuals will contain (a) two cases of type O and one case of each of the others; (b) three cases of type O and two of type A; (c) no case of type AB.

$Ans.$ (a) .0168; (b) .1557; (c) .8587.

5. Using the information of Exercise 4, compute the entire distribution for random samples of two. (a) How many distinct allocations are there? (b) What is the total probability of the two most likely allocations? (c) What is the total probability of the four most likely allocations? (d) What is the total probability of the two least likely allocations? $Ans.$ (a) 10; (b) .5796; (c) .8408; (d) .0075.

6. A box contains 10 light bulbs, two of which are burned out. (a) What is the distribution of the number of good bulbs in a conditionally random sample of eight? (b) What is the probability of drawing no defective bulb? (c) Two defective bulbs?

$Ans.$ (a) $f(x) = C(8,x)C(2, 8 - x)/C(10,8)$ $(x = 6, 7, 8)$; (b) $\frac{1}{45} \approx .022$; (c) $\frac{28}{45} \approx .622$.

7. A five-card hand contains three aces. If another player is allowed to withdraw any two cards sight unseen, what is the distribution (a) of the number of aces withdrawn? (b) The number of aces left? Compute each distribution in full.

$Ans.$ (a) $f(x) = C(3,x)C(2, 2 - x)/C(5,2)$ $(x = 0, 1, 2)$; (b) $f(x) = C(3,x)C(2, 3 - x)/C(5,3)$ $(x = 1, 2, 3)$.

8. In research on drugs to counteract the intoxicating effects of alcohol, 10 subjects were used to test the relative merits of benzedrine and caffeine. Benzedrine brought about more rapid recovery in 9 cases. Basing your analysis on the null hypothesis of a binomial distribution with $p = .5$, determine the probability of obtaining results by

distribution is an equation in terms of x where x is defined

chance which favor one drug to this extent or more.   Assume that there was no a priori reason to suppose one drug more effective than the other.   *Ans.* $P = \frac{11}{512} \approx .0215$.

9. Under the usual assumptions as to randomness, what is the distribution of the number of diamonds in a 13-card hand?

$$Ans.\ f(x) = C(13,x)C(39,\ 13 - x)/C(52,13)\ (x = 0,\ 1,\ 2,\ \ldots,\ 13).$$

10. The probability of "making the green light" at a certain intersection is .2.   (a) In a series of independent trials, what is the distribution of the number of trials required for the first success?   (b) What is the probability of obtaining a success in less than four trials?   *Ans.* (a) $f(x) = (.2)(.8^{x-1})\ (x = 1, 2, 3, \ldots)$; (b) .488.

11. Using the information of Exercise 4, find the sample size needed so that the probability of yielding at least one case of blood type AB will be at least .95.   Solve this problem from the viewpoint of the binomial distribution and then explain the connection with the geometric distribution.   *Ans.* 99.

12. How many times must a die be cast in order that the probability of three occurring will be at least .8?   *Ans.* 9.

13. A magazine has 100 pages and 100 misprints distributed at random.   Assuming a Poisson distribution with μ equal to the average number of misprints per page, estimate the probability that a page contains at least two misprints.   *Ans.* .264.

14. Given that the distribution of x is Poisson and (to six decimals) $f(0) = .049787$, find $P(x \geq 4)$.   *Ans.* .353.

15. In four independent rolls of a die, find the probability of obtaining (a) at least one six, (b) exactly one six, (c) exactly two sixes.   Compare these results with the Poisson approximations.

Ans. Binomial: (a) .518, (b) .386, (c) .116; Poisson: (a) .487, (b) .342, (c) .114.

16. The probability of obtaining a bulls-eye for a particular person is $\frac{1}{3}$.   Ten shots are fired.   (a) What is the probability of obtaining at least three bulls-eyes?   (b) What is the conditional probability of obtaining at least three bulls-eyes, knowing that at least one bulls-eye has been scored?   *Ans.* (a) .701, (b) .714.

17. A chance event E has a constant probability p of occurring on any trial.   Letting x denote the number of trials up to and including the rth success, find the distribution of x.   This is called the *Pascal distribution*.

$$Ans.\ f(x) = C(x - 1, r - 1)p^r q^{x-r}\ (x = r, r + 1, \ldots).$$

18. A finite population contains N objects, of which the number a belong to type A, b to type B, and c to type C, where $a + b + c = N$.   If a conditionally random sample of n objects is taken (without replacements), find the compound distribution of the number of objects (say x_1, x_2, x_3) of each type.

Ans. $f(x_1,x_2,x_3) = C(a,x_1)C(b,x_2)C(c,x_3)/C(N,n)$ where $x_1 = 0,\ 1,\ 2,\ \ldots\ [n,a]$; $x_2 = 0, 1, 2, \ldots\ [n,b]$; $x_3 = 0, 1, 2, \ldots\ [n,c]$; and $x_1 + x_2 + x_3 = n$.

19. If x has the Poisson distribution, and μ is an integer, show that there is some value of x for which $f(x) = f(x + 1)$.

20. A series of forecasts were made by method A and the errors were recorded.   For a subset comprising the worst errors, independent forecasts (not utilizing any information which would not have been available to the user of A) were made by method B. The differences between the absolute errors would be judged highly significant in favor of method B, provided that the requisite conditions were met.   What is the catch?

Ans. Stacked deck; sample not random.

21. In normal use, a certain natural fiber is exposed to outdoor weathering.   A synthetic fiber, intended as a substitute, was developed for greater breaking strength after exposure.   Five strands of each fiber were chosen at random from typical lots, and each strand of natural fiber was paired at random with a strand of synthetic.   The pairs were then exposed to weather at different places, which were far enough apart to justify the assumption of independence from pair to pair. Later tested for breaking strength, the two samples gave the following results:

Pair.............	1	2	3	4	5
Synthetic	18	15	25	13	17
Natural...........	10	16	11	6	8

(a) At the least, what must the significance level α be in order that the above results would be judged significant by the sign test, using the appropriate one-sided critical region? State the critical region which corresponds. (b) How small could α be in order that the same data would be judged significant by the magnitude test? State the critical region which corresponds.

Ans. (a) $\alpha = \frac{3}{16}$; $u = 4,\ 5$ where $u =$ no. positive differences, synthetic minus natural. (b) $\alpha = \frac{1}{16}$; $v = 37,\ 39$ where $v =$ sum of differences, synthetic minus natural, in 5 trials.

22. If the fiber experiment of Exercise 21 could be carried out under uniform weather conditions, pairing would become irrelevant and it would be correct to regard the observations as constituting two independent samples of five each. In that case, we could employ another form of the magnitude test in which the two sets of 5 are regarded as (conditionally) random selections from a combined set of 10, and the corresponding test variate is the difference D between the two sums of 5 observations. Using the data of Exercise 21, verify the following portion of the frequency table of D, wherein n denotes the number of ways (out of 252 possible samples) of obtaining a given value of D, and P denotes the probability that D will equal or exceed a stated value. Notice that the value of D actually obtained would be significant even if α were appreciably less than .05.

D	43	39	37	35	33	31	29
n	1	1	1	2	3	2	4
P	.004	.008	.012	.020	.032	.040	.056

23. In two random samples of five observations the *relative* frequencies of attribute A are respectively 0 and 1. (a) Using the hypergeometric test with a two-sided region, determine the probability of this result under the hypothesis that both samples are taken from the same population. (b) Repeat if the relative frequencies are .2 and .8 respectively. Ans. (a) $P = \frac{1}{126} \approx .008$. (b) $P = \frac{26}{126} \approx .206$.

24. A simple waiting line has an arrival rate of A and a servicing rate which increases with the length of line such that the serving rate $= nS$ where n is the number in line. Show that the probability of a line of length n is

$$P_n = \frac{1}{n!} \left(\frac{A}{S}\right)^n e^{-A/S}$$

CHAPTER 4

CONTINUOUS RANDOM VARIABLES

4-1. Introduction. Ordinarily, the specification of the admissible values of a continuous random variable is perfectly straightforward and can be done simply by stating the range or ranges of continuous variation, as $A \leq x \leq B$, but a valid association with probability is less direct. No one-to-one correspondence can be set up between the admissible values of a continuous variate and any infinite ordinal series of events E_1, E_2, E_3, . . . because the points on a continuum are not subject to enumeration. Therefore, the problem of defining the distribution of a continuous random variable calls for some ingenuity. Fortunately, however, an elementary idea proves powerful enough to cope with the most general situation.

Choosing an arbitrary number a, let us define two mutually exclusive and complementary classes of values: (I) $x \leq a$, and (II) $x > a$. With class I we associate the event E_a in the sense that any value of the variate belonging to class I corresponds to the occurrence of E_a; similarly, we associate the event $\bar{E}_a$ with class II. Thus $P(E_a)$ and $P(\bar{E}_a)$ are rigorously definable, but since they are complementary, it is sufficient to know $P(E_a)$. This construction can be carried out for any value of a whatever, and the result will obviously be a function of a. Hence we could replace $P(E_a)$ by the equivalent functional notation

$$F(a) \equiv P(E_a) \equiv P(x \leq a) \qquad (4\text{-}1)$$

but since we are going to allow a to take on all possible values and thus serve much the same purpose as the symbol x, it is more sensible to adopt the notation $F(x)$ rather than $F(a)$. That is, $F(x)$ denotes the probability that the random variable in question assumes any value less than or equal to x. A table, graph, or mathematical formula giving $F(x)$ for all possible values of x uniquely defines the distribution of x as a random variable, and for this reason $F(x)$ is called the *distribution function* of x. In a rigorous development of this subject, a distinction is made between the random variable itself and the real variable which includes all of its possible values; thus X is used for the former and x for the latter. This distinction is usually troublesome to the beginner, and we shall not stress it in this text. However, it must be understood that the variable x in the mathematical expression for $F(x)$ or $f(x)$ is a pure number; for instance, if the actual random variable assumes the value 15 volts, then x is the pure number 15.

In contrast to the distribution function of a discrete variate, which is necessarily a step function, the distribution function of a continuous variate is commonly continuous throughout its range of definition. Although discontinuities do sometimes occur, they are usually confined to a few isolated points. A typical distribution function of a continuous

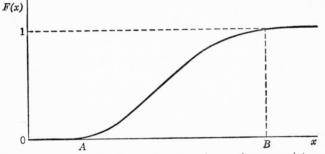

Fig. 4-1. Typical distribution function of a continuous variate.

variate x, the admissible values of which include all points in the range $A \leq x \leq B$, is illustrated in Fig. 4-1.

4-2. Use of Distribution Functions in Defining Distributions. We have previously defined the distribution of a discrete variate by stating the equation of its point-probability function $f(x)$ together with the specification of admissible values. For reasons soon to become apparent, a point-probability function is meaningless when the distribution function is continuous, although we are going to develop an analogous function in terms of point density. In lieu of the probability function, however, we may define the distribution of a continuous variate (or a discrete variate, too, for that matter) by stating the equation of its distribution function $F(x)$ supplemented by the specification of admissible values. This notion is best elucidated through specific illustrations.

Example 4-1. From geometric probability, we draw an example of a continuous variate. The permissible region, shown in Fig. 4-2, consists of the line segment OL.

Fig. 4-2

If points are picked at random on OL, their distances from O will generate a continuous random variable, the admissible values of which will range from 0 to L inclusive. Assuming all points equally likely, let us find the distribution of this variate. Let X denote an arbitrary point on OL and x its distance from O. The probability that any point X' picked at random will fall somewhere on the segment OX is

$$P(X' \text{ on } OX) = \frac{OX}{OL} = \frac{x}{L}$$

But having X' fall on OX is precisely the condition that the distance OX' be less than or equal to x. Hence by definition of the distribution function, we have

$$F(x) = \frac{x}{L}$$

an equation which holds everywhere in the admissible range of x, namely $0 \leq x \leq L$. Adopting the convention that the distribution function is identically zero for all values of x below the minimum admissible value of the variate and identically 1 for all values of x above the maximum admissible value of the variate, we may express the

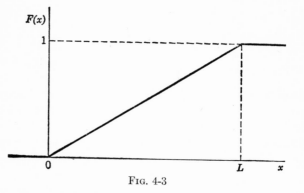

Fig. 4-3

distribution of x in one statement by combining the range of definition with the equation of $F(x)$. Thus the distribution of x is

$$F(x) = \frac{x}{L} \qquad (0 \leq x \leq L)$$

The graph of the distribution function is shown in Fig. 4-3. Although this distribution function is linear over the allowable range of x, geometric problems readily give rise to curved distribution functions, as illustrated by the next example.

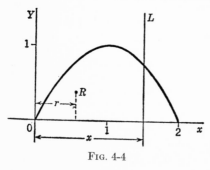

Fig. 4-4

Example 4-2. The permissible region, indicated by heavy lines in Fig. 4-4, is bounded below by the X axis and above by the parabola $y = 2x - x^2$. If all points within the region are equally likely, let us find the distribution of the distances of random points to the Y axis. At any distance $x \leq 2$ to the right of the Y axis, pass the straight line L parallel to OY. The distance of a random point R from OY is equal to its abscissa r, and the probability that $r \leq x$ is the same as the probability that R lies on or to the left of L. Hence

$$F(x) = P(r \leq x) = \frac{\text{area to left of } L}{\text{total area}} = \frac{\displaystyle\int_0^x y\,dx}{\displaystyle\int_0^2 y\,dx} = \frac{3x^2 - x^3}{4}$$

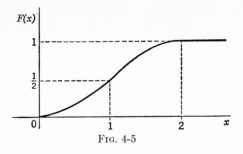

FIG. 4-5

Thus the distribution of the random variable x is

$$F(x) = \frac{3x^2 - x^3}{4} \quad (0 \leq x \leq 2)$$

The graph of $F(x)$ is shown in Fig. 4-5.

4-3. Computation of Probabilities. The probability that x lies in any particular range $a < x < b$ may be computed from the distribution function of x in the following manner. Since the event $x \leq b$ can be decomposed into two mutually exclusive events $x \leq a$ and $a < x \leq b$, it follows from the law of total probability that

$$P(x \leq b) = P(x \leq a) + P(a < x \leq b) \qquad (4\text{-}2)$$

whence $\qquad P(a < x \leq b) = P(x \leq b) - P(x \leq a)$

$$= F(b) - F(a) \qquad (4\text{-}3)$$

Thus, in Example 3-1, the probability that x exceeds 0 but does not exceed 2 is

$$P(0 < x \leq 2) = F(2) - F(0) = \tfrac{26}{27} - \tfrac{8}{27} = \tfrac{18}{27} = f(1) + f(2)$$

In passing, we note that Eq. (4-3) implies that $F(b) \geq F(a)$ whenever $b > a$, for the left-hand side of this equation can never be negative, since it is the probability of a definable event.

a		b
$\xi-\epsilon$	ξ $\qquad x$	$\xi+\epsilon$

FIG. 4-6

Suppose now that $F(x)$ is continuous, and let $a = \xi - \epsilon$, $b = \xi + \epsilon$ where ξ is any value which x can assume and ϵ is an arbitrarily small, positive number (see Fig. 4-6). Now any point which lies in the interval $\xi \leq x \leq \xi + \epsilon$ necessarily lies also in the interval $\xi - \epsilon < x \leq \xi + \epsilon$ because the former interval is entirely contained in the latter. Therefore, it follows that $P(\xi \leq x \leq \xi + \epsilon) \leq P(\xi - \epsilon < x \leq \xi + \epsilon)$, and so, applying Eq. (4-3), we have

$$P(\xi \leq x \leq \xi + \epsilon) \leq P(\xi - \epsilon < x \leq \xi + \epsilon) = F(\xi + \epsilon) - F(\xi - \epsilon)$$

$$(4\text{-}4)$$

In the limit as $\epsilon \to 0$, the extreme left-hand side of Eq. (4-4) may be interpreted as $P(x = \xi)$, while on the right-hand side, the hypothesized continuity of $F(x)$ requires that $F(\xi - \epsilon) \to F(\xi)$ and $F(\xi + \epsilon) \to F(\xi)$, whence $F(\xi + \epsilon) - F(\xi - \epsilon) \to 0$. Hence, for any variate x having a continuous-distribution function, it follows that

$$P(x = \xi) = 0 \qquad \text{for all } \xi \qquad (4\text{-}5)$$

In words: The probability that any continuous variate x which has a continuous distribution function $F(x)$ will take on a value exactly equal to any preassigned number ξ is vanishingly small. Consequently, if $F(x)$ is continuous, any interval may be so defined as to include or exclude one or both end points without affecting the probability that a random point will belong to it; that is,

$$P(a < x \le b) = P(a \le x \le b) = P(a \le x < b) = P(a < x < b)$$
$$= F(b) - F(a) \qquad (4\text{-}6)$$

Thus, in Example 4-2 the probability that a random value of distance lies in the open interval $1 < x < 2$ and the probability that it lies in the closed interval $1 \le x \le 2$ are both given by the same subtraction $F(2) - F(1) = 1 - \frac{1}{2} = \frac{1}{2}$.

As explained in Chap. 2, the zero probability given by Eq. (4-5) for $x = \xi$ does not mean that the value $x = \xi$ is impossible, but merely that it fades into immeasurable insignificance as compared to the total, inexhaustible field of distinct possibilities.

4-4. Density Functions. The concept of density, which has proved fruitful and convenient in physics, also aids in the study of random variables. Consider the physical notion of density as applied to a long, thin wire. For a homogeneous wire, the linear mass density is constant and is simply the mass per unit length, but for a nonhomogeneous wire, it varies as a function of the distance x measured from the origin, taken at one end of the wire. Hence if $M(x)$ represents the mass of the segment of wire from the origin to any point x, the linear mass density $\rho(x)$ is defined as the limit of the ratio of the mass increment $\Delta M(x)$ to the length increment Δx as $\Delta x \to 0$. Thus $\rho(x)$ is the derivative of the mass function $M(x)$, and in turn, $M(x) = \int_0^x \rho(\xi)\, d\xi$. (Note: When x is a limit of integration, it is conventional to use some other letter, say ξ, to represent the variable with respect to which the integration is performed.)

Provided that the distribution function of a variate is differentiable (hence certainly continuous), we may define probability density in a similar fashion. The probability that a random value r of the variate will lie between x and $x + \Delta x$ may be interpreted as the probability increment at the point x and (for simplicity) represented by ΔP.

$$\Delta P = P(x \le r \le x + \Delta x) = F(x + \Delta x) - F(x) = \Delta F(x) \qquad (4\text{-}7)$$

At the same time, the average "concentration" of probability in the neighborhood of x will be given by the relative increment $\Delta P/\Delta x = \Delta F(x)/\Delta x$ and under the assumption that $F(x)$ is differentiable, this ratio will approach a limit as $\Delta x \to 0$. This limit, which will be the derivative of the distribution function at the point x, will be called the *probability density* at x and will be denoted by $f(x)$. That is,

$$f(x) = \frac{dF(x)}{dx} \tag{4-8}$$

Correspondingly, the infinitesimal element of probability $dF(x)$ is given by

$$dF(x) = f(x)\,dx \tag{4-9}$$

and represents the probability that the variate will assume a value lying somewhere in the range x to $x + dx$. The geometric connection between $F(x)$ and $f(x)$ is shown schematically in Fig. 4-7.

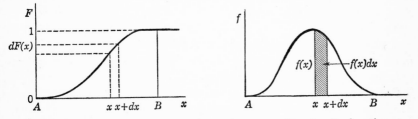

Fig. 4-7. Typical distribution function and corresponding density function.

Although we are using the notation $f(x)$ both for the probability that a discrete variate assumes a particular admissible value x and for the probability density of a continuous variate at the point x, this usage need not cause confusion, for the defining equation of the function will always be accompanied by a statement of admissible values. In the discrete case, these will be indicated as a series, but in the continuous case, by a range of continuous variation.

4-5. Properties of Density Functions. From the fact that $F(x + \Delta x) \geq F(x)$, and hence $\Delta F(x) \geq 0$ for all $\Delta x \geq 0$, it follows at once that the density function $f(x)$, being the derivative of the distribution function, is inherently non-negative. If A and B represent, respectively, the minimum and maximum admissible values of any variate x, then $F(A) \equiv P(x \leq A) = P(x = A)$ and $F(B) \equiv P(x \leq B) = 1$. Now if the variate possesses a density function, its distribution function is certainly continuous, because continuity is a necessary condition for the existence of the derivative; therefore, by virtue of Eq. (4-5), $P(x = A) = 0$, whence $F(A) = 0$.   Consequently, we arrive at the following general conclusions with regard to density functions:

(1) $$f(x) \geq 0 \qquad \text{for all } x$$

(2) $$\int_A^{x'} f(x)\, dx = F(x') - F(A) = F(x')$$

(3) $$\int_A^B f(x)\, dx = F(B) = 1 \qquad\qquad\qquad (4\text{-}10)$$

(4) $$P(a \leq x \leq b) = \int_a^b f(x)\, dx = P(a < x < b)$$

In words: The probability density function $f(x)$ of a variate x is a non-negative function having unit area when integrated over the admissible range of x.   When integrated from the lower limit of x up to any point x', it yields the corresponding value of the distribution function at $x = x'$, and when integrated between any two limits (a,b) it yields the probability that x lies in the interval (a,b).

4-6. Examples of Density Functions.   Examples 4-1 and 4-2 serve as illustrations of the density function.   The distribution function found in

FIG. 4-8. Density functions corresponding to the variates defined in Examples 4-1 and 4-2.

Example 4-1 was $F(x) = x/L$ in the range $0 \leq x \leq L$.   Therefore, in the same range,

$$f(x) = \frac{dF(x)}{dx} = \frac{1}{L}$$

and $f(x) \equiv 0$ for $x < 0$ and $x > L$.   Again, the distribution function found in Example 4-2 was $F(x) = (3x^2 - x^3)/4$ in the range $0 \leq x \leq 2$. Therefore, in the same range,

$$f(x) = \frac{dF(x)}{dx} = \frac{6x - 3x^2}{4} = \tfrac{3}{4}x(2 - x)$$

and $f(x) \equiv 0$ for $x < 0$ and $x > 2$.   These two density functions are exhibited in Fig. 4-8.

Both of these density functions admit of simple geometric interpretations.   In Example 4-1, for instance, the probability that a random point X' falls in any segment of length S is equal to S/L.   Hence if x' is the abscissa of X', we have

$$f(x)\, dx = P(x \leq x' \leq x + dx) = \frac{dx}{L}$$

whence $f(x) = 1/L$. In Example 4-2 (see Fig. 4-9) let M and M' denote two straight lines parallel to OY and cutting the x axis at x and $x + dx$ respectively. The probability that a random point R will fall between M

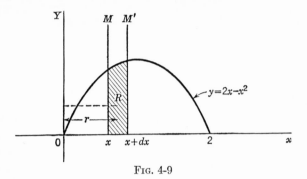

FIG. 4-9

and M' is equal to the ratio of the area included between these lines to the total area. Hence if r denotes the abscissa of the point R, we have

$$f(x)\, dx \equiv P(x \leq r \leq x + dx) = \frac{\text{area between } M \text{ and } M'}{\text{total area}}$$

$$= \frac{y\, dx}{\int_0^2 y\, dx} = \frac{(2x - x^2)\, dx}{\tfrac{4}{3}} = \tfrac{3}{4}x(2 - x)\, dx$$

whence $f(x) = \tfrac{3}{4}x(2 - x)$.

4-7. Use of Density Functions in Defining Distributions. When the density function exists, its equation, supplemented by the specification of the admissible range, can be used to define the distribution of the random variable. If the range is $A \leq x \leq B$, which includes both limits, we shall adopt the abbreviated notation (A,B); but if the admissible range excludes one or both of the limits, we shall write out the specification in full, for example $(A < x \leq B)$, $(A < x < B)$, etc. Thus the distributions of the variates considered in Examples 4-1 and 4-2 may be expressed as follows:

Example 4-1: $f(x) = \dfrac{1}{L}$ $(0, L)$

Example 4-2: $f(x) = \tfrac{3}{4}x(2 - x)$ $(0, 2)$

Outside of the *expressed range* of definition, it shall be taken for granted that the *density function* is *identically* zero.

In defining a distribution by either the distribution function or the density function, the specification of the admissible range must always be included. Otherwise the definition of the distribution is incomplete, and substitution of inadmissible values into the formulas could lead to absurdities, such as negative probabilities or probabilities greater than one.

4-8. Exceptional Situations. From the elementary standpoint, the density function is more convenient to work with and more appealing to the intuition than the distribution function, but whereas the latter always exists for any definable distribution, the density function exists only when the distribution function is differentiable. This condition, however, is not very restrictive in practice, inasmuch as most applications of probability theory are confined to variates which do have differentiable distribution functions. Even the few exceptions to this rule are usually amenable to rather obvious modifications of the ordinary analysis. A case in point is the poundage of brass rod shipped daily by a dealer in nonferrous metals. Since the minimum value, zero, has a finite probability of occurrence, the distribution function takes a finite jump at $x = 0$ as we cross from the left to the right of the origin; but thereafter it behaves in a perfectly regular manner. Therefore, a density function could be defined in the range $x > 0$. A similar situation is presented by the amount of rainfall over a particular city in a 24-hr period. Here there is a finite probability of a zero amount and also of a detectable but nonmeasurable amount called a "trace," but in the measurable range beyond, a density function is definable.

Later on, in the solution of some fairly simple problems, we shall encounter a few instances of another type of irregularity, such that the density function must be defined by two or more equations, each of which holds for a specified interval. Strictly speaking, the distribution function might not be differentiable at boundary points between adjacent intervals, and so the density function would be undefined there. Nevertheless, because of the continuity of the distribution function, it is not necessary to distinguish between the integral of the density function over the rigorously correct open interval which excludes the boundary points and over the more convenient closed interval which includes them. Therefore, it is permissible to define the density function at a boundary point arbitrarily by the equation which holds for the interior of either interval. This convention applies also when the distribution function becomes non-differentiable at the extremes of the admissible region. Let us consider two examples.

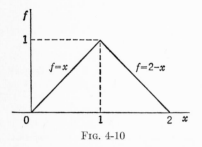

Fig. 4-10

Example 4-3. (see Fig. 4-10)

$$f(x) = x \quad (0, 1)$$
$$f(x) = 2 - x \quad (1, 2)$$

Here both equations yield the same value, $f = 1$, at the boundary point $x = 1$; hence the distribution function is differentiable at $x = 1$, and the density function is rigorously defined as its derivative. To put it another way, we note that for any value $0 < a < 1$, the distribution function

is given by

$$F(a) = \int_0^a x \, dx = \frac{a^2}{2}$$

whereas for any value $1 \leq b \leq 2$, it is given by

$$F(b) = \int_0^1 x \, dx + \int_1^b (2 - x) \, dx = 2b - \frac{b^2}{2} - 1$$

Both formulas yield the same value at their common point, that is $F(1) = \frac{1}{2}$, and both have the same derivative, $f = 1$.

Example 4-4. (see Fig. 4-11)

$$f(x) = \tfrac{1}{3} \qquad (0, 1) \qquad f(x) = \tfrac{2}{3} \qquad (1 < x \leq 2)$$

Here we exclude $x = 1$ from the definition of $f(x)$ in the second interval in order to avoid a contradiction of the definition in the first interval. However, in the integrals

Fig. 4-11

by which probabilities are computed, it is permissible to include $x = 1$ in both formulas. For if the lower limit of the second one were taken as $1 + \epsilon$, the ultimate value of the integral as $\epsilon \to 0$ would equal that obtained by taking the lower limit as 1 to begin with. For any value $0 \leq a \leq 1$, the distribution function is given by

$$F(a) = \int_0^a \tfrac{1}{3} \, dx = \frac{a}{3}$$

while for any value $1 \leq b \leq 2$ it is given by

$$F(b) = \int_0^1 \tfrac{1}{3} \, dx + \int_1^b \tfrac{2}{3} \, dx = \frac{2b}{3} - \tfrac{1}{3}$$

both of which yield $F(1) = \frac{1}{3}$. However, the two functions yield different derivatives at $x = 1$, and so the density function is not defined at this point except by the stated arbitrary convention. In this example also, the strict definition of the density function as a derivative breaks down at the extremes of the admissible region $(0,2)$. At the lower extreme, we have $F(x) = 0$ if $x \leq 0$ but $F(x) = x/3$ if $0 \leq x \leq 1$; and although $F(0) = 0$ in either case, the two functions have different derivatives at $x = 0$. At the upper extreme, $F(x) = (2x - 1)/3$ if $1 \leq x \leq 2$ but $F(x) = 1$ if $x \geq 2$; and as before, the functions agree at their common point, yielding $F(2) = 1$, but their derivatives are different. Consequently, the definition of the density function at $x = 0$ and at $x = 2$ must rest upon convention. Finally, we note the same situation in the density function associated with Example 4-1. Here the equation $f(x) = 1/L$ represents the derivative of $F(x)$ only in the range $0 < x < L$, but no inconsistency is caused by setting $f(0) = 1/L = f(L)$, thereby extending the definition of the density function to the end points of the range. So much for this type of irregularity—hereafter we shall take it in stride.

4-9. The Gamma Distribution. The rest of this chapter is devoted to the study of three families of continuous distributions which are useful in formulating mathematical models of random processes. These three are known, respectively, as the gamma, the beta, and the normal distributions, and it so happens that in each case the common forms of their density functions contain two parameters. We discuss the gamma distribution at some length because of the simple introduction it offers to certain concepts and methods of approach having wide application in the field of random variables.

The ordinary form of the gamma distribution pertains to a continuous variate x which may assume any non-negative value $0 \leq x < \infty$ and is defined in terms of its density function as follows:

$$f(x) = \frac{1}{\beta^{\alpha+1}\Gamma(\alpha + 1)} x^\alpha e^{-x/\beta} \qquad (\alpha > -1; \beta > 0; 0 \leq x < \infty) \qquad (4\text{-}11)$$

Gamma Distribution

This distribution is skewed to the right for all values of the parameters α, β but as α increases, the skewness becomes less pronounced. We shall see that the conventional practice of writing the coefficient of x in the exponential factor as $1/\beta$ simplifies the physical and geometrical interpretation of this parameter.

The general effect of each parameter on the shape of the curve can be investigated by the usual method of examining ordinates and derivatives for points of interest. We readily find that β operates mainly as a scale factor, whereas α produces qualitatively different effects depending on its magnitude.

The special case with $\alpha = 0$ is important enough to have a name of its own and is known as the *exponential* distribution. Thus, the exponential distribution is defined in terms of its density function as

$$f(x) = \frac{1}{\beta} e^{-x/\beta} \qquad (\beta > 0; 0 \leq x < \infty) \qquad (4\text{-}12)$$

Exponential Distribution

The first two derivatives in the exponential case are

$$f'(x) = -\frac{1}{\beta^2} e^{-x/\beta} \qquad f''(x) = \frac{1}{\beta^3} e^{-x/\beta} \qquad (4\text{-}13)$$

Figure 4-12 displays the exponential distribution for three values of β ($\beta = .5, 1, 2$).

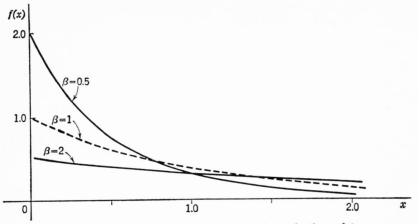

FIG. 4-12. Exponential distribution for various selections of β.

Letting $k = 1/\beta^{\alpha+1}\Gamma(\alpha + 1)$ we may write the first two derivatives for values of α other than zero as follows:

$$f'(x) = \frac{k}{\beta} x^{\alpha-1} e^{-x/\beta}(\alpha\beta - x) \qquad \text{root: } x = \alpha\beta \qquad (4\text{-}14)$$

$$f''(x) = \frac{k}{\beta^2} x^{\alpha-2} e^{-x/\beta}[\alpha(\alpha - 1)\beta^2 - 2\alpha\beta x + x^2] \qquad \text{roots: } x = \beta(\alpha \pm \sqrt{\alpha})$$
$$(4\text{-}15)$$

except that the second derivative, when $\alpha = 1$, has the special form

$$f''(x) = \frac{1}{\beta^4} e^{-x/\beta}(x - 2\beta) \qquad \text{root: } x = 2\beta \qquad (4\text{-}16)$$

Considering ordinates and derivatives under the restriction that negative values of x (and, of course, imaginary values) are excluded, we may now draw the following conclusions. In all cases, the curve approaches the X axis asymptotically for large values of x. If α has a negative value $-1 < \alpha < 0$, the ordinate of the curve increases without limit as x becomes small, approaching the vertical axis as an asymptote, but the curve falls off steadily as x increases. The ordinates remain finite if $\alpha \geq 0$. If $\alpha = 0$, the curve assumes its highest value $1/\beta$ at $x = 0$; the initial slope is $-1/\beta^2$, and although the slope gradually decreases in magnitude, it never changes sign. If $\alpha > 0$, the curve starts at the origin (that is, $f(0) = 0$), rises to a maximum at $x = \alpha\beta$ and then falls off. The curve is tangent to the vertical axis at the origin if α lies in the range $0 < \alpha < 1$, it has an initial slope equal to $1/\beta^2$ if $\alpha = 1$ (just opposite to the slope if $\alpha = 0$), and it is tangent to the X axis at the origin if $\alpha > 1$. There is one point of inflection, located at a distance $\beta \sqrt{\alpha}$ to the right of the maximum, if α lies in the range $0 < \alpha \leq 1$; but if $\alpha > 1$, there are two points of inflection, symmetrically placed at a distance $\beta \sqrt{\alpha}$ to either side of the maximum.

Curves which rise to an asymptote or to a cusp at one extreme but fall off steadily in the opposite direction are called *J-shaped*, although the "J" is often backwards. Thus the gamma distribution is J-shaped if $\alpha \leq 0$.

FIG. 4-13. Gamma distributions with unit β but different values of α.

Curves with a single rounded peak are called *unimodal*, and the value of x (the abscissa) at which the peak occurs is called the *mode*. Accordingly, the gamma distribution is unimodal when $\alpha > 0$. By an extension of the term, the mode is also understood as the point of highest density or, in the discrete case, the point of highest probability. However, it is not customary to refer to J-shaped curves as unimodal, even though we may be willing to call the high end of the curve the "mode." Curves with two, three, or more peaks are called *bimodal, trimodal,* or *multimodal,* respectively.

The gamma distribution is exhibited in the following figures. The effect of α is illustrated in Fig. 4-13, where β is held constant ($\beta = 1$) and

α is given a series of values ($\alpha = -.5, 0, .5, 1, 2, 5$). The effect of β is displayed in Fig. 4-14 where α is held constant ($\alpha = 1$) and β is given a series of values ($\beta = .5, 1, 2$). The combined effect of α and β is indicated in Fig. 4-15 by means of three pairs of values ($\alpha = 5, \beta = .4; \alpha = 10, \beta = .2; \alpha = 20, \beta = .1$) which yield the same mode ($\alpha\beta = 2$).

FIG. 4-14. Gamma distributions with unit α but different values of β.

FIG. 4-15. Gamma distribution with fixed mode.

A modified form of the gamma distribution with arbitrary minimum value A instead of zero is given by

$$f(x) = \frac{1}{\beta^{\alpha+1}\Gamma(\alpha+1)}(x-A)^\alpha e^{-(x-A)/\beta} \qquad (A \leq x < \infty) \quad (4\text{-}17)$$

Gamma with Arbitrary Minimum

This form is applicable when the conditions of the problem exclude values of x smaller than a stated value A. The gamma distribution can be used as a satisfactory approximation in many situations wherein the upper limit is finite, because the exponential factor $e^{-x/\beta}$ can be so adjusted as to render negligibly small the probability of exceeding the actual physical limit. Moreover, the gamma distribution often furnishes an excellent approximation to discrete distributions provided that (1) the probability function of the discrete variate is smooth and either unimodal or J-shaped and (2) the separation between consecutive admissible values is small compared to the total range. For instance, the distribution of cash receipts of a retail store, which would be a discrete variate measured in cents, might well be smooth enough to be approximated adequately by a gamma distribution.

Example 4-5. The distribution of length of life (i.e., hours of service before burning out) of a certain type of transmitter tube used in aircraft radar sets is exponential with $\beta = 180$. What is the probability that a tube will last less than 90 hr? More than 360 hr? If three tubes are picked at random for life testing, what is the probability that one will last 90 hr or less, another between 90 and 360 hr, and another more

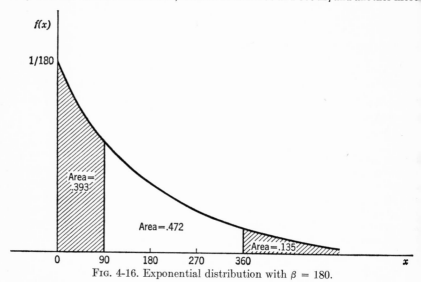

Fig. 4-16. Exponential distribution with $\beta = 180$.

than 360 hr?   (See Fig. 4-16.)   Here, the distribution is given by

$$f(x) = (\tfrac{1}{180})e^{-x/180} \qquad (0 \leq x < \infty)$$

In general, the exponential-distribution function with arbitrary β is

$$F(x) = 1 - e^{-x/\beta} \tag{4-18}$$

and in this case, the distribution function is $F(x) = 1 - e^{-x/180}$. The respective values of this distribution function at the points 90 and 360 are

$$F(90) = 1 - e^{-.5} = .393 \qquad F(360) = 1 - e^{-2} = .865$$

Hence the probability that a tube will last less than 90 hr is

$$P(x < 90) = F(90) = .393$$

The probability that a tube will last between 90 and 360 hr is

$$P(90 \leq x \leq 360) = F(360) - F(90) = .472$$

and the probability that a tube will last more than 360 hr is

$$P(x > 360) = 1 - F(360) = .135$$

The probability that a random sample of three will contain one instance of each of these three ranges is given by the multinomial law of probability as

$$\frac{3!}{1!1!1!} (.393)(.472)(.135) = .150$$

Example 4-6. Expressed as excess over \$500, annual family income in dollars in a certain city follows the gamma distribution with $\alpha = 1$, $\beta = 2,000$. If advertising circulars are sent out to 1,000 families picked at random, what is the probability that more than 15 circulars will be sent to families with annual income less than \$800? The distribution, in terms of its density function, is

$$f(x) = \frac{1}{(2,000)^2} (x - 500)e^{-(x-500)/2,000} \qquad (500 \leq x < \infty)$$

and the distribution function is

$$F(x) = \int_{500}^{x} f(\xi)\, d\xi = 1 - \frac{1,500 + x}{2,000} e^{-(x-500)/2,000}$$

The probability p that any family with income less than \$800 will be selected at random is given by

$$p = P(x < 800) = F(800) = 1 - (1.15)e^{-.15} = 1 - .9898 \approx .01$$

Strictly speaking, the distribution of the number of low-income families selected in a (conditionally) random sample of 1,000 is hypergeometric, but assuming that sampling depletions are negligible, we may regard the distribution as binomial with $n = 1,000$, $p = .01$. Again, since n is large and p is small, we may make the further simplification that the binomial distribution, in turn, may be replaced by the Poisson with $\mu = np = 10$. Hence, letting c denote the number of circulars sent to families with income less than \$800, we obtain the required probability from Molina's tables. This is

$$P(c > 15) = .049 \approx .05$$

The density function of the gamma distribution can be integrated exactly if α is an integer, but the work becomes inordinately laborious for hand computation if α is at all large; and for an arbitrary value of α not an integer, numerical integration is necessary. For this reason, suitable tables are a practical necessity. Extensive tables of the gamma distribution with $\beta = 1$, entitled "Tables of the Incomplete Γ-Function," were published in 1922 by the office of *Biometrika*, under the editorship of Karl Pearson. These tables may be applied to arbitrary $\beta > 0$ by the change of variable $v = x/\beta$. For

$$F(x) = \frac{1}{\beta^{\alpha+1}\Gamma(\alpha + 1)} \int_0^x y^\alpha e^{-y/\beta}\, dy = \frac{1}{\Gamma(\alpha + 1)} \int_0^{x/\beta} v^\alpha e^{-v}\, dv \quad (4\text{-}19)$$

In Pearson's tables, a further change of scale $u = v/\sqrt{\alpha + 1}$ was made in order to facilitate tabulation. Hence, to evaluate $F(x)$ one enters the tables under the appropriate α with the figure $u = x/(\beta\sqrt{\alpha + 1})$. Selected percentage points of the gamma distribution, obtained by adapt-

TABLE 4-1. SELECTED PERCENTAGE POINTS OF THE GAMMA DISTRIBUTION: VALUES OF x/β CORRESPONDING TO STATED VALUES OF $F(x)$[†]

α \ F	.01	.05	.10	.25	.50	.75	.90	.95	.99
$-.5$	.0000785	.00197	.00790	.0508	.227	.662	1.353	1.921	3.317
0	.01005	.0513	.105	.288	.693	1.386	2.303	2.996	4.605
.5	.0574	.176	.292	.606	1.183	2.054	3.126	3.907	5.672
1.0	.149	.355	.532	.961	1.678	2.693	3.890	4.744	6.638
1.5	.277	.573	.805	1.337	2.176	3.313	4.618	5.535	7.543
2.0	.436	.818	1.102	1.727	2.674	3.920	5.322	6.296	8.406
2.5	.620	1.084	1.417	2.127	3.173	4.519	6.008	7.034	9.238
3.0	.823	1.366	1.745	2.535	3.672	5.109	6.681	7.754	10.045
3.5	1.044	1.663	2.084	2.949	4.171	5.694	7.342	8.460	10.833
4.0	1.279	1.970	2.433	3.369	4.671	6.274	7.994	9.154	11.605
4.5	1.527	2.287	2.789	3.792	5.170	6.850	8.638	9.838	12.362
5.0	1.785	2.613	3.152	4.219	5.670	7.423	9.275	10.513	13.108
5.5	2.053	2.946	3.521	4.650	6.170	7.992	9.906	11.181	13.844
6.0	2.330	3.285	3.895	5.083	6.670	8.558	10.532	11.842	14.571
6.5	2.615	3.630	4.273	5.518	7.169	9.123	11.154	12.498	15.289
7.0	2.906	3.981	4.656	5.956	7.669	9.684	11.771	13.148	16.000
7.5	3.204	4.336	5.043	6.396	8.169	10.244	12.384	13.794	16.704
8.0	3.507	4.695	5.432	6.838	8.669	10.802	12.995	14.435	17.403
8.5	3.816	5.058	5.825	7.281	9.169	11.359	13.602	15.072	18.095
9.0	4.130	5.425	6.221	7.726	9.669	11.914	14.206	15.705	18.783
9.5	4.449	5.796	6.620	8.172	10.169	12.467	14.808	16.335	19.466
10.0	4.771	6.169	7.021	8.620	10.668	13.020	15.407	16.962	20.145
11.0	5.428	6.924	7.829	9.519	11.668	14.121	16.598	18.208	21.490
12.0	6.099	7.690	8.646	10.422	12.668	15.217	17.782	19.443	22.821
13.0	6.782	8.464	9.470	11.329	13.668	16.310	18.958	20.669	24.139
14.0	7.477	9.246	10.300	12.239	14.668	17.400	20.128	21.886	25.446
15.0	8.180	10.035	11.135	13.152	15.668	18.487	21.293	23.098	26.744
20.0	11.825	14.072	15.382	17.755	20.668	23.883	27.045	29.062	33.104
25.0	15.623	18.218	19.717	22.404	25.667	29.234	32.711	34.916	39.308
30.0	19.532	22.444	24.113	27.085	30.667	34.552	38.315	40.691	45.401

[†] Adapted from Catherine M. Thompson, Tables of Percentage Points of the Chi-square Distribution, *Biometrika*, vol. 32, pt. II, p. 187, October, 1941.

ing Thompson's tables of chi-square,[1] are given in Table 4-1. This table gives values of x which correspond to fixed values of $F(x)$. For such a value of x, corresponding to a stated fraction of the total area, Hald[2] has

[1] Catherine M. Thompson, Tables of Percentage Points of the Chi-square Distribution, *Biometrika*, vol. 32, pt. II, p. 187, October, 1941.

[2] A. Hald, "Statistical Theory with Engineering Applications," p. 66, John Wiley & Sons, Inc., New York, 1952.

TABLE 4-2. RATIOS FACILITATING THE ESTIMATION OF THE PARAMETERS α, β
OF THE GAMMA DISTRIBUTION

α	D_1/M	D_5/M	D_9/M	D_1/D_5	D_9/D_5	D_1/D_9
$-.5$	Curve J-shaped			.0348	5.960	.0058
0	Curve J-shaped			.152	3.323	.0455
.5	†	2.366	6.252	.247	2.642	.0934
1.0	.532	1.678	3.890	.317	2.318	.137
1.5	.537	1.451	3.079	.370	2.122	.174
2.0	.551	1.337	2.661	.412	1.990	.207
2.5	.567	1.269	2.403	.447	1.893	.236
3.0	.582	1.224	2.227	.475	1.819	.261
3.5	.595	1.192	2.098	.500	1.760	.284
4.0	.608	1.168	1.999	.521	1.711	.304
4.5	.620	1.149	1.920	.539	1.671	.323
5.0	.630	1.134	1.855	.556	1.636	.340
5.5	.640	1.122	1.801	.571	1.606	.355
6.0	.649	1.112	1.755	.584	1.579	.370
6.5	.657	1.103	1.716	.596	1.556	.383
7.0	.665	1.096	1.682	.607	1.535	.396
7.5	.672	1.089	1.651	.617	1.516	.407
8.0	.679	1.084	1.624	.627	1.499	.418
8.5	.685	1.079	1.600	.635	1.483	.428
9.0	.691	1.074	1.578	.643	1.469	.438
9.5	.697	1.070	1.559	.651	1.456	.447
10.0	.702	1.067	1.541	.658	1.444	.456
11.0	.712	1.061	1.509	.671	1.423	.472
12.0	.720	1.056	1.482	.682	1.404	.486
13.0	.728	1.051	1.458	.693	1.387	.500
14.0	.736	1.048	1.438	.702	1.372	.512
15.0	.742	1.045	1.420	.711	1.359	.523
20.0	.769	1.033	1.352	.744	1.309	.569
25.0	.789	1.027	1.308	.768	1.274	.603
30.0	.804	1.022	1.277	.786	1.249	.629

† Mode to left of D_i.
KEY: $D_i = i$th decile; M = mode.

proposed the convenient term *fractile*. Thus a value of x, say x_p, is a fractile of level p if $F(x_p) = p$.

The problem of estimating the parameters of a distribution from empirical data comes under the heading of *statistical estimation*, a branch of statistics for which a well-developed theory exists. However, in areas to which the application of probability represents an innovation or a comparatively recent approach, one must be prepared to face the obstacle of extreme paucity of data. Often the most that can be elicited from available records or from experienced workers in the field is a reasonable guess as to certain features of the distribution—for instance, whether the curve is J-shaped or unimodal, and if the latter, the approximate location of the mode or, in either case, perhaps a pair of percentage points. Under economic or military pressure, the incentive to attack the problem may be compelling, whereas the procurement of substantially more detailed information might be out of the question. (This is true particularly of data which require years to accumulate.) The gamma distribution, because of the variety of shapes it can assume with only two parameters, is often hypothesized as the form of the probability distribution, and the next step is to decide upon plausible values of its parameters. With the aid of Table 4-2 (or a similar one especially suited to the information at hand) these parameters can be evaluated from estimates of 2 percentage points or, as the case may be, the mode and 1 percentage point. The percentage points chosen for this table are *deciles*. The ith decile D_i is defined as that value of x for which $F(x) = i(.1)$. Thus, $F(D_1) = .10; F(D_5) = .50;$ $F(D_9) = .90$. A more common name for the fifth decile D_5 is the *median*.

Example 4-7. A city undertaking a study of corrosion of water pipes has records of total footage of each type of pipe laid yearly since the inauguration of public water supply, but breakage data for only the last five years. Hypothesizing a gamma distribution for the length of life of a foot of pipe, estimate α, β if the median is 30 years and the ninth decile is 60 years; again, if the mode is 22 years and the first decile is 12 years. From the median and ninth decile we compute the ratio $D_9/D_5 = {}^{60}\!/_{30} = 2$. Referring to Table 4-2, we find that the nearest value given is $D_9/D_5 = 1.99$ at $\alpha = 2$. Hence we take α as equal to 2. To determine β we refer to Table 4-1 and find that $D_5/\beta = 2.674$ when $\alpha = 2$. Hence

$$\beta = \frac{D_5}{2.674} = \frac{30}{2.674} = 11.2 \approx 11$$

As a tentative hypothesis, then, we put

$$f(x) = \frac{1}{2,662} x^2 e^{-x/11}$$

Alternatively, using the estimates of the mode and D_1 we have $D_1/M = {}^{12}\!/_{22} = .545$. Again, the nearest value in Table 4-2 corresponds to $\alpha = 2$, and since the mode is $M = \alpha\beta$, we obtain $\beta = M/\alpha = {}^{22}\!/_2 = 11$, as before.

When α is an integer, an interesting connection exists between the upper tail area of the gamma distribution and the Poisson distribution function. Considering the gamma distribution with α an integer and $\beta = 1$, let $G(\mu)$ denote the probability $P(x \geq \mu)$ that x assumes a value equal to or greater than an arbitrary positive quantity μ:

$$G(\mu) = \frac{1}{\Gamma(\alpha + 1)} \int_\mu^\infty x^\alpha e^{-x} \, dx \tag{4-20}$$

Integrating by parts, we obtain

$$G(\mu) = \frac{1}{\Gamma(\alpha + 1)} \mu^{\alpha} e^{-\mu} + \frac{1}{\Gamma(\alpha)} \int_{\mu}^{\infty} x^{\alpha-1} e^{-x} \, dx \qquad (4\text{-}21)$$

Now if α is an integer, the exponent of x can be reduced one unit at a time to zero; moreover, the gamma functions become factorials of integers. Consequently

$$G(\mu) = e^{-\mu} \left[\frac{\mu^{\alpha}}{\alpha!} + \frac{\mu^{\alpha-1}}{(\alpha - 1)!} + \cdots + \frac{\mu^2}{2!} + \mu + 1 \right] \qquad (4\text{-}22)$$

which we recognize as the distribution function of some discrete variate, call it y, having the Poisson distribution with parameter μ. Thus we conclude that

$$P(y \le \alpha) = \sum_{y=0}^{\alpha} e^{-\mu} \frac{\mu^y}{y!} = \frac{1}{\Gamma(\alpha + 1)} \int_{\mu}^{\infty} x^{\alpha} e^{-x} \, dx = G(\mu) \quad (4\text{-}23)$$

Therefore, the Poisson distribution function can be evaluated from the incomplete gamma function and vice versa. This result was first published by E. C. Molina in 1915.

Example 4-8. In 1920, Rutherford, Chadwick, and Ellis studied the emission of alpha particles from a radioactive substance. It was found empirically that the distribution of the number of particles emitted during a time interval of 7.5 sec was adequately represented by a Poisson distribution with $\mu = 3.87$, or more generally that the number of particles emitted in t sec was a Poisson variate with $\mu = \rho t$ where $\rho = 3.87/7.5 = .516$. Instrumentally, it is customary to clock the length of time taken to register a fixed number of particles rather than to count the number of particles emitted during a fixed interval of time. Let us find the distribution of the length of time required to register 40 particles. In general, let $G(t)$ denote the probability that it will take more than t sec for the emission of $n + 1$ particles. Clearly, this can happen in $n + 1$ mutually exclusive ways, namely by the emission of any smaller number of particles 0, 1, 2, . . . , n in t sec. Hence the corresponding total probability, obtained by summing the separate probabilities of each number of particles as given by the Poisson distribution, is

$$G(t) = \sum_{y=0}^{n} e^{-\mu} \frac{\mu^y}{y!}$$

But by Eq. (4-23), the latter sum can be expressed as an integral, which yields

$$G(t) = \frac{1}{\Gamma(n + 1)} \int_{\mu}^{\infty} x^n e^{-x} \, dx$$

Now the distribution function $F(t)$ is the complement of $G(t)$, whence

$$F(t) = 1 - G(t) = \frac{1}{\Gamma(n + 1)} \int_{0}^{\mu} x^n e^{-x} \, dx$$

and the density function $f(t)$ is given by

$$f(t) = \frac{dF(t)}{dt} = \frac{dF(\mu)}{d\mu}\frac{d\mu}{dt} = \frac{\rho^{n+1}}{\Gamma(n+1)} t^n e^{-\rho t}$$

Therefore, the distribution of waiting time t for the emission of $n+1$ particles is

$$f(t) = \frac{\rho^{n+1}}{\Gamma(n+1)} t^n e^{-\rho t} \qquad (0, \infty) \tag{4-24}$$

Distribution of Waiting Time for
Emission of $n+1$ Alpha Particles

This is a gamma distribution with $\alpha = n$, $\beta = 1/\rho$. In particular, for the problem at hand, $n = 39$, $\rho = .516$ and the distribution is

$$f(t) = \frac{(.516)^{40}}{39!} t^{39} e^{-(.516)t} \qquad (0 \le t < \infty)$$

Further interesting deductions follow readily from this result. Setting $n = 0$ in Eq. (4-24) we find that the distribution of waiting time for one particle is given by the exponential distribution

$$f(t) = \rho e^{-\rho t} \qquad (0 \le t < \infty) \tag{4-25}$$

Waiting Time for One Particle

Now it is obvious that the length of time required for the emission of a total of $n+1$ particles is equal to the sum of the waiting times for $n+1$ individual particles. Moreover, since these are emitted independently, their waiting times are independent. Therefore we arrive at the following theorem:

THEOREM 4-1. If $t_1, t_2, \ldots, t_k$ are independent variates all governed by the same exponential distribution,

$$h(t_i) = \frac{1}{\beta} e^{-t_i/\beta} \qquad (0, \infty) \tag{4-26}$$

then their sum $t = t_1 + t_2 + \cdots + t_k$ is a gamma variate with the same β and with $\alpha = k - 1$:

$$f(t) = \frac{1}{\beta^k \Gamma(k)} t^{k-1} e^{-t/\beta} \qquad (0, \infty) \tag{4-27}$$

More generally, the length of time for any number of particles can be regarded as the sum of times for sets of smaller numbers that add up to the same total. Hence we may state:

THEOREM 4-2. If $x_1, x_2, \ldots, x_k$ are independent gamma variates with common β and integral values of α, namely $\alpha_1, \alpha_2, \ldots, \alpha_k$, then their sum $x = x_1 + x_2 + \cdots + x_k$ is a gamma variate with the same β and with $\alpha = \alpha_1 + \alpha_2 + \cdots + \alpha_k + k - 1$.

In a later chapter we shall see that this result holds even when the α's are not integers, but we are not yet prepared for the proof.

Example 4-9.   The distribution of length of telephone calls in minutes was found by Molina to be exponential with $\beta = 2.26$ for calls between a pair of adjacent cities in 1925.   Let us suppose (for the sake of illustration) that the same applies today for any random selection of local calls.   A man goes to a public telephone booth and finds that five people are ahead of him, the first having just stepped into the booth.   Neglecting dialing time, what is the probability that this man will have to wait more than 18 min for his turn?   Assuming that the five people ahead of him constitute a random sample, the distribution of their total length of call will be gamma with $\alpha = 5 - 1 = 4$ and $\beta = 2.26$.   Here $x/\beta = 18/2.26 = 7.96$.   Referring to Table 4-1 under $\alpha = 4$, we find that the probability of exceeding this value of x/β is just over .10.   Hence the probability is about .10 that he will have to wait more than 18 min for his turn.

We have previously noted that exact values of the binomial distribution function can be obtained from the incomplete beta function, and approximate values for large n either from the Poisson or from the normal distribution (Sec. 4-11), depending on the circumstances.   The gamma distribution also can be used as an approximation, filling the gap for intermediate values of n beyond existing tables of the binomial but not large enough to yield good approximations by the normal.   Even within the tabulated range of n, the gamma distribution is also useful in situations wherein a continuous variate is easier to handle.

The problem of adjusting the parameters of a curve so that it will pass through or close to a given set of points comes under the general heading of *curve fitting*, and several techniques are available for this purpose.   Whereas most of these rest on principles which we have not yet discussed, the method we are about to employ is based on simple geometry.

Fig. 4-17

Letting r stand for any value of the binomial variate and $f(r)$ the corresponding value of the probability function of that variate, consider the line segment joining the tops of the two ordinates $f(r), f(r + 1)$ (see Fig. 4-17).   The slope of this line segment is

$$\frac{f(r + 1) - f(r)}{(r + 1) - r} = f(r + 1) - f(r)$$

and the mid-height (i.e., the height at the midpoint) is $[f(r + 1) + f(r)]/2$. Since the recursion formula for the binomial probability function gives $f(r + 1)$ in terms of $f(r)$ as

$$f(r + 1) = \frac{(n - r)p}{(r + 1)(1 - p)} f(r)$$

it is evident that both the slope and mid-height contain $f(r)$ as a factor. Hence $f(r)$ will cancel if we form the ratio of slope to mid-height, and the simplified expression becomes

$$\frac{\text{Slope}}{\text{Mid-height}} = 2\,\frac{(n+1)p - r - 1}{(n-1)p + r(1-2p) + 1} \qquad (4\text{-}28)$$

Let us now determine a smooth curve $g(x)$ which will yield this same ratio of slope to ordinate when $x = r + \frac{1}{2}$. Substituting $r = x - \frac{1}{2}$ in Fq. (4-28) we obtain

$$\frac{1}{g(x)}\frac{dg(x)}{dx} = 2\,\frac{(n+1)p - x - \frac{1}{2}}{np + \frac{1}{2} + x(1-2p)} = \frac{-2(x-a)}{bx + c} \qquad (4\text{-}29)$$

where $a = (n+1)p - \frac{1}{2}$ $b = 1 - 2p$ $c = np + \frac{1}{2}$

Hereafter we shall assume that $0 < p < .5$ so that b will be positive. A curve which satisfies Eq. (4-29) for all values of x will certainly satisfy it at the particular points $x = r + \frac{1}{2}$ ($r = 0, 1, 2, \ldots, n$). Hence we may integrate, obtaining

$$\ln g(x) = \ln K_1 + \frac{2(ab + c)}{b^2}\ln(bx + c) - \frac{2x}{b}$$

whence $g(x) = K_2(x + A)^\alpha e^{-x/\beta} = k(x + A)^\alpha e^{-(x+A)/\beta}$

where
$$A = \frac{c}{b} = \frac{2np + 1}{2(1 - 2p)}$$
$$\alpha = \frac{2(ab + c)}{b^2} = \frac{4(1 + n)p(1 - p)}{(1 - 2p)^2} \qquad (4\text{-}30)$$
$$\beta = \frac{b}{2} = \frac{1 - 2p}{2}$$

If we now choose k so that the curve has unit area over the range $-A \le x < \infty$ we arrive at a gamma distribution:

$$g(x) = \frac{1}{\beta^{\alpha+1}\Gamma(\alpha+1)}(x + A)^\alpha e^{-(x+A)/\beta} \qquad (-A \le x < \infty) \qquad (4\text{-}31)$$

Gamma Approximation to Binomial Distribution with $0 < p < .5$

where the parameters A, α, β are defined by Eq. (4-30). In applying this approximation, we must remember to evaluate the gamma distribution function at $x = r + \frac{1}{2}$ in order to estimate the binomial distribution function at r. Two sample cases using $n = 9, p = .2$ and $n = 16, p = .2$ are shown in Table 4-3. The approximations are good enough for most practical or even theoretical purposes.

TABLE 4-3. COMPARISON OF EXACT BINOMIAL DISTRIBUTION FUNCTION (F) AND APPROXIMATION (Γ) USING GAMMA DISTRIBUTION

	$n = 9, p = .2$			$n = 16, p = .2$	
r	F	Γ	r	F	Γ
0	.13	.15	0	.03	.04
1	.44	.43	1	.14	.16
2	.74	.72	2	.352	.357
3	.91	.89	3	.598	.595
4	.98	.97	4	.798	.791
5	.997	.993	5	.918	.909
6	.9997	.9985	6	.973	.967
7	.99998	.99975	7	.993	.990
			8	.999	.997
			9	.9998	.9993
			10	.99997	.99985

4-10. The Beta Distribution. In its standard form, the beta distribution applies to a continuous variate the admissible values of which lie between 0 and 1 with probability density

$$f(x) = \frac{1}{\beta(\alpha + 1, \lambda + 1)} x^{\alpha}(1 - x)^{\lambda} \qquad (\alpha, \lambda > -1; 0 \leq x \leq 1) \qquad (4\text{-}32)$$

Beta Distribution

This distribution is often a suitable model for the random behavior of percentages.

The effects of the parameters α, λ on the shapes of the curves are indicated in Fig. 4-18. The special case with both parameters equal to zero is called the *rectangular* distribution, for the density function reduces to the constant $f = 1$, and the figure resembles a rectangle, except that the two ends are not actually part of the density function. Another special case, called the *triangular* distribution, arises when one parameter is zero and the other unity. The curve then becomes a straight line with slope $+2$ if $\alpha = 1$, or -2 if $\lambda = 1$. The curve is U-shaped if both parameters are negative, J-shaped if only one is negative, and unimodal if both are positive. When both parameters have the same sign the curve has one turning point, which occurs at $x = \alpha/(\alpha + \lambda)$; this is the mode if the parameters are positive, but the lowest point if they are negative. If both α, λ exceed unity, there are two points of inflection, located at a distance $\sqrt{\alpha\lambda(\alpha + \lambda - 1)}/(\alpha + \lambda)(\alpha + \lambda - 1)$ to either side of the mode. If one parameter equals unity and the other exceeds unity, there is one point of inflection; if $\alpha = 1$, $\lambda > 1$ the inflection point is located at

$x = 2/(1 + \lambda)$; if $\alpha > 1$, $\lambda = 1$ the inflection point occurs at

$$x = \frac{\alpha - 1}{\alpha + 1}$$

In either case the location is given as a special case of the general formula, except that there is only one true root. The curve is symmetrical if $\alpha = \lambda$, skewed to the right if $\alpha < \lambda$, and skewed to the left if $\alpha > \lambda$. An

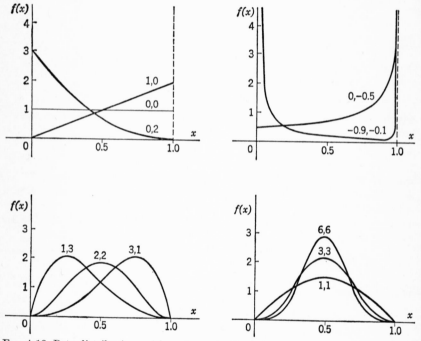

FIG. 4-18. Beta distributions with various selections of parameters α, λ. The symbol a, b means $\alpha = a$, $\lambda = b$.

interchange of parameters yields the mirror image of the initial curve. If the mode is held fixed, the concentration in the neighborhood of the mode increases as the parameters increase.

Example 4-10. Ceramic parts for various electrical devices are manufactured to order, and as a concession to the manufacturer, the customer placing an order for a given number of items N is willing to accept at the same unit price up to 10 per cent more than the number ordered. However, the manufacturer must supply at least the number ordered. Because of cracking, chipping, and other defects, the number of pieces S of standard quality is a fraction x ($0 \leq x \leq 1$) of the initial number I put into the molds. For a particular type of part, the distribution of this fraction is beta with $\alpha = 8$, $\lambda = 2$; that is,

$$f(x) = 495x^8(1 - x)^2 \qquad (0, 1)$$

If the initial number is chosen as a multiple m of the number of items ordered ($I = mN$), determine as a function of m the probability: (a) that the number of standard pieces will fall short of the number ordered, (b) that the number of standard pieces will exceed the maximum the customer will accept at the same unit price. Since $x = S/I$ we have

$$S = xI = xmN$$

Hence $S < N$ whenever $xm < 1$, which implies that $x < 1/m$; again, $S > 1.1N$ whenever $xm > 1.1$, or $x > 1.1/m$. Consequently,

$$P(S < N) = P\left(x < \frac{1}{m}\right) = F\left(\frac{1}{m}\right)$$

and

$$P(S > 1.1N) = P\left(x > \frac{1.1}{m}\right) = 1 - F\left(\frac{1.1}{m}\right)$$

Now in the range $0 \leq x \leq 1$ the distribution function of x is defined as

$$F(x) = \int_0^x f(\xi)\, d\xi = x^9(55 - 99x + 45x^2)$$

but $F(x) \equiv 1$ if $x > 1$. Hence, provided $m \geq 1$, the probability of falling short is given by

$$P(S < N) = P\left(x < \frac{1}{m}\right) = \frac{(55m^2 - 99m + 45)}{m^{11}}$$

However, if $m < 1$, this means that the initial number of items I is less than the number ordered, and so it is obvious that $P(S < N) \equiv 1$ if $m < 1$. In the same way, it is impossible to exceed the number $1.1N$ which the customer has agreed to buy unless $I > 1.1N$ whence $m > 1.1$. Thus $P(S > 1.1N) \equiv 0$ if $m \leq 1.1N$, and otherwise it is given by

$$P(S > 1.1N) = P\left(x > \frac{1.1}{m}\right) = 1 - (1.1)^9 \frac{55m^2 - 99(1.1)m + 45(1.1)^2}{m^{11}}$$

These two functions are displayed in Fig. 4-19.

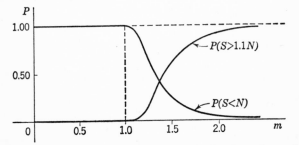

FIG. 4-19. Respective probabilities of falling short of ordered number and of exceeding the acceptable number.

In general, it is costly to fall short of the number ordered, because the manufacturing process has to be repeated, and this entails set-up time, schedule delays, tying up equipment, and increased costs of labor and power for the same item. The risk of falling short can be fixed at any desired level >0 by choosing I sufficiently large. However, playing it safe in this respect incurs its own penalty in occupying equipment and labor, which could be more profitably employed, and in wasting power and raw materials. The aims of ensuring the required number of items and of making profitable use of limited resources are in conflict. The problem of striking an optimum balance involves relative costs, and its solution entails the concept of mathematical expectation, which we treat in Chap. 7.

The beta density function cannot be integrated formally from 0 to x unless α and λ are both integral multiples of $\frac{1}{2}$. Unlike the gamma distribution, which permits the simplification of one-parameter tabulation because all gamma integrals with arbitrary parameter β can be obtained from the integral with $\beta = 1$, the beta distribution requires tabulation with respect to both parameters. Pearson's "Tables of the Incomplete Beta-Function," to which we referred in Chap. 3, stands as the most comprehensive work thus far produced on this distribution. Very often, however, it is convenient to have a table of fractiles, that is, one giving the values of x which correspond to selected levels of probability. A good table of this type has been constructed by Catherine M. Thompson.[1]

The scope of the beta distribution can be broadened by allowing the variate to range between any pair of finite limits A, B. The modified distribution then becomes

$$f(x) = \frac{1}{C}\,(x - A)^\alpha (B - x)^\lambda \qquad (A, B) \qquad (4\text{-}33)$$

Beta with Arbitrary Limits

where $\qquad\qquad C = (B - A)^{\alpha+\lambda+1}\beta(\alpha + 1, \lambda + 1)$

Fortunately the two extra parameters A, B do not necessitate additional tables, for if we substitute $u = (x - A)/(B - A)$ we obtain an integral in standard form.

Thus $\qquad \displaystyle\int_A^\xi f(x)\,dx = \frac{1}{\beta(\alpha + 1, \lambda + 1)} \int_0^{\xi'} u^\alpha (1 - u)^\lambda\,du \qquad (4\text{-}34)$

where $\xi' = (\xi - A)/(B - A)$. From the equation for u, we see that the effect of A and B is to shift the origin and change the scale of the conventional beta variate, but otherwise the density curves are similar.

4-11. The Normal Distribution. The normal distribution was discovered by De Moivre, whose published works as early as 1733 contained a derivation of it as the limiting form of the binomial. It was also known to Laplace no later than 1774, but through historical error, it has been attributed to Gauss, whose earliest published reference to it appeared in 1809. Nevertheless, the term "Gaussian distribution" is an accepted synonym for "normal distribution." During the eighteenth and nineteenth centuries, various attempts were made to establish this distribution as the underlying law governing all continuous variates—hence the name

[1] Catherine M. Thompson, Percentage Points of the Incomplete Beta-function, *Biometrika*, vol. 32, pt. II, pp. 168–181, October, 1941.

"normal." Although these attempts failed, being based on false premises, the normal distribution rightly occupies a preeminent place in the field of probability; for besides having exceptionally convenient properties of its own, it also serves as a useful approximation to many other distributions which are less tractable. In particular, the averages of n observations taken at random from almost any population tend to become normally distributed as n increases.

A variate x is said to be normally distributed if its density function $f(x)$ is given by an expression of the form

$$f(x) = \frac{1}{\sigma\sqrt{2\pi}}\, e^{-(x-\mu)^2/2\sigma^2} \qquad (-\infty, \infty) \qquad (4\text{-}35)$$

Normal Distribution

where μ can be any real number and σ any real number which is greater than zero. The distribution is unimodal, the mode being $x = \mu$, and

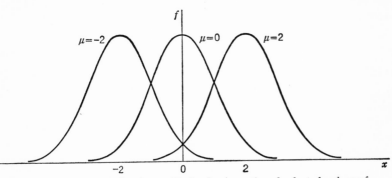

FIG. 4-20. Normal distributions with fixed σ ($\sigma = 1$) and selected values of μ.

there are two points of inflection, located at a distance σ to either side of the mode. By inspection, it is evident that the density curve is symmetrical about $x = \mu$ and falls off rapidly as the magnitude of $(x - \mu)$ increases. Although the normal distribution has an infinite range, the probability of very large deviations from μ is small enough to be neglected for most practical purposes; hence this distribution is capable of approximating others for which the true range is finite. Figure 4-20 shows the distribution for three values of μ and a constant value of σ; in Fig. 4-21, μ is constant and three values of σ are used. Clearly, a shift in μ displaces the curve as a whole, whereas a change in σ alters its relative proportions with reference to a fixed scale. In view of the symmetry of the curve about the mode, it is an accepted idiom to say that x is "normally distributed about λ" when we mean that the distribution of x is normal with $\mu = \lambda$.

A normal distribution with $\mu = 0$ and $\sigma^2 = 1 = \sigma$ is termed a *unit normal* distribution. Accordingly, this distribution is as follows:

$$f(x) = \frac{1}{\sqrt{2\pi}} e^{-x^2/2} \qquad (-\infty, \infty) \tag{4-36}$$

Unit Normal Distribution

Since the density function of the normal distribution cannot be integrated explicitly, the evaluation of probabilities would entail numerical

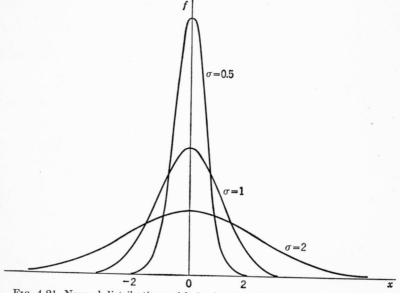

FIG. 4-21. Normal distributions with fixed μ ($\mu = 0$) and selected values of σ.

integration were it not for extensive tables already available. These tables have been constructed for the unit normal distribution only, but can be adapted to any other normal distribution by the substitution $u = (x - \mu)/\sigma$. For example, if x is a normal variate with arbitrary parameters, then

$$P(a \leq x \leq b) = \int_a^b \frac{1}{\sigma \sqrt{2\pi}} e^{-(x-\mu)^2/2\sigma^2} dx = \int_{a'}^{b'} \frac{1}{\sqrt{2\pi}} e^{-u^2/2} du \tag{4-37}$$

where $\qquad a' = \dfrac{a - \mu}{\sigma} \qquad b' = \dfrac{b - \mu}{\sigma}$

A brief tabulation of ordinates, areas, and fractiles of the unit normal distribution is given in Table 4-4, where only positive values of x are recorded, inasmuch as $f(-x) = f(x)$ and $F(-x) = 1 - F(x)$. We have used the notation $R(x)$ to denote the area to the right of x, and the notation $W(x)$ to denote the area within $-x$ and x. Thus if ξ denotes a

TABLE 4-4. UNIT NORMAL DISTRIBUTION

x	$f(x)$	$F(x)$	$R(x)$	$2R(x)$	$W(x)$
.0	.3989	.5000	.5000	1.0000	0
.1	.3970	.5398	.4602	.9203	.0797
.2	.3910	.5793	.4207	.8415	.1585
.3	.3814	.6179	.3821	.7642	.2358
.4	.3683	.6554	.3446	.6892	.3108
.5	.3521	.6915	.3085	.6171	.3829
.6	.3332	.7257	.2743	.5485	.4515
.7	.3123	.7580	.2420	.4839	.5161
.8	.2897	.7881	.2119	.4237	.5763
.9	.2661	.8159	.1841	.3681	.6319
1.0	.2420	.8413	.1587	.3173	.6827
1.1	.2179	.8643	.1357	.2713	.7287
1.2	.1942	.8849	.1151	.2301	.7699
1.3	.1714	.9032	.0968	.1936	.8064
1.4	.1497	.9192	.0808	.1615	.8385
1.5	.1295	.9332	.0668	.1336	.8664
1.6	.1109	.9452	.0548	.1096	.8904
1.7	.0940	.9554	.0446	.0891	.9109
1.8	.0790	.9641	.0359	.0719	.9281
1.9	.0656	.9713	.0287	.0574	.9426
2.0	.0540	.9772	.0228	.0455	.9545
2.1	.0440	.9821	.0179	.0357	.9643
2.2	.0355	.9861	.0139	.0278	.9722
2.3	.0283	.9893	.0107	.0214	.9786
2.4	.0224	.9918	.0082	.0164	.9836
2.5	.0175	.9938	.0062	.0124	.9876
2.6	.0136	.9953	.0047	.0093	.9907
2.7	.0104	.9965	.0035	.0069	.9931
2.8	.0079	.9974	.0026	.0051	.9949
2.9	.0060	.9981	.0019	.0037	.9963
3.0	.0044	.9987	.0013	.0027	.9973
Fractiles					
1.2816	.1755	.9000	.1000	.2000	.8000
1.6449	.1031	.9500	.0500	.1000	.9000
1.9600	.0584	.9750	.0250	.0500	.9500
2.0537	.0484	.9800	.0200	.0400	.9600
2.3263	.0267	.9900	.0100	.0200	.9800
2.5758	.0145	.9950	.0050	.0100	.9900

random value of a unit normal variate, and $x \geq 0$, then

$$P(\xi \leq x) = F(x) = \int_{-\infty}^{x} \frac{1}{\sqrt{2\pi}} e^{-y^2/2} \, dy = \int_{-\infty}^{x} f(y) \, dy$$

$$P(\xi \geq x) = R(x) = \int_{x}^{\infty} f(y) \, dy = 1 - F(x)$$

$$P(\xi \leq -x) = F(-x) = \int_{-\infty}^{-x} f(y) \, dy = R(x) = 1 - F(x) \qquad (4\text{-}38)$$

$$P(|\xi| \geq x) = \int_{-\infty}^{-x} f(y) \, dy + \int_{x}^{\infty} f(y) \, dy = F(-x) + R(x) = 2R(x)$$

$$P(-x \leq \xi \leq x) = W(x) = \int_{-x}^{x} f(y) \, dy$$

Example 4-11. By route A, the travel time in minutes from hotel to airport is normal with $\mu = 27$, $\sigma = 5$; by route B, the distribution is normal with $\mu = 30$, $\sigma = 2$. Which route is the better choice if (a) one has 30 min, (b) 34 min? In either situation, we shall choose the route for which the probability of exceeding the allotted travel time is the smaller. Let t denote any value of travel time. In case a we have,

Route A: $P(t > 30) = R\left(\dfrac{30 - 27}{5}\right) = R(.6) = .27$

Route B: $P(t > 30) = R\left(\dfrac{30 - 30}{2}\right) = R(0) = .50$

Hence in case a, route A is the better risk. In case b we have,

Route A: $P(t > 34) = R\left(\dfrac{34 - 27}{5}\right) = R(1.4) = .08$

Route B: $P(t > 34) = R\left(\dfrac{34 - 30}{2}\right) = R(2.0) = .02$

Hence in case b, route B is the better risk.

Suppose n independent observations $x_1, x_2, \ldots, x_n$ of the same variate x are taken at random, and the sample average $\bar{x}$ is computed in the usual way, i.e., by adding the numbers and then dividing by n. Every time this experiment is performed, a particular value of $\bar{x}$ will result from the computation, and if we imagine the experiment repeated indefinitely with the same number of observations n each time, the computed averages will range over a series of values according to some definite law of probability. A theorem of far-reaching importance and known as the *central limit theorem* asserts that the sample averages from almost any population likely to be encountered in practice tend to become normally distributed as the sample size increases, despite the fact that no value of $\bar{x}$ can possibly be smaller than the smallest admissible value of x or larger than the largest admissible value. The reason is that the parameter σ which figures in the normal approximation to the distribution of $\bar{x}$ decreases with increasing n (actually σ is proportional to $1/\sqrt{n}$) at such a rate that the total probability associated with the region which lies outside the true physical limits of variation is negligibly small for sufficiently large n.

Example 4-12. To a good approximation, the individual values of the average monthly temperatures for a given locality are normally distributed about the climatological mean temperature at that locality for the month in question. Toward the end of December, a meteorologist predicts that at two localities A and B the average temperatures for the following January will be at least 5° above the corresponding climatological means. These forecasts prove to be correct. If σ for the distribution of the average January temperature is 2° at A and 4° at B, what are the respective probabilities of obtaining average temperatures within the ranges forecast? Which forecast is the more indicative of skill? Let $\bar{T}_A$ denote the average temperature for any January and μ_A the climatological mean at locality A. According to the forecast, $\bar{T}_A \geq \mu_A + 5°$, whence $\bar{T}_A - \mu_A \geq 5°$. The probability is

$$P(\bar{T}_A \geq \mu_A + 5°) = R(\tfrac{5}{2}) = R(2.5) = .006$$

Similarly, for locality B, the forecast asserts that $\bar{T}_B \geq \mu_B + 5°$, and the probability of such an occurrence is

$$P(\bar{T}_B \geq \mu_B + 5°) = R(\tfrac{5}{4}) = R(1.25) = .106$$

The forecast for locality A is the more indicative of skill, because it correctly calls for a much rarer event.

The normal distribution is the limiting form of a great many distributions; in particular, it is the limiting form approached by the binomial for large n. Thus, if x is binomially distributed,

$$f(x) = C(n,x)p^x q^{n-x} \qquad (x = 0, 1, 2, \ldots, n)$$

then as n increases,

$$f(x) \rightarrow \frac{1}{\sqrt{npq}\,\sqrt{2\pi}}\, e^{-(x-np)^2/2npq} \qquad (-\infty, \infty) \qquad (4\text{-}39)$$

Normal Approximation to Binomial

which is of normal form with $\mu = np$, $\sigma^2 = npq$. For moderately large values of n, the binomial distribution is adequately approximated for most purposes by the normal with $\mu = np$, $\sigma^2 = npq$ provided that $np \geq 5$. However, in applying the normal approximation, a compensation is made for the fact that the variate is actually discrete and n is finite. The conventional correction consists of changing the numerical deviation from μ by one-half unit before dividing by σ, on the grounds that the discrete value $x = a$ should correspond on a continuous scale to the interval $a - \tfrac{1}{2} \leq x \leq a + \tfrac{1}{2}$. Thus to estimate the probability

$$P(x \geq a) = \sum_{x=a}^{n} C(n,x)p^x q^{n-x}$$

where $a \geq \mu + \frac{1}{2}$ we set

$$u = \frac{a - \frac{1}{2} - \mu}{\sigma}$$

and look up $R(u)$ in the unit normal table. Again, to estimate the probability

$$P(x \leq a) = \sum_{x=0}^{a} C(n,x) p^x q^{n-x}$$

where $a \leq \mu - \frac{1}{2}$ we set

$$u' = \frac{\mu - (a + \frac{1}{2})}{\sigma}$$

and look up $R(u')$. Finally, to estimate $P(a \leq x \leq b)$ we extend the interval one-half unit to either side before dividing by σ.

Example 4-13. In the manufacture of 1-in. wood screws at a certain plant, it occasionally happens that a screw is not slotted. This occurs at random, and the compound probability of its taking place and escaping notice on inspection is .02. If a retail hardware dealer purchases a batch of 2,500 screws, what is the probability that 64 or more will lack slots? 36 or less? Between 36 and 64 inclusive? The true distribution, which is binomial with $n = 2,500$, $p = .02$, was given in Table 3-19. The respective probabilities are

$$P(x \geq 64) = 1 - F(63) = .031$$
$$P(x \leq 36) = F(36) = .023$$
$$P(36 \leq x \leq 64) = F(64) - F(35) = .962$$

For the normal approximation we have $\mu = np = 50$, $\sigma^2 = npq = 49$, $\sigma = 7$, and the corresponding probabilities are

$$P(x \geq 64) \approx R\left(\frac{13.5}{7}\right) = R(1.93) = .027$$

$$P(x \leq 36) \approx R\left(\frac{13.5}{7}\right) = R(1.93) = .027$$

$$P(36 \leq x \leq 64) \approx W\left(\frac{14.5}{7}\right) = W(2.07) = .962$$

A comparison between the normal and Poisson approximations to this binomial is given in Table 4-5. The Poisson is closer for this small value of p, but the normal is adequate for most purposes, and for larger values of p the normal approximation improves.

As suggested by Table 4-5, the fact that the Poisson distribution with $\mu = np$ approximates the binomial for sufficiently small p, while the normal approximates the binomial for large n provided that np is not too small, implies that the normal approximates the Poisson when μ is sufficiently large. Here the normal approximation uses the same μ as the Poisson, and σ is taken as $\sqrt{\mu}$.

TABLE 4-5. COMPARISON OF NORMAL AND POISSON APPROXIMATIONS TO THE BINOMIAL PROBABILITY FUNCTION $f(x)$ WITH $n = 2,500$, $p = .02$

x	Binomial	Normal	Poisson
25	.0000	.0001	.0000
30	.0006	.0010	.0007
35	.0052	.0057	.0054
40	.0212	.0205	.0215
45	.0460	.0442	.0458
50	.0569	.0570	.0563
55	.0424	.0442	.0422
60	.0199	.0205	.0201
65	.0061	.0057	.0063
70	.0013	.0010	.0014
75	.0002	.0001	.0002

The gamma distribution also approaches the normal as α increases. In this case, we take $\mu = \beta(1 + \alpha)$ and $\sigma = \beta \sqrt{1 + \alpha}$. R. A. Fisher showed that a more nearly normal variate y can be derived from a gamma variate x with parameters α, β by putting $y = 2\sqrt{x/\beta}$. When α exceeds 14, the distribution of y becomes approximately normal with $\mu = \sqrt{4\alpha + 3}$, $\sigma = 1$. A still more rapid approach to normality may be obtained by another transformation of a gamma variate due to Wilson and Hilferty. Here if we put $w = [x/\beta(\alpha + 1)]^{1/3}$ it turns out that the distribution of w is approximately normal with $\mu = (9\alpha + 8)/(9\alpha + 9)$, $\sigma = 1/(3\sqrt{\alpha + 1})$. A comparison between the exact values of $F(x)$ for the gamma distribution with $\alpha = 15$, $\beta = 1$ and the approximate values, first treating the gamma itself as normal and then treating the two functions y and w as normal, is presented in Table 4-6. Even the first approximation, treating the gamma itself as normal, is close enough

TABLE 4-6. COMPARISON BETWEEN EXACT AND APPROXIMATE VALUES OF $F(x)$ FOR GAMMA DISTRIBUTION WITH $\alpha = 15$, $\beta = 1$

x	$F(x)$	Direct normal	Fisher's transformation	Wilson-Hilferty
8.180	.01	.025	.013	.0101
10.035	.05	.068	.055	.0497
11.135	.10	.112	.103	.0999
13.152	.25	.238	.247	.2498
15.668	.50	.467	.492	.5000
18.487	.75	.733	.746	.7501
21.293	.90	.907	.902	.9001
23.098	.95	.962	.953	.9501
26.744	.99	.996	.992	.9900

for many qualitative uses; Fisher's transformation, which is fairly easy to use, is in error only in the third decimal; and the Wilson-Hilferty transformation yields results which differ from the exact values only in the fourth decimal.   Since the parameter β can be eliminated in computing probabilities, equally good results will be obtained with any value of β; moreover, the approximations improve with increasing values of α.

The foregoing transformations were originally developed in connection with a certain variate known as *chi-square*, the distribution of which is gamma with $\beta = 2$, $\alpha = (n/2) - 1$ where n is a positive integer.   The effectiveness of the transformations illustrates the general rule that if x is a non-negative variate with a skewed distribution, then the distributions of $\sqrt{x}$ and $x^{1/3}$ tend to be more nearly symmetrical and more nearly normal than the distribution of x.   The same is true of log x provided that $f(0) = 0$.   Other normalizing transformations have also been devised for special uses.   Besides the obvious advantage that existing probability tables may be applied, normalizing transformations serve the purpose of reducing many difficult analytical problems to solvable forms.

4-12. Confidence Limits (Interval Estimation).   In this chapter we have considered continuous density functions $f(x)$.   This function may contain unknown parameters which one would like to estimate, even though the general form of the function is known.   Therefore, in this section we shall consider how to bracket the true value of a single parameter by an interval called a "confidence interval."   It should be kept in mind in all of this discussion that the parameter itself has a definite value, and therefore, in general, has no probability distribution.   While there are several methods of determining confidence limits, we shall use the one which seems to have the widest application, inasmuch as it is a direct approach to the problem.

Let us denote this probability density function by $f(x,\theta)$ and therefore the probability that x will lie between x and $x + dx$ as $f(x,\theta)\, dx$.   (Actually, the variable x may be a function of other random variables such as the average of n observations drawn from a particular distribution.)   Since we do not know the true value of θ in a particular instance, we must allow for the possibility of its assuming any value which is logically admissible, even though its actual value is unique.   Thus both x and θ are defined jointly over a range of possible values, which may or may not be infinite in extent.   The limits on x may well be functions of θ itself, such as $a(\theta) \leq x \leq b(\theta)$.

If we fix the parameter θ at a specific value, then a value of x may be chosen, say x_1, so that

$$\int_{a(\theta)}^{x_1} f(x,\theta)\, dx = p_1$$

and a value of x_2 chosen so that

$$\int_{x_2}^{b(\theta)} f(x,\theta) \, dx = p_2$$

where p_1 and p_2 are constants whose sum is less than unity. It is clear, then, that the probability that $x_1 \leq x \leq x_2$ is $1 - p_1 - p_2$. These two integral equations actually give x_1 as a function of θ and p_1 and x_2 as a function of θ and p_2. If we denote these relationships as $x_1 = w_1(\theta,p_1)$ and $x_2 = w_2(\theta,p_2)$ it is now possible to visualize graphically the behavior of these two monotonically increasing functions of the variable θ as in Fig. 4-22. The area between the two curves shown represents what is termed the *confidence belt*, in that no matter what the value of θ is during

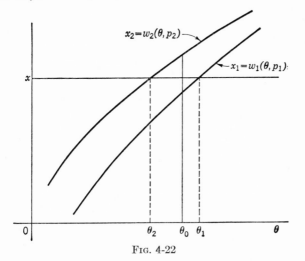

FIG. 4-22

a single experiment, the probability is $1 - p_1 - p_2$ that a random observation (from that particular population determined by θ) will yield a value of x inside that region.

Now let us start from the opposite direction and assume we have a value of x given and now wish to say something about the likelihood of certain values of θ. A horizontal line through the given observed point x cuts each of the two curves $x_2 = w_2(\theta,p_2)$ and $x_1 = w_1(\theta,p_1)$ at one point because of the monotonic and continuous character of the curves. Let these two points have the θ coordinate of θ_2 and θ_1 respectively. If θ_0 is the true value of the parameter, then the interval $\theta_1 - \theta_2$ will include θ_0 provided x lies between $x_1 = w_1(\theta_0,p_1)$ and $x_2 = w_2(\theta_0,p_2)$. This, however, will occur exactly $(1 - p_1 - p_2)$ fraction of the time. Thus, if θ_0 is the true value of the parameter, the probability that $\theta_1 - \theta_2$ will overlap θ_0 is also $(1 - p_1 - p_2)$. This same probability, however, equally well applies to any value of the parameter which may be the true one that we are estimating. In the long run, therefore, considered over a large number of experiments in which the value of x is calculated from observed data, and the interval $\theta_1 - \theta_2$ computed according to the above scheme, $(1 - p_1 - p_2)$ fraction of the time the interval will cover the true value of the parameter which gave rise to the calculated x. It is important to realize that this statement holds *only* in the *long run*, inasmuch as in a particular instance the point either is covered or not. In the first instance, the probability is 1 and in the second, zero. There are obviously an infinite number of values of p_1 and p_2 which will give a series of confidence intervals based on the same confidence coefficient $(1 - p_1 - p_2)$. Intuitively one would feel that the value of p_1 and p_2 which made the length of the confidence intervals as small as possible should be the one preferred. If the function $f(x,\theta)$ is reasonably symmetrical for a fixed θ, then a fairly good approximation to the intervals of shortest length would be obtained by setting $p_1 = p_2$ which is customarily chosen.

Example 4-14. Given that the distribution of the mean of a sample of size n is normally distributed as $(\sqrt{n}/\sigma \sqrt{2\pi}) \exp [-n(\bar{x} - \mu)^2/2\sigma^2]$ $(-\infty, \infty)$, what are the 95 per cent confidence limits for $\bar{x}$ if σ is known?

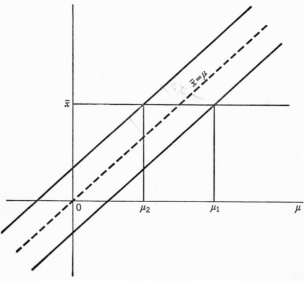

FIG. 4-23

For a fixed value of μ, $\bar{x}$ will lie within the limits $\mu \pm (1.96/\sqrt{n}) \sigma$ about 95 per cent of the time. Since both σ and n are constant, the functions w_1 and w_2 are two lines parallel to the line $\bar{x} = \mu$ as in Fig. 4-23. Therefore, for a fixed value of $\bar{x}$ we have the two limits of a confidence interval as $\mu_2 = \bar{x} - 1.96\sigma/\sqrt{n}$ and $\mu_1 = \bar{x} + 1.96\sigma/\sqrt{n}$. Thus 95 per cent of the time, irrespective of the true value of μ, this parameter will be overlapped by this confidence interval calculated on the basis of the observed value of $\bar{x}$, or $P(\mu_2 \leq \mu \leq \mu_1) = .95$.

Example 4-15. The percentage of defects is observed in a random sample of size n taken from a large lot. Assuming that for a fixed value of the parameter p (percentage of defects for the entire lot) the number of defects is binomially distributed in the sample, what are the 50 per cent confidence limits in estimating the lot parameter p?

Since for a fixed value of this parameter p a binomial distribution is hypothesized for the sample, the observed p' will lie 50 per cent of the time within the limits $p' = p \pm .67 \sqrt{pq/n}$ approximately. Therefore, $p_2' = w_2(p,.25) = p + .67 \sqrt{(p)(1-p)/n}$ and $p_1' = w_1(p,.25) = p - .67 \sqrt{(p)(1-p)/n}$. Since n is fixed, these two equations in p and p_2' and p and p_1' form the top and bottom of an ellipse (see Fig. 4-24).

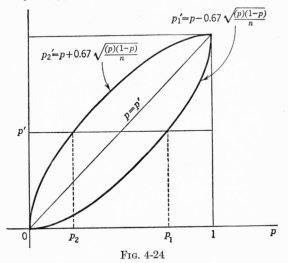

FIG. 4-24

The p_1 and p_2 which form the upper and lower confidence limits are thus the two roots of the above quadratic equations and are as follows:

$$\frac{n}{n + (.67)^2} \left[p' + \frac{(.67)^2}{2n} \pm .67 \sqrt{\frac{p'q'}{n} + \frac{(.67)^2}{4n^2}} \right]$$

EXERCISES

1. Points are uniformly distributed inside a circle of radius R. (a) In terms of the distribution function, find the distribution of the distance x of interior points from the center. (b) For what value of x are the chances even that a random interior point will be nearer to the center than that distance or farther away?

Ans. (a) $F(x) = x^2/R^2$ $(0 \le x \le R)$; (b) $x = R/\sqrt{2}$

2. Points are uniformly distributed along the periphery of a semicircle of radius R. (a) In terms of the distribution function, find the distribution of the shortest distance x from one end of the diameter to random points on the periphery. (b) Find $P(x \le R)$.

Ans. (a) $F(x) = (2/\pi) \sin^{-1} x/2R$ $(0 \le x \le 2R)$; (b) $P = \frac{1}{3}$.

3. Points are uniformly distributed on the periphery of the circle $x^2 - 2Rx + y^2 = 0$. (a) Express the distribution of x in terms of its distribution function. (b) In terms of its density function. (c) Sketch the density function. (d) Evaluate $P(R/2 \le x \le R)$. (e) Evaluate $P(x \ge 3R/2)$.

Ans. (a) $F(x) = \frac{1}{\pi} \cos^{-1} \frac{R - x}{R}$ $(0 \le x \le 2R)$; (b) $f(x) = \frac{1}{\pi} \frac{1}{\sqrt{2Rx - x^2}}$ $(0 \le x \le 2R)$; (c) U-shaped; (d) $\frac{1}{6}$; (e) $\frac{1}{3}$.

✦ **4.** The points inside a circle of radius R and center O are uniformly distributed. From a fixed external point E located at a distance D from O, a line EI is drawn to any point I chosen at random inside the circle. Letting x represent the distance $\overline{EI}$, find the density function of x. [HINT: Consider $P(x \leq \overline{EI} \leq x + dx)$.]

     Ans. $f(x) = (2/\pi R^2)x \cos^{-1}[(x^2 + D^2 - R^2)/2Dx]$ $(D - R \leq x \leq D + R)$.

✦ **5.** Given that

$$f(x) = x \quad (0,1) \qquad f(x) = 2 - x \quad (1,2)$$

find $P(\frac{1}{2} \leq x \leq \frac{3}{2})$.   *Ans.* .75.

✦ **6.** A density function is said to be symmetrical about zero when $f(-x) \equiv f(x)$. If a is any positive value of x, derive the following results, using geometric intuition freely.

     (a) $F(0) = .5$.

     (b) $P(x > a) \equiv P(x \geq a) = .5 - \int_0^a f(x)\, dx$.

     (c) $F(-a) + F(a) = 1$.

     (d) $P(-a < x < a) \equiv P(-a \leq x \leq a) = 2F(a) - 1$.

     (e) $P(|x| > a) \equiv P(|x| \geq a) = 2F(-a) = 2[1 - F(a)]$.

     A distribution is said to be unimodal if its density function has only one turning point, and this is a maximum value of the ordinate; the abscissa of the maximum is called the *mode*. In Exercises 7–11, show that the distributions are unimodal and find the mode in each case. Also determine k in each case so that the total area will be unity.

✦ **7.** $f(x) = kx^4 e^{-x}$ $(0, \infty)$.   *Ans.* $k = \frac{1}{24}$; mode $= 4$.

✦ **8.** $f(x) = kx e^{-ax}$ $(a > 0; 0 \leq x < \infty)$.   *Ans.* $k = a^2$; mode $= 1/a$.

9. $f(x) = kx e^{-x^2}$ $(0, \infty)$.   *Ans.* $k = 2$; mode $= 1/\sqrt{2}$.

10. $f(x) = kx(a - x)^2$ $(0,a)$.   *Ans.* $k = 12/a^4$; mode $= a/3$.

11. $f(x) = k(ax + x^2)e^{-bx}$ $(a, b > 0; 0 \leq x < \infty)$.

                         Ans. $k = b^3/(ab + 2)$; mode $= (2 - ab + \sqrt{4 + a^2b^2})/2b$.

✦ **12.** The *median* of a variate x which has a continuous distribution function $F(x)$ is defined as that value of c such that $F(c) = \frac{1}{2}$. If x has a density function $f(x)$ and the lower and upper limits of x are A and B respectively, show that the median satisfies the following equation:

$$\int_A^c f(x)\, dx = \int_c^B f(x)\, dx$$

✦ **13.** The variate x is distributed as follows:

$$f(x) = \frac{1}{\sigma \sqrt{2\pi}} e^{-(x-\mu)^2/2\sigma^2} \qquad (\sigma > 0; -\infty < x < \infty)$$

     (a) Show that the total area is a unity.   (b) Determine the points of inflection. (c) Locate the median and mode by inspection.   (d) Sketch the curve.

     Ans. (a) Reduce to gamma function by substituting $u = (x - \mu)/\sigma \sqrt{2}$. Thus obtain Area $= \Gamma(\frac{1}{2})/\sqrt{\pi} = 1$.   (b) Inflection points at $x = \mu + \sigma$ and $x = \mu - \sigma$. (c) Median $=$ mode $= \mu$.   (d) Bell-shaped, symmetrical about $x = \mu$.

✦ **14.** The variate x is distributed as follows:

$$f(x) = \frac{k}{a^2 + (x - b)^2} \qquad (-\infty, \infty)$$

(a) Determine k so that the total area will be unity. (b) Sketch the curve. (c) Locate the median and mode by inspection, checking the former by integration and the latter by differentiation.

Ans. (a) $k = a/\pi$. (b) Bell-shaped, symmetrical about $x = b$. (c) Median = mode = b.

15. A random observation x_1 is made of the variate x, the distribution of which is

$$f(x) = a^2x\, e^{-ax} \qquad (a > 0; 0 \leq x < \infty)$$

(a) What is the probability that x_1 will be less than the mode? (b) More than twice the mode? Ans. (a) .264, (b) .406.

16. The random variable x is distributed as follows:

$$f(x) = \frac{6x}{(1 + x)^4} \qquad (0, \infty)$$

(a) Show that the total area is unity and find the distribution function $F(x)$. (b) Find $P(x \leq \frac{1}{4})$, (c) $P(x \geq 4)$, (d) $P(1 \leq x \leq 2)$.

Ans. (a) $F(x) = 1 - 3/(1 + x)^2 + 2/(1 + x)^3$; $F(\infty) = 1$. (b) .104. (c) .104. (d) .241.

17. Given

$$P(x \geq a) = \frac{1}{(1 + a/k)^k} \qquad (k > 0; 0 \leq a < \infty)$$

(a) Find $F(x)$ and $f(x)$. (b) Plot $F(x)$ and $f(x)$ if $k = 2$. (c) If three observations are taken at random and $k = 2$, what is the probability that all three will exceed 4? (d) What is the probability that one will lie between 0 and 1, another between 2 and 3, and another between 4 and 5?

Ans. (a) $F(x) = 1 - \dfrac{1}{(1 + x/k)^k}$ $(0, \infty); f(x) = \dfrac{1}{(1 + x/k)^{k+1}}$ $(0, \infty)$.

(b) F starts at 0 and rises sharply at first, then more slowly, approaching the line $F = 1$ asymptotically; f starts at 1 and falls sharply at first, then more slowly, approaching the x axis asymptotically. Neither curve has inflection points.

(c) $\frac{1}{729}$; (d) 13/1,470.

18. To an adequate approximation, the distribution of length of life (period of satisfactory service) of a certain manufactured product is given by $f(x) = 2xe^{-x^2}$ $(0 \leq x < \infty)$. (a) To three decimals, find the value of a such that $P(x \geq a) = .99$. (b) If 1,000 articles are sold, what is the probability that the life of at least one will be less than this value a? Ans. (a) $a = .100; P = .999956$.

19. Scaled to convenient units, the daily electric power consumption in a certain locality is a gamma variate with $\alpha = 1.5$, $\beta = 1\frac{2}{3}$. How much power should a plant be able to supply in order that stand-by equipment will not be drawn upon more than 1 per cent of the time? Ans. 25.1.

20. Assuming a gamma variate, estimate the parameters of the distribution of precipitation (converted to inches of rainfall) for the month of January over a certain region given that the first decile is 1.33 and the ninth decile is 5.62.

Ans. $\alpha = 2.5$, $\beta = .94$.

21. In millions of cubic feet, the daily gas "sendout" of a certain company during the heating season is a modified gamma variate with $A = 30$, $\alpha = 6$, $\beta = 4.6$. Taken over the season, approximately what proportion of the daily sendouts would be expected to fall between 48 and 78 units? (Use nearest entries in table.) Ans. .8.

22. In months, the distribution of business life of a certain type of enterprise is exponential, the risk of failure in the early stages being fairly great. (a) What is the value of β if the first decile is 7.56? (b) If a man rents buildings to two such companies, and independence may be assumed, what is the median value of the total rent-months where, from the revenue standpoint, concurrent months are regarded as distinct?   *Ans.* (a) 72, (b) 120.82.

23. The distribution of x is known to be gamma with $\beta = 1$ but unknown α. A random observation of x turns out to have the value 7.5. (a) For what value of α would this value of x correspond to a fractile of .99? (b) of .01? These two values of α are called "98% confidence limits."   *Ans.* (a) $\alpha = 1.5$; (b) $\alpha = 14.0$.

24. Under the same conditions as Exercise 23, suppose that instead of one observation, three are drawn at random, and their sum S is computed. (a) If $S = 19.5$ what are the 98% confidence limits for α in the distribution of S? (b) What are the corresponding limits for α in the distribution of x? (Assume validity of Theorem 4-2 for non-integral α's.)   *Ans.* (a) 9.5 to 30.0, (b) 2.5 to 9.3.

25. An agricultural research farm is subdivided into experimental plots of $\frac{1}{500}$ acre each. The plots may be considered as members of a common population, and the yield of wheat in pounds per plot is normally distributed with $\mu = 4$, $\sigma = .5$. Letting x denote the yield of a plot chosen at random, determine the following probabilities:

(a) $P(x \leq 2.5)$, (b) $P(x \leq 4.5)$, (c) $P(x > 5)$, (d) $P(3.5 < x < 4.2)$, (e) $P(3.5 < x < 4.5)$, (f) $P(3 \leq x \leq 5)$.

Ans. (a) .001, (b) .841, (c) .023, (d) .497, (e) .683, (f) .955.

26. The annual rainfall (in inches) over a certain region is normally distributed with $\mu = 39.5$, $\sigma = 3.5$. Considering the annual amounts independent (an assumption which the actual observations seem to support), find the probability that in four consecutive years (a) the first two amounts will be less than 36.7 and the next two greater than 42.3, (b) some pair or other will be less than 36.7 and the remaining pair greater than 42.3.   *Ans.* (a) .002, (b) .012.

27. The average value $\bar{x}$ of a random sample of n observations from a certain population is normally distributed with $\mu = 20$, $\sigma = 5/\sqrt{n}$. How large a sample should we draw in order to have a probability of at least .90 that $\bar{x}$ will lie between 18 and 22?

Ans. 17.

28. Suppose $p = .2$ is the probability of success in a single trial. Estimate the total probability of obtaining less than 6 or more than 15 successes in 50 trials.

Ans. .082.

29. Given a Poisson distribution with $\mu = 25$, estimate $P(x > 35)$.   *Ans.* .018.

30. Using the Wilson-Hilferty transformation, estimate the ninth decile of the gamma distribution with $\alpha = 24$, $\beta = 1$. Check by linear interpolation in Table 4-1.   *Ans.* 31.58. Interpolation gives same value.

31. In Chap. 6 it is proved that if x is normally distributed with parameters (μ, σ) then $\bar{x}$, the average of n independent observations of x, is also normally distributed with corresponding parameters $(\mu, \sigma/\sqrt{n})$. This result is not merely approximate, in this case, but exact. Given a normal population with $\sigma = 1$, plot the distance between the lower and upper 98% confidence limits for μ as a function of the sample size n on which the sample mean $\bar{x}$ is based.   *Ans.* Graph of $(4.65)/\sqrt{n}$.

32. The breaking strength (in pounds) of string manufactured by an established process is normally distributed with $\mu = 15$, $\sigma = 3$. A new process is tried, and a random sample of 9 pieces of standard length have an average breaking strength of 18. (a) Under the null hypothesis that these pieces are random selections from the original population, what is the probability that their average would differ from μ as much as this or more in either direction? (b) Regarding the new breaking strengths as belonging to another normal population, with σ the same as before, find 98% confidence limits for μ.   *Ans.* (a) .0027, (b) 15.7 to 20.3.

33. A certain probability distribution is a function of a single parameter a. If the value of a is fixed and an extremely large number of observations are made on this population, 95 per cent of them will always lie in the region $a \pm (a - 1)(3 - a)$. It is known that all the possible values of the parameter a are between $1 < a < 3$. Construct the 95 per cent confidence belt. If an observation is made on the population experimentally, it is found that $a' = 1.5$. What is the confidence interval in this case and exactly what is meant by that figure?   *Ans.* $(5 - \sqrt{7})/2$, $(3 + \sqrt{3})/2$.

34. Given the simple hypothesis $f(x) = (1/\pi)/(1 + x^2)$ $(-\infty, \infty)$, determine the limits of the critical region in the following cases, where α denotes the chosen level of significance. (*a*) One-sided region in right-hand tail, $\alpha = .05$. (*b*) One-sided region in left-hand tail, $\alpha = .05$. (*c*) Two-sided region, $\alpha = .05$. (*d*) Two-sided region, $\alpha = .01$.   *Ans.* (*a*) 6.313, (*b*) -6.313, (*c*) ± 12.716, (*d*) ± 63.704.

CHAPTER 5

JOINT DISTRIBUTIONS

5-1. Fundamental Concepts. So far we have been concerned with distributions of single variates. These are called *univariate* distributions to distinguish them from *bivariate* distributions, which involve two variates simultaneously, or *multivariate* distributions, which are generally understood to involve three or more variates simultaneously. The term "multivariate" may also be used broadly to designate an arbitrary number of variates, and in that sense would include univariate and bivariate distributions as special cases. Since natural phenomena are characterized by the coexistence of many attributes and dimensions, it is often necessary to consider multivariate distributions in representing the relevant conditions of practical problems. Once the conceptual step is taken from univariate to bivariate distributions, the transition to higher dimensions involves nothing essentially new. Therefore, let us consider some concrete examples of bivariate distributions.

Example 5-1. The team for a competitive game consists of two players, each of whom can score 0, 1, or 2 points. Player 1 has the probability .2 of scoring 0, .5 of scoring 1, and .3 of scoring 2, while for player 2 the corresponding probabilities are .1, .4, .5. The problem is to derive the joint distribution of the scores of these two teammates, assuming their performances are independent. Let x_1 denote any possible score of player 1 and $f_1(x_1)$ his probability of gaining that score; also let x_2 denote any possible score of player 2 and $f_2(x_2)$ the corresponding probability. This much is univariate material; we now introduce the bivariate aspect by letting $f(x_1,x_2)$ denote the probability of the compound event that player 1 scores x_1 points while in the same game player 2 scores x_2 points. By the assumption of independence we have

$$f(x_1,x_2) = f_1(x_1)f_2(x_2)$$

Thus, the probability that both players score 0 is

$$f(0,0) = f_1(0)f_2(0) = (.2)(.1) = .02$$

Again, the probability that player 1 scores 0 while player 2 scores 1 is

$$f(0,1) = f_1(0)f_2(1) = (.2)(.4) = .08$$

and so on. Table 5-1 presents the complete bivariate distribution, comprising nine distinct possibilities together with their associated probabilities. The margins of the table contain the sums of the tabular entries $f(x_1,x_2)$ by rows (horizontal) and columns (vertical). Each row total yields precisely the probability $f_1(x_1)$ that player 1 scores

x_1 points, and each column total yields the probability that player 2 scores x_2 points. Because of the fact that the single distributions are thus displayed in the margins of the bivariate table, single distributions have come to be called *marginal* distributions.

TABLE 5-1. BIVARIATE DISTRIBUTION OF SCORES

x_1 \ x_2	0	1	2	Sum $= f_1(x_1)$
0	.02	.08	.10	.20
1	.05	.20	.25	.50
2	.03	.12	.15	.30
Sum $= f_2(x_2)$	.10	.40	.50	1.00

Supposing now that the score for the team is the sum of the scores gained by the two players, let us find the distribution of the team score t. Clearly the possible values of t are 0, 1, 2, 3, 4 and the probability $p(t)$ of any particular value is equal to the sum of the probabilities of the distinct ways in which that combined score can be obtained. Hence

$$p(0) = f(0,0) = .02$$
$$p(1) = f(0,1) + f(1,0) = .08 + .05 = .13$$
$$p(2) = f(0,2) + f(1,1) + f(2,0) = .10 + .20 + .03 = .33$$
$$p(3) = f(1,2) + f(2,1) = .25 + .12 = .37$$
$$p(4) = f(2,2) = .15$$

In this way, we arrive at the distribution of the team score t as shown in Table 5-2.

TABLE 5-2. DISTRIBUTION OF TEAM SCORE

t	0	1	2	3	4	Sum
$p(t)$	.02	.13	.33	.37	.15	1.00

A joint distribution can be synthesized from the marginal distributions only if the variates are independent. The joint distribution of dependent variates can be derived only when there is sufficient mathematical information to determine the compound probabilities either directly or by analytic deduction; without such information, one must resort to empirical estimates based on relative frequencies of compound events. A bivariate distribution with dependent coordinates is illustrated in the next example.

Example 5-2. Companies A and B control respectively 50 per cent and 20 per cent of the market for a certain commodity. The problem is to derive the bivariate distribution of the numbers of customers patronizing each company in random samples of two buyers. The symbol (x_1,x_2) will represent the event that x_1 of the two are customers of A while x_2 are customers of B; also $f(x_1,x_2)$ will represent the probability of this event. Since the two companies together sell to only 70 per cent of the market, the remaining 30 per cent goes to neither. Letting N denote neither A nor B, the possible allocations of two buyers are shown in Table 5-3, wherein compound probabilities are computed on the assumption that sampling depletions may be ignored. The bivariate distribution itself is presented compactly in Table 5-4. As in the previous example, the row and column totals yield the marginal distributions, for even though the variates are not independent, the separate combinations along a row or column represent the exhaustive and mutually exclusive ways in which a fixed value of one of the variates can occur.

TABLE 5-3

Allocation		Compound probability of this allocation	Corresponding bivariate event	Total probability of bivariate event
Buyer 1	Buyer 2			
N	N	$(.3)(.3) = .09$	$(0,0)$	$f(0,0) = .09$
N	B	$(.3)(.2) = .06$	$(0,1)$	
B	N	$(.2)(.3) = .06$	$(0,1)$	$f(0,1) = .06 + .06$ $= .12$
B	B	$(.2)(.2) = .04$	$(0,2)$	$f(0,2) = .04$
N	A	$(.3)(.5) = .15$	$(1,0)$	
A	N	$(.5)(.3) = .15$	$(1,0)$	$f(1,0) = .15 + .15$ $= .30$
B	A	$(.2)(.5) = .10$	$(1,1)$	
A	B	$(.5)(.2) = .10$	$(1,1)$	$f(1,1) = .10 + .10$ $= .20$
A	A	$(.5)(.5) = .25$	$(2,0)$	$f(2,0) = .25$

TABLE 5-4. BIVARIATE DISTRIBUTION OF CUSTOMERS

x_1 \ x_2	0	1	2	Sum $= f_1(x_1)$
0	.09	.12	.04	.25
1	.30	.20	0	.50
2	.25	0	0	.25
Sum $= f_2(x_2)$	.64	.32	.04	1.00

In Chap. 2 the conditional probability of an event B given the occurrence of another event A was obtained as the ratio of the compound probability of (A,B) to the unconditional probability of A; that is, $P(B|A) = P(A,B)/P(A)$. Similarly, the conditional probability that a discrete variate x_2 takes on a certain admissible value b when another discrete variate x_1 takes on a specific value a is given by

$$\phi(b|a) = \frac{f(a,b)}{f_1(a)}$$

Holding x_1 fixed at the value a but letting x_2 vary over all of its (conditionally) admissible values, we obtain what is known as the *conditional distribution* of x_2, given that $x_1 = a$. It should be noted that the conditional distribution summed for all possible values of x_2 always equals unity. Inasmuch as a, in turn, can represent any admissible value of x_1, we represent the conditional-probability function of x_2 by the symbol $\phi(x_2|x_1)$ for general reference, or more specifically by $\phi(x_2|x_1 = a)$ when a particular value a of x_1 is intended. The conditional distributions of x_2 for successive choices of x_1 in Example 5-2 are shown in Table 5-5.

TABLE 5-5. CONDITIONAL DISTRIBUTIONS

	Value of x_2			Sum
	0	1	2	
$\phi(x_2\|x_1 = 0)$	.36	.48	.16	1.00
$\phi(x_2\|x_1 = 1)$	.60	.40	0	1.00
$\phi(x_2\|x_1 = 2)$	1.00	0	0	1.00

An advantage of the conditional distribution is the comparative ease with which it often can be derived by elementary changes of variable or deduced from physical reasoning.

Summarizing the fundamental concepts: The joint distribution of *independent* variates can be synthesized from the respective marginal distributions; but for *dependent* variates, either the joint or conditional distribution must be known in advance or derivable from the given information. For discrete variates, the marginal probabilities may be obtained by summing the appropriate joint probabilities, and conditional probabilities may be obtained by dividing joint probabilities by associated marginal probabilities; in turn, the joint distribution can be constructed if the marginal and conditional distributions are known.

Geometric language is helpful in discussing multivariate distributions. The simultaneously admissible values of n variates may be thought of as cutting out a region in n-dimensional space, the coordinate axes of which represent the respective variates. We shall develop this idea as we proceed.

5-2. Multivariate Distribution Functions and Density Functions. In the joint distribution of several random variables x_1, x_2, x_3, . . . the joint-distribution function $F(a,b,c, . . .)$ yields the probability that the inequalities $x_1 \le a$, $x_2 \le b$, $x_3 \le c$, . . . are simultaneously satisfied. As suggested by the univariate case, the general notation employed for the joint-distribution function is $F(x_1,x_2,x_3, . . .)$ inasmuch as the symbols a, b, c, . . . merely represent arbitrary values of the given variates. Several random variables are *mutually independent* provided that their joint-distribution function factors identically into the product of their separate (i.e., marginal) distribution functions, as

$$F(x_1, x_2, \ldots, x_n) = F_1(x_1) F_2(x_2) \cdots F_n(x_n) \qquad (5\text{-}1)$$

We shall take this equation as the general definition of independence for random variables. It is, of course, compatible with the definition previously laid down for qualitative events, but we shall not go through the algebraic manipulation necessary to establish the connection.

The density concept introduced for continuous univariate distributions can be extended to any number of dimensions, and although the joint-distribution function has the mathematical advantage of complete generality, the joint density function, when it exists, is much easier to work with from the elementary viewpoint. If the joint-distribution function is continuous and differentiable, the joint density function may be defined as its nth partial derivative wherein each variate in turn is taken once:

$$f(x_1, x_2, \ldots, x_n) = \frac{\partial^n}{\partial x_1 \, \partial x_2 \, \cdots \, \partial x_n} [F(x_1, x_2, \ldots, x_n)] \qquad (5\text{-}2)$$

While Eq. (5-2) constitutes a formal definition, in this book the joint density function itself will be taken as primary information or else derived under stated hypotheses, without first explicitly solving for the corresponding distribution function. The meaning of the joint density function is analogous to that of the univariate density function; that is, the expression

$$f(x_1, x_2, \ldots, x_n) \, dx_1 \, dx_2 \, \cdots \, dx_n$$

represents the probability that a random point $x_1', x_2', \ldots, x_n'$ will fall within an infinitesimal region such that $x_1 < x_1' < x_1 + dx_1$; $x_2 < x_2' < x_2 + dx_2$; $\ldots$; $x_n < x_n' < x_n + dx_n$. The total integral of any joint density function over the entire region for which it is defined is necessarily equal to unity.

By taking the appropriate nth partial derivatives of both sides of (5-1), we see at once that if the variates are independent, their joint density function factors identically into the product of their marginal density functions:

$$f(x_1, x_2, \ldots, x_n) = f_1(x_1) f_2(x_2) \cdots f_n(x_n) \qquad (5\text{-}3)$$

From this fact it follows that the joint density function of independent variates can be constructed by taking the product of their respective marginal density functions, just as the joint-probability function of independent discrete variates can be analogously constructed. Equation (5-3) will serve as an alternative definition of independence, applicable to continuous variates for which the joint density function exists and also formally applicable to discrete variates with the understanding that f then represents the discrete-probability function.

From now on, for the sake of simplicity of exposition, we shall concentrate on bivariate distributions, although general results will be stated where feasible. The student can easily work out the n-dimensional analogies if he understands the bivariate case, particularly with the aid of Chap. 2.

5-3. Admissible Regions. The mathematical specification of a joint distribution can be expressed either in terms of the joint-distribution function or the joint density function, but the region of definition must

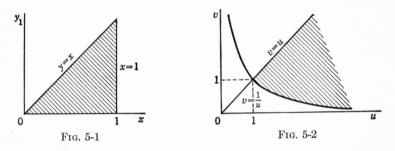

FIG. 5-1   FIG. 5-2

always be stated to make the specification complete. One way of defining the admissible region is to describe its geometric boundaries. For example, we might say: "The admissible region of x and y consists of the triangle (Fig. 5-1) bounded by the lines $y = 0$, $y = x$, and $x = 1$." Or in another case we might say: "The admissible region of u and v (Fig. 5-2) lies in the first quadrant and consists of that infinite wedge bounded below by the hyperbola $v = 1/u$ and above by the straight line $v = u$." Verbal descriptions such as these are sometimes necessary for clarity, but if the geometric figure is simple enough, it often happens that the admissible region can be defined concisely by stating the extreme limits of one variate and then stating the functional limits of the other for an arbitrary value of the first. For instance, we may represent the triangular region of Fig. 5-1 by the analytic specification

$$(0 \leq x \leq 1 \qquad 0 \leq y \leq x)$$

This compact specification is interpreted to mean that the outside limits of the figure are the lines $x = 0$ and $x = 1$; then within these limits, the figure is further bounded by the lines $y = 0$ and $y = x$. The separate steps in the interpretation are indicated graphically in Fig. 5-3. For the same region, we could have written, equally well, the alternative specification

$$(0 \leq y \leq 1 \qquad y \leq x \leq 1)$$

FIG. 5-3. Steps in the visualization of an admissible region. (a) Outside limits; (b) complementary limits; (c) admissible region.

FIG. 5-4. Visualization of alternative construction. (a) Outside limits; (b) complementary limits; (c) admissible region.

FIG. 5-5. (a) Outside limits; (b) complementary limits; (c) admissible region.

for which the steps in the corresponding graphical interpretation are indicated in Fig. 5-4.

The infinite wedge-shaped region of Fig. 5-2 can be defined by the concise specification

$$1 \leq u < \infty \qquad \frac{1}{u} \leq v \leq u$$

for which the graphical interpretation is shown in Fig. 5-5. Here, however, in order to interchange the roles of u and v, as we did with x and y in the previous example, we would need two statements:

$$0 \leq v \leq 1; \frac{1}{v} \leq u < \infty \qquad \text{and} \qquad 1 \leq v < \infty; v \leq u < \infty$$

Thus the specification may be simpler from one viewpoint than another, and of course, we shall ordinarily choose the simpler one. Where geometrically feasible, we shall describe the admissible region by stating constant limits for one variate, followed by corresponding limits for the second when the first assumes an arbitrary value within those constant limits; and it is always understood that the density is identically zero outside of the admissible region. With a little practice, the student will rapidly acquire facility in the interpretation of compact representations of the admissible region.

5-4. Continuous Bivariate Distributions. As would be expected from analogy with discrete variates, the *marginal* density function of each variate can be obtained from the joint density function by integration with respect to the other variates. In the bivariate case, let the joint

$$(a) \qquad\qquad\qquad (b)$$

Fig. 5-6. (a) Path of integration for marginal density of x; (b) path of integration for marginal density of y.

density function of x and y be denoted by $f(x,y)$ and the marginal density function of x by $f_1(x)$. Consider the elementary rectangle which has its corners located at the points (x,y), $(x + dx, y)$, $(x, y + dy)$, $(x + dx, y + dy)$. The probability that a random point (x',y') will fall in this rectangle is given by $f(x,y)\, dx\, dy$, and the integral of such probability elements with respect to y, for a fixed value of x, will yield the sum of the probabilities of all of the mutually exclusive ways of obtaining points with abscissas lying between x and $x + dx$. Now unless $f(x,y)$ is defined for the entire plane, the admissible region will be bounded by lines or curves, and the integral with respect to y will be taken from the bottom to the top of the vertical strip [Fig. 5-6(a)] corresponding to the fixed value of x. The lower limit of y, ordinarily a point on a curve, will be expressed in terms of x as $a_1(x)$ and the upper limit expressed as $b_1(x)$. Consequently,

$$P(x \le x' \le x + dx) = \left[\int_{a_1(x)}^{b_1(x)} f(x,y)\, dy \right] dx = f_1(x)\, dx \qquad (5\text{-}4)$$

whence, equating coefficients of dx,

$$f_1(x) = \int_{a_1(x)}^{b_1(x)} f(x,y)\, dy \qquad (5\text{-}5)$$

By similar reasoning, the marginal density function of y is given by

$$f_2(y) = \int_{a_2(y)}^{b_2(y)} f(x,y) \, dx \qquad (5\text{-}6)$$

where $a_2(y)$ and $b_2(y)$ are the functional values of x in terms of y at the two ends of the horizontal strip [Fig. 5-6(b)] corresponding to a fixed value of y.

Given the information that the ordinate y' of a random point lies between y and $y + dy$, the conditional probability that its abscissa x' will lie between x and $x + dx$ can be obtained in the usual way from the joint and unconditional probabilities:

$$P[(x \le x' \le x + dx) | (y \le y' \le y + dy)]$$

$$= \frac{P[(x \le x' \le x + dx), (y \le y' \le y + dy)]}{P(y \le y' \le y + dy)}$$

$$= \frac{f(x,y) \, dx \, dy}{f_2(y) \, dy} = [f(x,y)/f_2(y)] \, dx \qquad (5\text{-}7)$$

We thus arrive at the *conditional* density function $\phi_1(x|y)$ defined by the equation

$$\phi_1(x|y) \equiv \frac{f(x,y)}{f_2(y)} \qquad (5\text{-}8)$$

and having the property that $\phi_1(x|y) \, dx$ yields the conditional probability that x' lies between x and $x + dx$ given that $y \le y' \le y + dy$.

The conditional density function $\phi_2(y|x)$ of y for a fixed value of x is correspondingly defined by the equation

$$\phi_2(y|x) \equiv \frac{f(x,y)}{f_1(x)} \qquad (5\text{-}9)$$

and has a similar interpretation. Reciprocally, the joint density function can be constructed as the product of the marginal density function of one variate and the conditional density function of the other:

$$f(x,y) = f_1(x)\phi_2(y|x) = f_2(y)\phi_1(x|y) \qquad (5\text{-}10)$$

By including the range of definition with the equation of the conditional density function, we obtain the complete specification of the conditional distribution. Thus, referring to Fig. 5-6(b), the conditional distribution of x for a fixed value of y would be defined by the equation for $\phi_1(x|y)$ together with the admissible range, $a_2(y) \le x \le b_2(y)$; similarly [Fig. 5-6(a)], the conditional distribution of y for a fixed value of x would be given by the equation for $\phi_2(y|x)$ together with the statement that $a_1(x) \le y \le b_1(x)$. As the student should verify by applying the appropriate definitions, the conditional density functions have unit area:

$$\int_{a_2(y)}^{b_2(y)} \phi_1(x|y) \, dx = 1 \qquad \int_{a_1(x)}^{b_1(x)} \phi_2(y|x) \, dy = 1 \qquad (5\text{-}11)$$

The importance of the conditional distribution resides principally in the fact that by means of it, certain multivariate problems can be reduced virtually to univariate problems and thus rendered easier to solve.

Let us now consider some specific examples. In each case the joint distribution will be given, and we shall derive the marginal and conditional distributions.

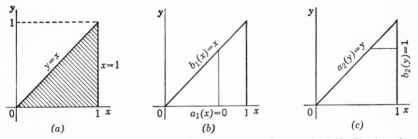

FIG. 5-7. (a) Admissible region; (b) path of integration for marginal distribution of x; (c) path of integration for marginal distribution of y.

Example 5-3

$$f(x,y) = 24y(1 - x) \qquad (0 \le x \le 1 \qquad 0 \le y \le x)$$

Marginal density functions:

$$f_1(x) = \int_0^x f(x,y) \, dy = 24(1 - x) \int_0^x y \, dy = 12x^2(1 - x)$$

$$f_2(y) = \int_y^1 f(x,y) \, dx = 24y \int_y^1 (1 - x) \, dx = 12y(1 - y)^2$$

Marginal distribution of x:

$$f_1(x) = 12x^2(1 - x) \qquad (0, 1)$$

Marginal distribution of y:

$$f_2(y) = 12y(1 - y)^2 \qquad (0, 1)$$

Conditional density functions:

$$\phi_1(x|y) = \frac{24y(1 - x)}{12y(1 - y)^2} = \frac{2}{(1 - y)^2}(1 - x)$$

$$\phi_2(y|x) = \frac{24y(1 - x)}{12x^2(1 - x)} = \frac{2}{x^2}y$$

Conditional distribution of x:

$$\phi_1(x|y) = \frac{2}{(1 - y)^2}(1 - x) \qquad (y \le x \le 1)$$

Conditional distribution of y:

$$\phi_2(y|x) = \frac{2}{x^2}y \qquad (0 \le y \le x)$$

Check:

$$\int_0^1 f_1(x)\, dx = 12 \int_0^1 x^2(1-x)\, dx = 12\beta(3,2) = \frac{12(2!)(1!)}{4!} = 1$$

$$\int_0^1 f_2(y)\, dy = 12 \int_0^1 y(1-y)^2\, dy = 12\beta(2,3) = 1$$

$$\int_y^1 \phi_1(x|y)\, dx = \frac{2}{(1-y)^2} \int_y^1 (1-x)\, dx = \frac{2}{(1-y)^2} \frac{(1-y)^2}{2} = 1$$

$$\int_0^x \phi_2(y|x)\, dy = \frac{2}{x^2} \int_0^x y\, dy = \frac{2}{x^2} \frac{x^2}{2} = 1$$

This example brings out an important fact which students sometimes overlook. Although the joint density function of independent variates factors into pure functions of each, factorization alone is not sufficient for independence; the factors must equal the respective marginal density functions. Moreover, whenever the conditional distribution of one variate depends either in form or in range of definition upon another variate, then the variates are dependent; however, when a conditional distribution does not involve another variate either explicitly in the equation of the density function or implicitly in the range of definition, the variates are independent. In the present example it is clear that $f(x,y) \neq f_1(x)f_2(y)$ despite the fact that $f(x,y)$ is a product of two pure functions, one in y and one in x. Here the conditional distributions depend both in form and in range upon the other variate, and neither agrees with the corresponding marginal distribution.

Example 5-4

$$f(x,y) = xe^{-x(1+y)} \qquad (0,\ \infty \text{ each})$$

Here the admissible region is the entire first quadrant, and so the limits of integration will be simply 0 to ∞ in each case. The total integral of the joint density function over the region for which it is defined equals unity, as it should, for

$$\int_0^\infty \int_0^\infty f(x,y)\, dx\, dy = \int_0^\infty e^{-x} \left(\int_0^\infty x e^{-xy}\, dy \right) dx = \int_0^\infty e^{-x}\, dx = 1$$

As already indicated by this integration, the marginal distribution of x is given by

$$f_1(x) = e^{-x} \qquad (0,\ \infty)$$

For the marginal density function of y, the integration with respect to x may be simplified by substituting $u = x(1+y)$, $x = u/(1+y)$, and since y is held fixed during the integration, $dx = du/(1+y)$. Then

$$f_2(y) = \int_0^\infty f(x,y)\, dx = \frac{1}{(1+y)^2} \int_0^\infty u e^{-u}\, du$$

$$= \frac{1}{(1+y)^2} \Gamma(2) = \frac{1}{(1+y)^2}$$

Thus the marginal distribution of y is given by

$$f_2(y) = \frac{1}{(1+y)^2} \qquad (0,\ \infty)$$

The conditional distributions are

$$\phi_1(x|y) = \frac{f(x,y)}{f_2(y)} = (1+y)^2 x e^{-x(1+y)} \qquad (0, \infty)$$

and
$$\phi_2(y|x) = \frac{f(x,y)}{f_1(x)} = x e^{-xy} \qquad (0, \infty)$$

Example 5-5

$$f(u,v) = \frac{1}{2u^2v} \qquad (1 \le u < \infty ; \frac{1}{u} \le v \le u)$$

The marginal density function of u is given by

$$f_1(u) = \int_{1/u}^{u} f(u,v)\, dv = \frac{1}{2u^2} \left[\ln v\right]_{1/u}^{u} = \frac{\ln u}{u^2}$$

and the marginal distribution of u is

$$f_1(u) = \frac{\ln u}{u^2} \qquad (1, \infty)$$

The marginal distribution of v, however, involves an extra step. For all values of v, the upper limit of integration on u is ∞, but the lower limit assumes two distinct

FIG. 5-8. (a) Admissible region; (b) path of integration for marginal distribution of u; (c) paths of integration for marginal distribution of v.

functional forms, depending upon the value of v. When $v \le 1$ the lower limit lies on the hyperbola $u = 1/v$; but when $v \ge 1$ the lower limit lies on the straight line $u = v$; when $v = 1$ both functions yield the same value, $u = 1$. Consequently, the marginal density function will have two distinct equations, as follows:

Range I $(0 \le v \le 1)$: $\quad f_2(v) = \int_{1/v}^{\infty} f(u,v)\, du = \frac{1}{2v}\left[-\frac{1}{u}\right]_{1/v}^{\infty} = \frac{1}{2}$

Range II $(1 \le v < \infty)$: $\quad f_2(v) = \int_{v}^{\infty} f(u,v)\, du = \frac{1}{2v}\left[-\frac{1}{u}\right]_{v}^{\infty} = \frac{1}{2v^2}$

The marginal distribution of v thus requires two statements:

$$f_2(v) = \frac{1}{2} \qquad (0,1) \qquad\qquad f_2(v) = \frac{1}{2v^2} \qquad (1, \infty)$$

Corresponding to these two equations, the conditional distribution of u given v assumes two separate forms:

If $0 \le v \le 1$, $\qquad \phi_1(u|v) = \frac{1}{u^2v} \qquad \left(\frac{1}{v} \le u < \infty\right)$

and if $1 \le v < \infty$, $\qquad \phi_1(u|v) = \frac{v}{u^2} \qquad (v \le u < \infty)$

On the other hand, the conditional distribution of v given u requires only one statement:

$$\phi_2(v|u) = \frac{1}{2 \ln u} \frac{1}{v} \qquad \left(\frac{1}{u} \leq v \leq u\right)$$

5-5. Illustrations of the Use of General Principles. The ideas developed in this chapter in conjunction with those from previous chapters now expand the range and type of problem that can be handled. The following illustrative examples are presented to clarify these basic principles further and to indicate how these tools and concepts may be used in practical application. It will be clear from the following that applications are very numerous so that those considered are merely indicative of a general class of problems.

Example 5-6. The probability of success on a single trial is constant from trial to trial and equal to p. After 10 trials it is known that the number of successes was greater than 4. What is the probability of the various remaining possibilities?

The result must be a conditional-probability function which sums to unity over the remaining possible outcomes. Therefore, the probability of exactly x successes is given by

$$P(x|x > 4) = \frac{C(10,x)p^x q^{10-x}}{1 - \displaystyle\sum_{y=0}^{4} C(10,y)p^y q^{10-y}} \qquad (x = 5, 6, \ldots, 10)$$

Example 5-7. The mail arrives at company A sometime between 8 and 9 A.M., and for practical purposes it is equally likely to be any time within that hour. The office boy must have the president's mail delivered to him by 9 A.M. The boy apparently delivers the mail any time between its arrival at the company and 9 A.M., and again, the time of this delivery is equally likely within the limits of the possible time interval. What is the probability that the mail will reach the president's desk between t and $t + dt$?

The probability that the mail will be delivered to the company between T and $T + dT$ is $dT/1$ (since the unit of time is an hour) while the conditional probability that it will be delivered to the president's desk between t and $t + dt$ knowing that it arrived at the company in the neighborhood of T is $dt/(9 - T)$. By definition the joint probability that the mail will arrive at the company between T and $T + dT$ and be delivered to the president between t and $t + dt$ is

$$P(T,t)\, dT\, dt = \frac{dT\, dt}{9 - T} \qquad (8 < T < 9;\ T < t < 9)$$

Having obtained the joint distribution, the two marginals can be evaluated by means of integration. However, the marginal or total probability of T is already known and the answer to our question involves the marginal distribution of t, which is

$$P_1(t)\, dt = dt \int_8^t \frac{dT}{9 - T} = -\ln (9 - t)\, dt \qquad (8 < t < 9)$$

where again the unit of time is an hour (see Fig. 5-9). The area under the $P_1(t)$ curve is, of course, unity.

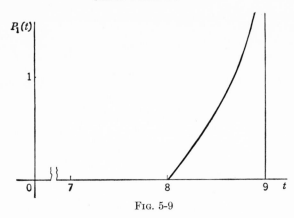

$$\text{FIG. 5-9}$$

Example 5-8. The average number of cars per day that take a country-road connection between two main roads is 15. The only building located on this road is an antique shop, and the percentage of cars which go through this road that stop at the shop is .12. What is the chance that exactly x cars stop at the antique shop on a given day?

Since the average number of cars per day is given and no further information regarding their destination or reason for traveling the road is contained in the statement, the only reasonable assumption one can make is that the number of cars is Poisson distributed on any given day. This would be equivalent to assuming that the cars go through this road individually and collectively at random. However, if it is known that n cars travel through this road on a given day with a constant probability of .12 of stopping, then the conditional probability of exactly x stops out of n cars must be binomially distributed. These two distributions are

$$P_1(n) = \frac{e^{-15}(15)^n}{n!} \qquad (n = 0, 1, 2, \ldots, \infty)$$

and

$$P_2(x|n) = C(n,x)(.88)^{n-x}(.12)^x \qquad (x = 0, 1, \ldots, n)$$

The joint probability of n cars and x stops will thus be the product of these two probabilities. The answer to our problem is, of course, the marginal distribution of x and this is obtained by summing over n. It is to be observed that n must be at least as large as x or otherwise it would be impossible to have available the x cars to stop at the antique shop. Therefore,

$$P_3(x) = \sum_{n=x}^{\infty} \frac{e^{-15}(15)^n}{n!} C(n,x)(.88)^{n-x}(.12)^x$$

By setting $n - x = y$ and observing that the resulting summation is merely the expansion for e^z, one obtains the result

$$P_3(x) = \frac{e^{-15}(.12)^x(15)^x}{x!} \sum_{y=0}^{\infty} \frac{(15)^y(.88)^y}{y!} = \frac{e^{-(15)(.12)}[(15)(.12)]^x}{x!}$$

The student should note that this result is very general, and if the average number of cars were λ and the probability of a car stopping p, then the probability of exactly x

stops on any one day would be given by a Poisson distribution with the parameter μ equal to λp.

Example 5-9. For brand A the distribution of breaking strength (x) of synthetic fiber is given approximately by

$$f_1(x) = 3ax^2 e^{-ax^3} \qquad (0, \infty) \qquad a > 0$$

and for brand B the breaking strength (y) is given by

$$f_2(y) = 3by^2 e^{-by^3} \qquad (0, \infty) \qquad b > 0$$

If a piece of each brand of synthetic fiber is chosen at random and tested, what is the probability that the sample of brand A will withstand greater tension than the sample of brand B? If $a = b$, what is the probability that five such tests will all turn out to be favorable to brand A?

Although the actual breaking strength cannot be infinite, the cubic exponent in each density function makes the probability of very large values negligibly small, and for practical purposes the distributions may be accepted as described. The two distributions give the means of computing the probability of a sample value falling between x and $x + dx$ in the case of brand A, and between y and $y + dy$ for brand B. Since these events are independent, the joint probability is $f_1(x)f_2(y)\,dx\,dy$. The entire field of possible sample results (i.e., simultaneous values of x and y) is represented by the first quadrant of the xy plane. However, all possible pairs of sample values (x,y) such that brand B breaks before brand A are represented by that portion of the first quadrant which lies below the line $y = x$ if we assume x is the abscissa and y the ordinate. Therefore, the probability $P(E)$ of the event E that y be less than x is found by integrating the joint density function over this region; thus

$$P(E) = \int_0^\infty dx \int_0^x f_1(x)f_2(y)\,dy = \int_0^\infty f_1(x)(1 - e^{-bx^3})\,dx = 1 - \frac{a}{a+b}$$

In the case of $a = b$, we have $P(E) = \frac{1}{2}$ and, accordingly, if five tests were made, the probability that all will be favorable to brand A is $(\frac{1}{2})^5 = \frac{1}{32}$. This latter result depends only on the fact that x and y have the same density function. Let us suppose that this is the case and that the common range of definition is (L,U). Then the previous argument gives us

$$P(E) = \int_L^U f_1(x)\,dx \int_L^x f_1(y)\,dy$$

If now we define w as

$$w = \int_L^x f_1(y)\,dy$$

then $dw = f_1(x)\,dx$. Also, we have $w = 0$ when $x = L$ and $w = 1$ when $x = U$.

Consequently, $$P(E) = \int_0^1 w\,dw = \frac{1}{2}$$

which shows that the result is independent of the form of the function.

Example 5-10. In a department store customers arrive in the time interval from 9 A.M. to 5 P.M. according to some distribution, which may be interpreted as a density function of time at arrival. Thus the total number of customers entering the store between τ and $\tau + d\tau$ is $Nf(\tau)\,d\tau$ where N is the total number of customers in any one day. The probability that a person coming in at time τ will leave between t and $t + dt$ will be denoted by $g(t|\tau)\,dt$. What is the distribution of the number of people in the store between the hours of 9 A.M. and 5 P.M.?

If we change the scale so that 0 corresponds to 9 A.M. and 1 to 5 P.M. and redefine our notation accordingly, we have the condition that the integral of $Nf(\tau)\, d\tau$ from 0 to 1 is equal to N. We also have the condition that the integral of the conditional distribution $g(t|\tau)\, dt$ from τ to 1 must equal unity. The average number of people actually in the store at any time T is given by $Nw(T)$ where $w(T)$ is the function to be determined. Now

$$Nf(\tau)\, d\tau = \text{number who enter between } \tau \text{ and } \tau + d\tau$$

$$\int_\tau^T g(t|\tau)\, dt = \text{fraction of those people who come in at } \tau \text{ and leave between } \tau$$
$$\text{and } T$$

$$1 - \int_\tau^T g(t|\tau)\, dt = \text{fraction who enter at } \tau \text{ and are still in store at time } T$$

Then
$$Nw(T) = N \int_0^T f(\tau)\, d\tau \left[1 - \int_\tau^T g(t|\tau)\, dt\right]$$

which now permits $w(T)$ to be evaluated if $f(\tau)$ and $g(t|\tau)$ are known.

Example 5-11. Given a rectangular distribution $f(x) = 1$ $(0 < x < 1)$. Five observations are drawn at random from this distribution and then ordered by size so that s represents the smallest of the five. What is the probability that s will lie between x_1 and $x_1 + dx_1$? This type of problem, which comes under the general heading of ordered statistics, is solved by considering the general multinomial law introduced in Chap. 2. It will be remembered that if the possible outcomes of a trial are $E_1, E_2, \ldots, E_r$ with corresponding probabilities $p_1, p_2, \ldots, p_r$ then the probability that in n trials E_1 occurs k_1 times, E_2 occurs k_2 times, etc., is

$$\frac{n!}{k_1! k_2! \cdots k_r!}\, p_1^{k_1} p_2^{k_2} \cdots p_r^{k_r} \qquad \text{where } k_1 + k_2 + \cdots + k_r = n$$
$$p_1 + p_2 + \cdots + p_r = 1$$

In this particular problem we desire the probability that, in picking x five times at random from the rectangular distribution, it falls 0 times in the interval $(0, x_1)$, once in $(x_1, x_1 + dx_1)$, and four times in $(x_1 + dx_1, 1)$. Substituting the corresponding probabilities in the multinomial we have

$$\frac{5!}{0!\,1!\,4!} \left(\int_0^{x_1} dx\right)^0 (dx_1)^1 \left(\int_{x_1}^1 dx\right)^4 = 5(1 - x_1)^4\, dx_1 \qquad (0 \le x_1 < 1)$$

which gives as the coefficient of dx_1 the probability density of the smallest observation. It is to be noted that this distribution has a very high ordinate when $x_1 = 0$ and drops off very rapidly as x increases, reaching 0 when $x_1 \to 1$. This then is the distribution obtained by sampling in groups of five and noting the smallest observation in each case. A large number of these smallest observations are now considered together and they would generate the above density function.

Example 5-12. Given the probability density function ae^{-at} $(0, \infty)$. Four observations are drawn at random from this population and ordered according to their magnitude. What is the joint distribution of the smallest (x_1) and the largest (x_4)?

In this particular case we have no observations between 0 and x_1, one observation between x_1 and $x_1 + dx_1$, two observations between $x_1 + dx_1$ and x_4, one between x_4 and $x_4 + dx_4$, and none between $x_4 + dx_4$ and infinity. Substituting the individual probabilities in the multinomial, we have the joint probability of x_1 and x_4 as follows:

$$f_1(x_1, x_4)\, dx_1\, dx_4 = \frac{4!}{1!\,2!\,1!}\, ae^{-ax_1}\, dx_1 \left(\int_{x_1}^{x_4} ae^{-ax}\, dx\right)^2 ae^{-ax_4}\, dx_4$$
$$= 12a^2 e^{-a(x_1 + x_4)} (e^{-ax_1} - e^{-ax_4})^2\, dx_1\, dx_4 \qquad (0 < x_4 < \infty;\ 0 \le x_1 < x_4)$$

where $f_1(x_1, x_4)$ represents the probability density of x_1 and x_4 simultaneously.

Example 5-13. Five observations are drawn at random from the density function $f(x) = 6x(1 - x)$ $0 < x < 1$ and these observations are ordered from the smallest to the largest. What is the probability density function of the median (x_3)?

The solution follows a pattern of the previous two problems and is as follows:

$$f_1(x_3)\ dx_3 = \frac{5!}{1!2!2!} \left[6 \int_0^{x_3} x(1 - x)\ dx \right]^2 6x_3(1 - x_3)\ dx_3 \left[6 \int_{x_3}^1 x(1 - x)\ dx \right]^2$$

$$= 30 \times 6^5 x_3(1 - x_3) \left(\frac{x_3^2}{2} - \frac{x_3^3}{3} \right)^2 \left[\tfrac{1}{6} - \left(\frac{x_3^2}{2} - \frac{x_3^3}{3} \right) \right]^2 dx_3$$

Example 5-14. In the inspection of light bulbs, vacuum tubes, condensers, and many other items, where a destructive test is necessary in order to determine their life or other characteristics, it is desirable often to simplify the testing techniques. For example, if one is testing electric light bulbs in order to determine the length of life, out of n bulbs tested, it is possible that some will continue to burn for a long while and that a test rack or shipment will be held up for this period. One technique to overcome this difficulty is to test a large number of items, but on the basis of the time to failure of the first few, determine the characteristics of the entire lot. Assuming a very simple life curve for electric light bulbs of the form $p(t) = \frac{1}{\tau} e^{-t/\tau}$ where τ is the mean life of a large lot, the probability that an individual bulb will burn out between t and $t + dt$ is $p(t)\ dt$. For a fixed value of τ, what is the probability of obtaining a pair of values for t_1 and t_2 which would be less probable than a given observed pair?

If n bulbs are placed on the test rack and the time to failure observed in all cases, we would produce a series of times $t_1, t_2, \ldots, t_n$ which we might consider in a sequence of order in which t_1 is the shortest and t_n the longest. The joint distribution of t_1 and t_2 may be obtained in the usual way as

$$p(t_1,t_2)\ dt_1\ dt_2 = \frac{n!}{1!1!(n - 2)!} \left(\frac{1}{\tau} e^{-t_1/\tau}\ dt_1 \right) \left(\frac{1}{\tau} e^{-t_2/\tau}\ dt_2 \right) \left(\frac{1}{\tau} \int_{t_2}^{\infty} e^{-t/\tau}\ dt \right)^{n-2}$$

$$0 < t_1 < \infty$$
$$t_2 > t_1$$

$$= \frac{(n)(n - 1)}{\tau^2} e^{[t_1 + (n-1)t_2]/\tau}\ dt_1\ dt_2$$

It must be true, of course, that

$$\int_0^{\infty} \int_{t_1}^{\infty} p(t_1,t_2)\ dt_1\ dt_2 = 1$$

If the experiment is conducted as outlined, it means that the time of the failure of the first bulb is noted and we will call this value a, and the time to the second failure will be b. Thus, in each case the experiment would result in an actual pair of values (t_1,t_2) denoted as (a,b). Since the probability density function is constant, if the exponent of e is constant, all pairs of values which satisfy the condition

$$t_1 + (n - 1)t_2 = a + (n - 1)b = c$$

have the same probability of occurrence for a given value of τ as the observed point (a,b). In reference to Fig. 5-10, it is now possible to find the probability that (t_1,t_2) will fall in the shaded area having observed the fixed point (a,b) as

$$p = \frac{n(n - 1)}{\tau^2} \int_0^{c/n} e^{-t_1/\tau}\ dt_1 \int_{t_1}^{(c-t_1)/(n-1)} e^{-(n-1)t_2/\tau}\ dt_2$$

$$= 1 - \left(1 + \frac{c}{\tau} \right) e^{-c/\tau}$$

Since c is fixed by the observed value of the first and second bulb to burn out, and if we know the value of τ, then the area as found from the above expression will give the probability that we would observe by chance a sample which might be considered "worse" than that which was observed.

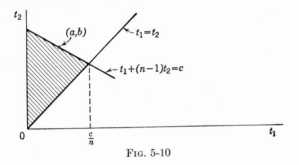

FIG. 5-10

Example 5-15. The selling price of a specific article to the public will vary somewhere between \$.25 and \$.35 per item, depending upon the final cost of production as determined from the initial run. It is assumed that any price within this range is equally likely to occur. However, the volume of the sales as a probability density function is dependent upon this final retail figure and, expressed in millions of pieces, is of the form $f(v|c) = (c^2v)e^{-cv}$ $(0 < v < \infty)$, where c is the cost per piece in dollars. The effect of substituting values of c ranging from .25 to .35 in this equation is gradually to move the mode of the curve toward the y axis; thus, increasing the price reduces the volume of sales. What is the probability that the sales will exceed 9 million pieces?

Since the probability that the price will lie between c and $c + dc$ is $10\,dc$ and the conditional probability of $v|c$ is as indicated above, the joint probability may be directly computed as

$$f(v,c)\ dv\ dc = (10\ dc)(c^2ve^{-cv}\ dv)$$

From this expression the marginal distribution of v can now be obtained by integrating over the variable c. Thus

$$g(v)\ dv = 10v\ dv \int_{.25}^{.35} c^2e^{-cv}\ dc = -10v\ dv \left[\frac{e^{-cv}}{v^3}\ (v^2c^2 + 2cv + 2)\right]_{.25}^{.35}$$

The probability that the sales will exceed 9 million is thus given by the area underneath the marginal distribution curve from 9 to infinity as

$$P(v > 9) =$$
$$10 \int_9^\infty \left\{\frac{e^{-.25v}}{v^2}\ [(.25)^2v^2 + 2(.25)v + 2] - \frac{e^{-.35v}}{v^2}\ [(.35)^2v^2 + 2(.35)v + 2]\right\}\ dv$$

The nonelementary parts of this integral offset each other in pairs, with the result that

$$P(v > 9) = {}^{10}\!/_9(4.25e^{-2.25} - 5.15e^{-3.15})$$
$$= .2525$$

Thus the probability in question is about .25.

As an alternative method of solution, which is somewhat simpler, we may reverse the order of integration over the joint distribution. To this end let $a = .25$, $b = .35$,

$M = 9$. Then

$$P(v > M) = \int_a^b 10c^2 \left(\int_M^\infty v e^{-cv}\, dv \right) dc$$

$$= 10 \int_a^b (Mc + 1)e^{-Mc}\, dc$$

$$= \frac{10}{M} [(Ma + 2)e^{-Ma} - (Mb + 2)e^{-Mb}]$$

Upon substitution of numerical values for a, b, M, this expression yields the same result as before.

Example 5-16. Particles are emanating from a radioactive source at an average rate of a impulses per unit of time. Since these pulses occur at random, they can be described by a Poisson distribution which, for a given time period, t, gives the following probability for exactly x emanations:

$$P(x|t) = \frac{(at)^x e^{-at}}{x!} \qquad (x = 0, 1, 2, \ldots, \infty)$$

Let us assume that time is an equally likely variable over any range and therefore its density function can be represented by $g(t) = 1/T$ $(0 < t < T)$. Find the conditional distribution of t for a fixed value of x.

The joint probability that x emanations will be observed and the corresponding time t' falls between t and $t + dt$ is

$$f_1(x,t)\, dt = \frac{dt}{T} \frac{(at)^x e^{-at}}{x!}$$

Since this joint distribution is a function of x and t, it is now possible to integrate t over the appropriate limits and obtain the marginal distribution of x (the marginal distribution of t, of course, is known) as

$$f_2(x) = \frac{1}{T} \int_0^T \frac{(at)^x e^{-at}\, dt}{x!}$$

We know, however, that the required conditional probability $w(t|x)\, dt$ can be obtained by dividing the joint probability $f_1(x,t)\, dt$ by the marginal distribution $f_2(x)$. Thus

$$w(t|x)\, dt = \frac{(at)^x e^{-at}\, dt}{\int_0^T (at)^x e^{-at}\, dt}$$

It is now possible to let $T \to \infty$, thus permitting the denominator of the above expression to be evaluated as a gamma function. Thus the final probability that t' will lie between t and $t + dt$ at the same time that x (the number of emanations) assumes a given fixed value is given by

$$w(t|x)\, dt = \frac{a(at)^x e^{-at}\, dt}{x!} \qquad (0 < t < \infty)$$

It is interesting to note that the form of this answer is the same as that of Example 4-8 and that if x is set equal to 0 we have the density function as an exponential ae^{-at}. Actually, of course, the expression found in this problem involves time and n emanations, whereas the previous example involved the time necessary for the emission of $n + 1$ particles. In the case of the exponential, the difference between these two concepts is merely a question of semantics, since the distribution of time for no emissions is the same as the time between individual emissions in this case.

Example 5-17. The number of orders n per day for a certain chemical is Poisson-distributed (parameter μ), and the weight in pounds per order is exponentially distributed (parameter β). Assuming that the weights from order to order are independent, find the distribution of total weight of orders per day.

Denote the weight of the ith order in a day by y_i and the total weight of n orders by w. Since $w \equiv 0$ if $n = 0$, and the latter event has a finite probability of occurrence $(e^{-\mu})$, the distribution function of w is discontinuous at zero. Thus, for $w = 0$ we have

$$P(w = 0) = P(n = 0) = e^{-\mu}$$

However, a density function exists for $w > 0$.

Consider a fixed number of orders $n > 0$. Then $w = y_1 + y_2 + \cdots + y_n$ and by Theorem 4-1, the conditional distribution of w becomes

$$\phi(w|n) = \frac{1}{\beta^n \Gamma(n)} \, w^{n-1} e^{-w/\beta} \qquad (0, \infty)$$

Since n is an integer, we may replace $\Gamma(n)$ by $(n-1)!$ and write the joint distribution of n and w for $n > 0$ as follows:

$$
\begin{aligned}
f(n,w) &= e^{-\mu} \frac{\mu^n}{n!} \frac{1}{\beta^n (n-1)!} \, w^{n-1} e^{-w/\beta} \\
&= \frac{\mu}{\beta} e^{-\mu} e^{-w/\beta} \frac{(\mu w/\beta)^{n-1}}{n!(n-1)!} \qquad (n = 1, 2, \ldots, \infty; 0 < w < \infty)
\end{aligned}
$$

Therefore, the marginal distribution of w in the range $w > 0$ becomes

$$h(w) = \sum_{n=1}^{\infty} f(n,w) = \frac{\mu}{\beta} e^{-\mu} e^{-w/\beta} \sum_{k=0}^{\infty} \frac{(\mu w/\beta)^k}{k!(k+1)!} \qquad (0 < w < \infty)$$

where $k = n - 1$.

Students familiar with advanced calculus may be interested in the fact that this series can be identified with the modified Bessel function of the first kind of order unity. The latter function (symbol $I_1(u)$) may be expressed as follows:

$$I_1(u) = \frac{u}{2} \sum_{k=0}^{\infty} \frac{(u/2)^{2k}}{k!(k+1)!}$$

Substituting $\mu w/\beta = (u/2)^2$ we thus obtain

$$h(w) = e^{-\mu} \frac{\sqrt{\mu}}{\sqrt{\beta}} \, w^{-1/2} e^{-w/\beta} I_1 \left(2 \sqrt{\frac{\mu w}{\beta}} \right) \qquad (0 < w < \infty)$$

and this density function together with the equation $P(w = 0) = e^{-\mu}$ defines the distribution of w.

In the more general case in which the weight per order is a gamma variate (parameters α, β) we would still have $P(w = 0) = e^{-\mu}$, while for $n > 0$ the conditional distribution of w would be given by

$$\phi(w|n) = \frac{1}{\beta^{n\alpha+n} \Gamma(n\alpha + n)} \, w^{n\alpha+n-1} e^{-w/\beta} \qquad (0 < w < \infty)$$

and the marginal density function would be

$$h(w) = e^{-\mu} e^{-w/\beta} \sum_{n=1}^{\infty} \frac{\mu^n w^{n\alpha+n-1}}{n! \beta^{n\alpha+n} \Gamma(n\alpha + n)} \qquad (0 < w < \infty)$$

In this case, however, the series expansion for the marginal density does not reduce to a Bessel function.

Example 5-18. Ten observations are drawn at random from an arbitrary density function $f(x)$ which may be defined over a finite or infinite range of the variate x. Three more observations are drawn at random from $f(x)$. What is the probability that all 3 of these latter observations are larger than any of the previous 10? The probability that the largest of the original 10 observations falls at x_{10} is $g(x_{10})\,dx_{10}$ where

$$g(x_{10})\,dx_{10} = \frac{10!}{9!} \left[\int_{-\infty}^{x_{10}} f(x)\,dx \right]^9 f(x_{10})\,dx_{10}$$

If the largest of the group of 10 is at x_{10}, then the conditional probability that the three observations drawn subsequently will be greater than this given value is

$$\left[\int_{x_{10}}^{\infty} f(x)\,dx \right]^3$$

and the corresponding joint probability of the two events is then

$$g(x_{10})\,dx_{10} \left[\int_{x_{10}}^{\infty} f(x)\,dx \right]^3$$

Since x_{10} can take on any value in the range of definition of the variate—under our assumption $f(x)$ is continuous—the total probability of the event as stated will be

$$P(E) = \int_{-\infty}^{\infty} g(x_{10})\,dx_{10} \left[\int_{x_{10}}^{\infty} f(x)\,dx \right]^3$$

$$= 10 \int_{-\infty}^{\infty} \left[\int_{x_{10}}^{\infty} f(x)\,dx \right]^3 \left[\int_{-\infty}^{x_{10}} f(x)\,dx \right]^9 f(x_{10})\,dx_{10}$$

Let $u = \int_{-\infty}^{x_{10}} f(x)\,dx$ and then $du = f(x_{10})\,dx_{10}$; so

$$P(E) = 10 \int_0^1 (1 - u)^3 u^9\,du = 10\beta(4,10) = \frac{1}{286}$$

Thus the probability of the event is independent of the form of $f(x)$. Applications of this form of analysis to the evaluation of observational data is obvious and forms a class of techniques which are called *nonparametric*.

Example 5-19. Let $f(x)$ be the density function of an arbitrary probability distribution. Find the probability that $n + 2$ independent observations can be drawn from the distribution in the following way: If x_1 and x_n are the minimum and maximum of the first n observations, the $(n + 1)$th and $(n + 2)$th observations must lie outside the interval $x_1 \le x \le x_n$.

Following the argument in Example 5-18, it follows that

$$P = (n)(n - 1) \int_{-\infty}^{\infty} f(x_1)\,dx_1 \int_{x_1}^{\infty} f(x_n) \left[\int_{x_1}^{x_n} f(x)\,dx \right]^{n-2} \left[1 - \int_{x_1}^{x_n} f(x)\,dx \right]^2 dx_n$$

Let $u = \int_{-\infty}^{x_1} f(x)\,dx$ and $v = \int_{-\infty}^{x_n} f(x)\,dx$ $(u \le v \le 1)$. Then $v - u = \int_{x_1}^{x_n} f(x)\,dx$, $du = f(x_1)\,dx_1$ and $dv = f(x_n)\,dx_n$. Since, when $x_n = x_1$, $u = v$, we have

$$n(n - 1) \int_0^1 du \int_u^1 (v - u)^{n-2} [1 - (v - u)]^2\,dv$$

and

$$n(n - 1) \int_0^1 du \left[\frac{(v - u)^{n-1}}{n - 1} - 2\frac{(v - u)^n}{n} + \frac{(v - u)^{n+1}}{n + 1} \right]_u^1 = \frac{6}{(n + 1)(n + 2)}$$

It is interesting to note that, when $n = 23$, the probability is equal to .01.

5-6. Point Estimation of a Parameter. In Sec. 4-12, we considered the idea of confidence limits as an interval estimation of a parameter. In this section we shall consider the best estimate of a single value for the parameter as a function of observational data. Fisher's method of maximum likelihood often yields a "best estimate" in the sense that it satisfies certain criteria which are intuitively desirable. The student interested in the mathematical and intuitive foundations of maximum likelihood estimates should consult a text on statistical methods. The technique consists of computing the compound probability function (density function if a continuous variable) of a specific observed sample and then maximizing this function, called the *likelihood function*, with respect to the parameter. Assuming that a high turning point exists in the meaningful range of θ, this is accomplished in the usual way by computing the derivative and setting it equal to zero to find the stationary point. Thus, if we have the probability density $f(x,\theta)$ and observations $x_1, x_2, \ldots, x_n$ t he joint-probability density, assuming independence of the x's, would be

$$L = f(x_1,\theta)f(x_2,\theta) \cdots f(x_n,\theta) = \prod_{i=1}^{n} f(x_i,\theta) \qquad (5\text{-}12)$$

Since the logarithm of L is a maximum for the same value of θ as L itself, it is often convenient to take the natural logarithm of both sides before differentiation. Accordingly, we may put

$$\ln L = \ln f(x_1,\theta) + \ln f(x_2,\theta) + \cdots + \ln f(x_n,\theta) \qquad (5\text{-}13)$$

and $\qquad \dfrac{\partial(\ln L)}{\partial\theta} = \dfrac{1}{f(x_1,\theta)}\dfrac{\partial f(x_1,\theta)}{\partial\theta} + \cdots + \dfrac{1}{f(x_n,\theta)}\dfrac{\partial f(x_n,\theta)}{\partial\theta} = 0 \quad (5\text{-}14)$

This yields a single equation for the solution of θ in terms of the x's. If more than one parameter is to be estimated, one can differentiate with respect to each parameter partially, creating simultaneous equations in the unknown parameters when each partial derivative is set equal to zero.

Example 5-20. Observations $x_1, x_2, \ldots, x_n$ are drawn at random from a population which has the functional form $f(x) = ke^{-kx}$ $(0 < x < \infty)$. What is the maximum likelihood estimate of k? Computing the likelihood function, we have

$$L = k^n e^{-k(x_1+x_2+\cdots+x_n)}$$

or $\qquad\qquad \ln L = n \ln k - k(x_1 + x_2 + \cdots + x_n)$

The $\ln L$ is now differentiated with respect to k and a stationary point evaluated:

$$\frac{\partial}{\partial k}(\ln L) = \frac{n}{k} - (x_1 + x_2 + \cdots + x_n) = 0$$

so $\qquad\qquad k = \dfrac{1}{(x_1 + x_2 + \cdots + x_n)/n} = \dfrac{1}{\bar{x}}$

Thus the maximum likelihood estimator for k is $1/\bar{x}$.

Example 5-21. A set of observations $x_1, x_2, \ldots, x_n$ are drawn at random from a normal population with unknown mean μ but a known standard deviation σ. What combination of the x's is the maximum likelihood estimator for μ? Here, employing the more convenient notation $\exp[-h(x)]$ to represent $e^{-h(x)}$ we have

$$L = \frac{1}{(\sqrt{2\pi})^n \sigma^n} \exp\left[-\sum_{i=1}^{n} \frac{(x_i - \mu)^2}{2\sigma^2} \right]$$

$$\ln L = -\frac{n}{2} \ln 2\pi - n \ln \sigma - \frac{1}{2\sigma^2} \sum (x_i - \mu)^2$$

$$\frac{\partial (\ln L)}{\partial \mu} = \frac{1}{2\sigma^2} \sum_{i=1}^{n} (x_i - \mu) = 0$$

Since this equation is satisfied by setting $\Sigma x_i / n = \mu$, the sample mean is the maximum likelihood estimator of μ for a normal population.

Example 5-22. If in Example 5-21 the parameter μ is known but σ is unknown, what is the maximum likelihood estimator of σ? Here,

$$L = (2\pi\sigma^2)^{-n/2} e^{-\Sigma(x_i - \mu)^2 / 2\sigma^2}$$

or

$$\ln L = -n \ln \sigma - \left(\frac{n}{2}\right) \ln 2\pi - \frac{\Sigma(x_i - \mu)^2}{2\sigma^2}$$

$$\frac{\partial (\ln L)}{\partial \sigma} = -\frac{n}{\sigma} + \frac{\Sigma(x_i - \mu)^2}{\sigma^3} = 0$$

Thus the maximum likelihood solution is

$$\sigma^2 = \frac{\Sigma(x_i - \mu)^2}{n}$$

Example 5-23. Consider the Poisson distribution with the unknown parameter λ as $p(x) = e^{-\lambda} \lambda^x / x!$. Observations $x_1, x_2, \ldots, x_n$ are available from experimentation where, of course, each x_i represents the number of successes observed during a single experiment. What is the maximum likelihood extimate of λ? Here

$$L = \frac{e^{-n\lambda} \lambda^{(x_1 + x_2 + \cdots + x_n)}}{x_1! x_2! \cdots x_n!}$$

or

$$\ln L = -n\lambda + (x_1 + x_2 + \cdots + x_n) \ln \lambda - \ln \prod_{i=1}^{n} x_i!$$

$$\frac{\partial (\ln L)}{\partial \lambda} = -n + \frac{(x_1 + x_2 + \cdots + x_n)}{\lambda} = 0$$

and therefore

$$\lambda = \frac{(x_1 + x_2 + \cdots + x_n)}{n} = \bar{x}$$

EXERCISES

In Exercises 1 to 3 use the type of reasoning employed in establishing Theorems 4-1 and 4-2 rather than attempt an analytic proof.

1. The variate x has two admissible values 0, 1 and $f(0) = q$, $f(1) = p$. Given that $x_1, x_2, \ldots, x_n$ are random observations of x (hence independently distributed as x in repeated trials) and $y = x_1 + x_2 + \cdots + x_n$ show that the distribution of y in repeated independent trials is binomial with parameters n, p.

2. The variate u has the binomial distribution with parameters n_1, p while the independent variate v has the binomial distribution with parameters n_2, p (that is, p is the same in both). If $z = u + v$ show that the distribution of z is binomial with parameters n, p where $n = n_1 + n_2$.

3. The distribution of the variate x is geometric with parameter p. Given that $x_1, x_2, \ldots, x_n$ are random observations of x and $y = x_1 + x_2 + \cdots + x_n$ show that y has the Pascal distribution with the same parameter p (see Exercise 17 of Chap. 3).

4. The discrete variate x has the distribution $f(x) = \frac{1}{5}$ ($x = 1, 2, 3, 4, 5$). If two random observations x_1, x_2 are taken and $y = |x_1 - x_2|$, find the distribution of y.
Ans.

y	0	1	2	3	4	Sum
$g(y)$	.20	.32	.24	.16	.08	1.00

5. A game of skill is played by two teams of two players each. An individual player can score 0, 1, or 2 points, and the score for the team is the sum of the scores of the two players. Assuming independence, derive the distribution of scores for each team from the following information on the individual players. Compute the probability of a tie, the probability that team 1 defeats team 2, and the probability that team 2 defeats team 1. (Higher score wins.)

INDIVIDUAL DISTRIBUTIONS

Score	Team 1		Team 2	
	A	B	A	B
0	.5	.2	.3	.2
1	.3	.3	.5	.5
2	.2	.5	.2	.3

Ans.

TEAM DISTRIBUTIONS

Score..	0	1	2	3	4
Team 1	.10	.21	.38	.21	.10
Team 2	.06	.25	.38	.25	.06

Event	Tie	Team 1 wins	Team 2 wins
Probability.	.2614	.3693	.3693

6. Independent variates x_1, x_2 have the Poisson distribution with respective parameters μ_1, μ_2. Show that the variate $y = x_1 + x_2$ has the Poisson distribution with parameters $\mu = \mu_1 + \mu_2$. Extend by induction to any number of independent Poisson variates.

[HINT: Set up the joint distribution of x_1, x_2; replace x_2 by $y - x_1$; multiply and divide by $y!$, then sum over x_1 from $x_1 = 0$ to $x_1 = y$ using the binomial theorem.]

7. Using the same approach as in Exercise 6, show analytically that the sum of two independent binomial variates with respective parameters (n_1, p) and (n_2, p) is binomially distributed with parameters (n, p) where $n = n_1 + n_2$.

✗   **8.** The variate x has the Poisson distribution with parameter μ and the conditional distribution of y given x is binomial with parameters (x, p), that is, $\phi(y|x) = C(x,y)p^y q^{x-y}$ $(y = 0, 1, 2, \ldots, x)$. Show that the marginal distribution of y is Poisson with parameter μp.

[HINT: Set up the joint distribution of x, y. Introduce a new variable $u = x - y$ and sum over u from 0 to ∞ by recognizing the series expansion.]

9. Independent variates x_1, x_2, x_3 have the Poisson distribution with respective parameters $\mu_1 = .27$, $\mu_2 = .32$, $\mu_3 = .41$. Using the results of Exercise 6, determine the probability that $y \geq 4$, where $y = x_1 + x_2 + x_3$.   *Ans.* .019.

✗   **10.** The variates x and y are jointly distributed as follows:

$$f(x,y) = 24x^2y(1 - x) \qquad (0, 1 \text{ each})$$

Find the marginal distribution of each variate and show that they are independent.
Ans. $f_1(x) = 12x^2(1 - x)$ $(0, 1)$; $f_2(y) = 2y$ $(0, 1)$; $f(x,y) = f_1(x)f_2(y)$.

✗   **11.** Find the marginal and conditional distributions of x and y which are jointly distributed as follows: $f(x,y) = 6xy(2 - x - y)$ $(0, 1 \text{ each})$.
Ans. $f_1(x) = x(4 - 3x)$ $(0, 1)$; $\phi_1(x|y) = 6x(2 - x - y)/(4 - 3y)$ $(0, 1)$; $f_2(y) = y(4 - 3y)$ $(0, 1)$; $\phi_2(y|x) = 6y(2 - x - y)/(4 - 3x)$ $(0, 1)$.

✗   **12.** Find the marginal distribution of y and the conditional distribution of x given y if x and y are jointly distributed as follows:

$$f(x,y) = 4y(x - y)e^{-(x+y)} \qquad (0 \leq x < \infty; 0 \leq y \leq x)$$

Ans. $g(y) = 4ye^{-2y}$ $(0, \infty)$; $\phi(x|y) = (x - y)e^{-(x-y)}$ $(y \leq x < \infty)$.

✗   **13.** The joint distribution of x and y is

$$f(x,y) = \tfrac{1}{8}(x^2 - y^2)e^{-x} \qquad (0 \leq x < \infty; -x \leq y \leq x)$$

Find the marginal distribution of each variate and the conditional distribution of y for a fixed value of x.
Ans. $f_1(x) = \tfrac{1}{6}x^3 e^{-x}$ $(0, \infty)$; $f_2(y) = \tfrac{1}{4}e^{-|y|}(1 + |y|)$ $(-\infty, \infty)$; $\phi(y|x) = (3/4x^3)(x^2 - y^2)$ $(-x \leq y \leq x)$.

✗   **14.** On a line segment of unit length let x $(0 \leq x \leq 1)$ denote the distance from the initial point O to any point X. Assume that the probability that a point U chosen at random on this segment will fall between x and $x + dx$ equals dx. Representing the distance OU by u, let another point V be taken at random in the interval $u \leq x \leq 1$, and denote the distance OV by v. Find the joint distribution of u and v and also their marginal distributions.
Ans. $f_1(u) = 1$ $(0, 1)$; $f(u,v) = 1/(1 - u)$ $(0 \leq u \leq 1; u \leq v \leq 1)$; $f_2(v) = -\ln(1 - v)$ $(0, 1)$.

✗   **15.** Find the marginal distribution of x if x and y are jointly distributed as follows: $f(x,y) = \dfrac{2}{\pi}(1 - x^2 - y^2)$ $(0 \leq x^2 + y^2 \leq 1)$. Also show that the integral of $f(x,y)$ over its region of definition is unity.   *Ans.* $f_1(x) = (8/3\pi)(1 - x^2)^{3/2}$ $(-1, 1)$.

✗   **16.** The variates x and y are jointly distributed as follows (where $\alpha > 0$):

$$f(x,y) = \frac{\sqrt{3}}{6\pi\alpha^2}e^{-(x^2 - xy + y^2)/3\alpha^2} \qquad (-\infty, \infty \text{ each})$$

Find the marginal distributions of x and y and the conditional distribution of each variate for a given value of the other. Integrate by completing the square in the exponent.

Ans.

$$f_1(x) = \frac{1}{2\alpha\sqrt{\pi}} e^{-x^2/4\alpha^2} \quad (-\infty, \infty) \qquad f_2(y) = \frac{1}{2\alpha\sqrt{\pi}} e^{-y^2/4\alpha^2} \quad (-\infty, \infty)$$

$$\phi_1(x|y) = (1/\alpha\sqrt{3\pi})e^{-(x-\frac{1}{2}y)^2/3\alpha^2} \quad (-\infty, \infty)$$

$$\phi_2(y|x) = (1/\alpha\sqrt{3\pi})e^{-(y-\frac{1}{2}x)^2/3\alpha^2} \quad (-\infty, \infty)$$

17. Prove that a necessary and sufficient condition for the independence of two variates x, y is the two-fold requirement (a) that their joint density function $f(x,y)$ factor into pure functions of the separate variates (as $f(x,y) = kg(x)h(y)$, k = constant) and (b) that the admissible region be rectangular (as $A \le x \le B$; $a \le y \le b$ where A, B, a, b, are constants).

18. The marginal distribution of x is normal with parameters $\mu = 0$, $\sigma = 1$; the conditional distribution of y given x is normal with parameters $\mu = kx$, $\sigma = \sqrt{1-k^2}$; and the conditional distribution of z given any pair of values of x and y is normal with parameters $\mu = ky$, $\sigma = \sqrt{1-k^2}$. (a) State the joint distribution of x, y, z. (b) Find the marginal distributions of y and z. (c) Find the conditional distribution of x given y. (d) State the joint distribution of y and z. (e) Find the conditional distribution of z given x (but not given y). Integrations can be carried out by completing the square in the exponent. Make use of formal similarities.

Ans. (a)

$$f(x,y,z) = \frac{1}{(1-k^2)(\sqrt{2\pi})^3} e^{-Q/2} \quad (-\infty, \infty \text{ each variate})$$

where

$$Q = \frac{(1-k^2)x^2 + (y-kx)^2 + (z-ky)^2}{1-k^2}$$

(b) Both y and z are unit normal.

(c) Normal with parameters $\mu = ky$, $\sigma = \sqrt{1-k^2}$.

(d) $g(y,z) = \dfrac{1}{2\pi\sqrt{1-k^2}} e^{-(y^2-2kyz+z^2)/2(1-k^2)}$ $(-\infty, \infty \text{ each})$.

(e) Normal with parameters $\mu = k^2x$, $\sigma = \sqrt{1-k^4}$.

19. In the joint distribution of two independent unit normal variates x, y show that the probability that a random point will fall within the square enclosed by the lines $x = -a$, $x = a$, $y = -a$, $y = a$ is less than the probability that it will fall within the circle of equal area defined by $x^2 + y^2 = 4a^2/\pi$. With this fact in mind prove the inequality

$$\frac{1}{\sqrt{2\pi}} \int_{-a}^{a} e^{-x^2/2}\, dx \le \sqrt{1 - e^{-2a^2/\pi}}$$

[HINT: Express the square of the required integral as the product of two integrals of identical form but with one in x and the other in y. Rewrite this as a double integral, and then, changing to polar coordinates, integrate over the circle $r = 2a/\sqrt{\pi}$.]

20. The joint distribution of x and y is given by $f(x,y) = 1/x^2y^2$ $(1, \infty$ each). A point x', y' is chosen at random in the admissible region and the product $u = x'y'$ and the quotient $v = x'/y'$ of its coordinates are computed. By integrating $f(x,y)$ over the appropriate portions of the admissible region, find (a) $P(u \le 4)$, (b) $P(v \le 2)$, (c) the probability of the compound event $u \le 4$, $v \le 2$. (d) Do any points of the admissible region satisfy the simultaneous inequalities $u < 2$, $v > 2$?

Ans. (a) $(3 - \ln 4)/4$, (b) $\frac{3}{4}$, (c) $(5 - 3\ln 2)/8$, (d) no.

21. The results of Exercise 20 show that u and v are not independent. Nevertheless, show that the particular value $v = 1$ has the factorization property $P(u \le a, v \le 1) = P(u \le a)P(v \le 1)$ where a is any value which u can assume.

22. Given that the waiting time t for some chance event is exponentially distributed, and letting t_0 be an arbitrary fixed value of t, find the conditional distribution of waiting time under the restriction that $t > t_0$. Denoting a random value of t by t' deduce that $P(t' > t_0 + x|t' > t_0) = P(t > x)$. Express this proposition in words.

Ans. $\phi(t|t > t_0) = (1/\beta)e^{-(t-t_0)/\beta}$ $(t_0 < t < \infty)$.

23. Suppose that the orders for a certain article of merchandise come from two main sources, the demands per unit time being independent Poisson variates with respective parameters μ_1, μ_2. Appealing to Eq. (4-25), show that the elapsed time between orders is exponentially distributed with $\beta = 1/(\mu_1 + \mu_2)$. Do this from two points of view, first by applying Exercise 6 and second by considering the distinct ways of obtaining a stated waiting time.

24. The proposition proved in Exercise 22 for the exponential distribution may be stated analytically as follows:

$$\frac{f(x + y)}{\int_x^\infty f(z)\, dz} \equiv f(y) \qquad (y \geq 0)$$

Prove, conversely, that if this identity holds for all $y \geq 0$, and the variate is non-negative, then the distribution is exponential. This fact that the conditional probability of exceeding a given arbitrary value by a stated margin (or more) depends only on the margin stipulated and not on the arbitrary starting point is thus a definitive property of the exponential distribution.

[HINT: Simplify and differentiate with respect to x. To prove uniqueness, it is then sufficient to show that the differential equation obtained by setting $y = 0$ is satisfied only by an exponential function.]

25. In the theory of failure of mechanical systems, business enterprises, etc., the notation $Z(t) \equiv f(t)/[1 - F(t)]$ is used to denote the conditional density function of failure between time t and $t + dt$, given nonfailure prior to time t. For certain retail businesses, Lomax[1] found that this function is well represented by an expression of the form $Z(t) = b/(t + a)$ $(a, b > 0)$. Find $f(t)$, the probability density function of failure time. *Ans.* $f(t) = (b/a)[a/(t + a)]^{b+1}$ $(a, b > 0; 0 \leq t < \infty)$.

26. Given $f(x) = 2x$ $0 < x < 1$. Five observations are drawn at random from this distribution and ordered from the smallest to the largest. Find the distribution of (a) the second smallest, (b) the median, (c) the largest.

Ans. (a) $40x_2{}^3(1 - x_2{}^2)^3$ $(0, 1)$; (b) $60x_3{}^5(1 - x_3{}^2)^2$ $(0, 1)$; (c) $10x_5{}^9$ $(0,1)$.

27. Four observations are drawn at random from the distribution $f(x) = \alpha e^{-\alpha x}$ $(0, \infty)$. These are ordered from the smallest to the largest. (a) What is the joint distribution of the second and fourth? (b) What is the distribution of the largest?

Ans. (a) $24\alpha^2 e^{-\alpha(x_2 + x_4)}(1 - e^{-\alpha x_2})(e^{-\alpha x_2} - e^{-\alpha x_4})$ $(0 < x_4 < \infty; 0 \leq x_2 < x_4)$; (b) $4\alpha(1 - e^{-\alpha x_4})^3 e^{-\alpha x_4}$ $(0, \infty)$.

28. Given the density function $f(x) = x$ $(0 \leq x \leq 1)$; $f(x) = 2 - x$ $(1 \leq x \leq 2)$. Three observations are drawn at random from this distribution and arranged in order of magnitude. What is the distribution of the median?

Ans. $g(x_2) = \frac{3}{2}x_2{}^3(2 - x_2{}^2)$ $(0 \leq x_2 \leq 1)$; $g(x_2) = \frac{3}{2}[2(2 - x_2)^3 - (2 - x_2)^5]$ $(1 \leq x \leq 2)$.

29. Prove that the probability that the $(n + 1)$st observation is larger than the greatest of the first n is $1/(n + 1)$ for any continuous distribution.

30. The parameter m in the density function $f(x) = 1 + m(x - \frac{1}{2})$ $(0 < x < 1)$ is to be estimated from two observations x_1 and x_2 drawn at random. What is the maximum likelihood estimate of m? *Ans.* $2(x_1 + x_2)/[(x_1 + x_2) - 4x_1 x_2]$.

---

[1] *J. Am. Statist. Assoc.*, December, 1954.

CHAPTER 6

DERIVED DISTRIBUTIONS

6-1. Introduction. The province of any mathematical theory is the extension of knowledge by deduction from accepted premises. By this means, science is able to make full use of established principles and avoid degeneration into sheer empiricism. An important deductive problem in the field of random variables is the derivation of the distribution of some function (or the joint distribution of several functions) of initial variates, for which the joint distribution is already known.

In this chapter, we shall study this problem beginning with a function of a single variate and progressing to multivariate functions. In the univariate case, suppose that y is a known function of another variate x. Given the distribution of x, the problem is to determine the distribution of y. A general solution of this problem can be obtained in terms of density functions, provided that y is a monotonic function of x and its derivative with respect to x exists.

6-2. Monotonic Functions. If y increases whenever x increases, it is said to be a *monotonically increasing function;* if y decreases whenever x increases, it is said to be a *monotonically decreasing function.* For example, e^x is a monotonically increasing function, while e^{-x} is a monotonically decreasing function. The function x^2 is not monotonic if x can have negative as well as positive values. However, if $x \geq 0$, x^2 is monotonically increasing, whereas if $x \leq 0$, x^2 is monotonically decreasing.

The nature of a monotonic function necessitates a unique correspondence between the dependent and independent variable. Consequently, for mathematical purposes, the latter can be regarded in turn as a function of the former. Moreover, if the initial function can be differentiated with respect to x, the inverse function can be differentiated with respect to y.

6-3. The Density Function of a Monotonically Increasing Function. Assume that x has a density function $f(x)$ and let $F(x)$ and $G(y)$ denote, respectively, the distribution functions of x and y. Suppose that y is a differentiable, monotonically increasing function of x and that $y = b$ when $x = a$. Then since $y \leq b$ when and only when $x \leq a$, we have at once $P(y \leq b) = P(x \leq a)$, whence $G(b) = F(a)$. As stated in the previous paragraph, we may regard x as a function of y, say $\phi(y)$, so that $a = \phi(b)$.

147

Differentiating both sides of the equation $G(b) = F(a)$ with respect to b yields:

$$\frac{dG(b)}{db} = \frac{dF(a)}{db} = \frac{dF(a)}{da}\frac{da}{db} = \frac{dF(a)}{da}\frac{d\phi(b)}{db} \qquad (6\text{-}1)$$

By definition, however, the derivative of the distribution function is the density function. Hence

$$g(b) = f(a)\frac{d\phi(b)}{db} = f[\phi(b)]\frac{d\phi(b)}{db} \qquad (6\text{-}2)$$

Or, replacing b by y,

$$g(y) = f[\phi(y)]\frac{d\phi(y)}{dy} \qquad (6\text{-}3)$$

Example 6-1. Suppose that x has the probability density function $f(x) = e^{-x}$ $(0, \infty)$ and we wish to derive the probability density function of y where $y = \sqrt[3]{x}$.

Fig. 6-1

Here $x = y^3$ and $dx/dy = 3y^2$. Thus the distribution of y is given by

$$g(y) = 3y^2 e^{-y^3} \qquad (0, \infty)$$

The two density functions are shown in Fig. 6-1. To carry the example further, consider the probability that x lies between 0 and ln 2. This quantity is

$$P(x \leq \ln 2) \equiv F(\ln 2) = \int_0^{\ln 2} e^{-x}\, dx = \tfrac{1}{2}$$

At the same time that $x \leq \ln 2$ we have $y \leq \sqrt[3]{\ln 2}$, and

$$P(y \leq \sqrt[3]{\ln 2}) \equiv G(\sqrt[3]{\ln 2}) = \int_0^{\sqrt[3]{\ln 2}} 3y^2 e^{-y^3}\, dy = \tfrac{1}{2}$$

Thus, the two probabilities are equal and, in general, the two shaded areas of Fig. 6-1 are equivalent.

Example 6-2. Rounding errors in a computed quantity are often uniformly distributed over a range extending from $-.5$ to $.5$ unit in the last decimal place carried. Thus, if x represents the error in such a computed quantity, we may say $f(x) = 1$ $(-.5, .5)$ where it is understood that the scale of x is chosen so that one unit of x represents one unit in the last decimal place carried. Suppose that the quantity under consideration is the speed S of a moving particle and the corresponding computed value is C. Then, neglecting all sources of error other than that due to the computing process itself, we may put

$$x = S - C \qquad \text{and} \qquad f(x) = 1 \qquad (-.5, .5)$$

Assume that on the scale of x, both the actual and the computed values S, C are considerably greater than unity. Now let us determine the behavior of the errors in the computed value of *kinetic energy*. Here the true value is $(m/2)S^2$, while the computed value is $(m/2)C^2$, so that the error is

$$\frac{m}{2} (S^2 - C^2)$$

For the present let us put $y = S^2 - C^2$ and derive the distribution of y; afterward we

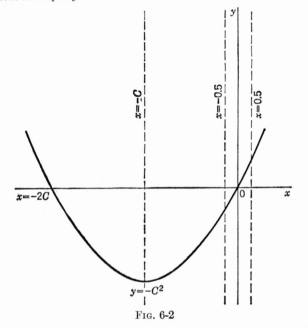

FIG. 6-2

can easily find the distribution of the error itself, which is $(m/2)y$. Rewriting S as $C + x$ we obtain

$$y = (C + x)^2 - C^2 = 2Cx + x^2$$

This equation (Fig. 6-2) represents a parabola with vertex (turning point) at $x = -C$, $y = -C^2$, and since $C > 1$ it follows that y is a monotonically increasing function of x over the permissible range $-.5 \leq x \leq .5$. The corresponding limits on y are $(-C + .25 \leq y \leq C + .25)$. From the equation of the parabola we have at once

$$(C + x)^2 = C^2 + y$$

and on the *right* side of the vertex,

$$x = -C + \sqrt{C^2 + y}$$

Since $f(x)$, being equal to unity, is independent of x, we have $f[\phi(y)] = 1$ and the only variable part of the density function of y is contributed by the derivative

$$\frac{dx}{dy} = \frac{1}{2\sqrt{C^2 + y}}$$

Hence (Fig. 6-3), $\quad g(y) = \dfrac{1}{2\sqrt{C^2 + y}} \qquad (-C + .25,\ C + .25)$

FIG. 6-3

The fact that there is nothing to substitute into $f(x)$ is often confusing to the student. Therefore we shall present an alternative derivation of $g(y)$ based on the distribution function $G(y)$. Let $y = b$ when $x = a$. Then $y \le b$ when, and only when, $x \le a$; and so

$$G(b) = F(a) = \int_{-.5}^{a} dx = a + .5$$

But the relation between x and y yields $a = -C + \sqrt{C^2 + b}$. Hence,

$$G(b) = -C + \sqrt{C^2 + b} + .5$$

Accordingly,

$$g(b) = \frac{dG(b)}{db} = \frac{1}{2 \sqrt{C^2 + b}}$$

and in general,

$$g(y) = \frac{1}{2 \sqrt{C^2 + y}} \qquad (-C + .25, \ C + .25)$$

Finally, denoting the actual error $(m/2)y$ by z, we have $y = (2/m)z$ and the density function of z, say $h(z)$, is

$$h(z) = \frac{1}{\sqrt{2m}} \frac{1}{\sqrt{k + z}} \qquad \left(-\frac{mC}{2} + \frac{m}{8}, \frac{mC}{2} + \frac{m}{8}\right)$$

where $k = mC^2/2$.

6-4. The Density Function of a Monotonically Decreasing Function.
If y is a monotonically decreasing function, and $y = b$ when $x = a$, then

$$P(y \le b) = P(x \ge a)$$

Thus, according to the previous assumptions and notation,

$$G(b) = 1 - F(a) \qquad g(b) = -f[\phi(b)] \frac{d\phi(b)}{db} \tag{6-4}$$

But if y is a monotonically decreasing function of x, $\phi(y)$ is likewise a monotonically decreasing function of y. Consequently, $d\phi(b)/db$ is always negative, and $-d\phi(b)/db$, being always positive, can be regarded as the absolute value of the derivative. Therefore, the equation for $g(b)$ can be rewritten as $g(b) = f[\phi(b)]|d\phi(b)/db|$ and in general,

$$g(y) = f[\phi(y)] \left| \frac{d\phi(y)}{dy} \right| \tag{6-5}$$

Note that Eq. (6-5) applies equally well to either case.

Example 6-3. Consider the function $y = 1/x$ where x is distributed as follows:

$$f(x) = \frac{6x}{(1 + x)^4} \qquad (0, \infty)$$

Here $x = 1/y$, $|dx/dy| = 1/y^2$, and

$$g(y) = \frac{6/y}{(1 + 1/y)^4} \frac{1}{y^2} = \frac{6y}{(1 + y)^4}$$

Since $y \to 0$ as $x \to \infty$, and $y \to \infty$ as $x \to 0$, the range of y is $(0, \infty)$; we do not say $(\infty, 0)$ because we are interested in the distribution of y, and we always represent the range of any variate as the interval from its lowest value to its highest value. In

Fig. 6-4

this example we have arrived at the rather unusual result that the reciprocal of a variate has the same form of distribution (Fig. 6-4) as the variate itself:

$$g(y) = \frac{6y}{(1 + y)^4} \qquad (0, \infty)$$

Example 6-4. Let x be normally distributed with parameters μ_1, σ_1 and let y be a linear function of x, say $y = a + bx$. If the coefficient b were zero, the linear function would degenerate to a constant, and we shall exclude this trivial case. For non-zero values of b, the function is monotonically increasing if b is positive and monotonically decreasing if b is negative. In either case, we have

$$x = \frac{y - a}{b} \qquad \left| \frac{dx}{dy} \right| = \frac{1}{|b|}$$

In the density function of x,

$$f(x) = \frac{1}{\sigma_1 \sqrt{2\pi}} e^{-(x-\mu_1)^2/2\sigma_1^2} \qquad (-\infty, \infty)$$

we must express x in terms of y and then multiply by $1/|b|$. Thus we put

$$x - \mu_1 = \frac{y - a - b\mu_1}{b} \qquad \frac{(x - \mu_1)^2}{2\sigma_1^2} = \frac{(y - a - b\mu_1)^2}{2b^2\sigma_1^2} = \frac{(y - \mu)^2}{2\sigma^2}$$

where $\mu = a + b\mu_1$ and $\sigma = |b|\sigma_1$. Accordingly,

$$g(y) = \frac{1}{|b|} \frac{1}{\sigma_1 \sqrt{2\pi}} e^{-(y-\mu)^2/2\sigma^2} = \frac{1}{\sigma \sqrt{2\pi}} e^{-(y-\mu)^2/2\sigma^2} \qquad (-\infty, \infty)$$

The range of y is $(-\infty, \infty)$ because a constant times infinity yields infinity. We have therefore proved that any nontrivial linear function of a normal variate is normally distributed.

This result is important enough to warrant a formal statement as a theorem.

THEOREM 6-1.   If x is normally distributed with parameters μ_1, σ_1, and y is any linear function $y = a + bx$ ($b \neq 0$), then y is normally distributed with corresponding parameters $\mu = a + b\mu_1, \sigma = |b|\sigma_1$.

6-5. The Probability Transformation.   A variable change of fundamental importance in distribution theory is known as the *probability transformation* and is defined by the equation $y = F(x)$, where $F(x)$ is the distribution function of x.   This transformation exists for all distributions, and in the class for which probability density functions exist, it has the interesting property of being rectangularly distributed.   It is obvious from the definition that the range of y is 0 to 1, and in case $f(x)$ exists we have

$$\frac{dy}{dx} = f(x) \qquad \frac{dx}{dy} = \frac{1}{f(x)}$$

whence
$$g(y) = \frac{f(x)}{f(x)} = 1 \qquad (0 \leq y \leq 1) \tag{6-6}$$

The probability transformation forms a theoretical link between any pair of distributions having probability densities.   Theoretically, any distribution for which the probability density exists can be transformed into any other by applying the probability transformation to each and thus bringing the variates into one-to-one correspondence.   The value of this lies in the fact that an initial variate having a distribution which is not suitable for certain types of standard statistical analyses can be replaced by another which is derived from the first by a definite transformation and which has a distribution that satisfies the conditions under which the proposed techniques apply.   Even when the distribution functions cannot be expressed as explicit closed functions of the variate values, they can be obtained in tabular form by numerical integration.   The transformation is then arrived at in the form of a table exhibiting the corresponding values of the two variates for selected values of the equated distribution functions.

Example 6-5.   Find a function of x having the distribution $g(y) = 3(1 - \sqrt{y})$ (0, 1), given that $f(x) = 6x(1 - x)$, (0, 1).   The distribution functions are

$$F(x) = \int_0^x f(x)\, dx = 3x^2 - 2x^3$$

$$G(y) = \int_0^y g(y)\, dy = 3y - 2y^{3/2}$$

Setting $G(y) = F(x)$ we get

$$3y - 2y^{3/2} = 3x^2 - 2x^3$$

Since this must be satisfied identically, the solution is unique and is found by inspection to be $y = x^2$.

6-6. Density Functions of the Square and the Absolute Value. If y is not a monotonic function of x, the foregoing formulas do not hold. We shall consider two cases of interest, which also indicate the general procedure in all cases where the variable change is not monotonic. First let $y = x^2$. Then $x = \pm \sqrt{y}$ and

$$G(y) = \int_{-\sqrt{y}}^{\sqrt{y}} f(x)\, dx$$

whence, differentiating the definite integral,

$$g(y) = \frac{f(\sqrt{y}) + f(-\sqrt{y})}{2\sqrt{y}} \tag{6-7a}$$

Density Function of $y = x^2$

Second, let $y = |x|$. Then

$$G(y) = \int_{-|x|}^{|x|} f(x)\, dx = \int_{-y}^{y} f(x)\, dx$$

and
$$g(y) = f(y) + f(-y) \tag{6-7b}$$

Density Function of $y = |x|$

Example 6-6. Let $y = x^2$ and

$$f(x) = \frac{1}{\sqrt{2\pi}}\, e^{-x^2/2} \qquad (-\infty, \infty)$$

Then $f(\sqrt{y}) = (1/\sqrt{2\pi})\, e^{-y/2} = f(-\sqrt{y})$ and so

$$g(y) = \frac{1}{\sqrt{2\pi}}\, y^{-\frac{1}{2}} e^{-y/2} \qquad (0, \infty)$$

Again, let $z = |x|$ with x the same as before. Then $f(z) = 1/\sqrt{2\pi}\, e^{-z^2/2} = f(-z)$ and

$$g(z) = \frac{2}{\sqrt{2\pi}}\, e^{-z^2/2} \qquad (0, \infty)$$

Example 6-7. The distribution of x is rectangular over the range $(-\frac{1}{2}, \frac{3}{2})$, that is,

$$f(x) = \frac{1}{2} \qquad (-\frac{1}{2}, \frac{3}{2})$$

and $y = x^2$. The total range of y is from 0 to $\frac{9}{4}$, but the fact that negative values of x cut off at $-\frac{1}{2}$ means that $f(-\sqrt{y}) \equiv 0$ as soon as y exceeds $\frac{1}{4}$. Therefore we must distinguish two ranges:

Range I $(0 \le y \le \frac{1}{4})$: $\qquad g(y) = \dfrac{\frac{1}{2} + \frac{1}{2}}{2\sqrt{y}} = \frac{1}{2} y^{-\frac{1}{2}}$

Range II $(\frac{1}{4} < y \le \frac{9}{4})$: $\qquad g(y) = \dfrac{0 + \frac{1}{2}}{2\sqrt{y}} = \frac{1}{4} y^{-\frac{1}{2}}$

Therefore the distribution of y (Fig. 6-5) has a discontinuity at $y = \frac{1}{4}$. The complete distribution of y is stated by writing these two equations in tandem:

$$g(y) = \frac{1}{2} y^{-\frac{1}{2}} \quad (0 \le y \le \frac{1}{4}) \qquad\qquad g(y) = \frac{1}{4} y^{-\frac{1}{2}} \quad (\frac{1}{4} < y \le \frac{9}{4})$$

6-7. The Distribution of a Function of Two or More Independent Variates. Most derived distributions involve more than a simple variable change. Typically, we are interested in variables which cannot be measured directly but can be constructed mathematically as functions (such as sums, products, quotients) of variables which are directly measurable. This introduces the consideration of a multidimensional space, but for the time being we shall confine our analysis to two dimensions. The general principles, however, apply to any number of dimensions.

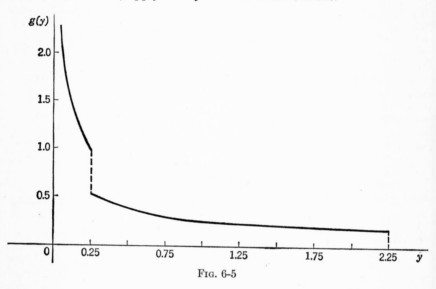

Fig. 6-5

Consider two independent variates x, y with marginal density functions $f_1(x)$ and $f_2(y)$ respectively. By hypothesis, their joint density function $f(x,y)$ is equal to the product of their marginal density functions, that is, $f(x,y) = f_1(x)f_2(y)$. Let u be a monotonic function of x and y in the sense that u behaves as a monotonic function of x when y is held fixed and as a monotonic function of y when x is held fixed. Some examples are $u = x + y$, $u = xy$, $u = x/y$, $u = ye^{-x}$. To obtain the distribution of u, we imagine that one of the initial variates x, y actually is held fixed at some arbitrary value, while the other varies over its possible range, according to its own marginal distribution. For definiteness, assume that x is fixed and y free to vary. The probability distribution of u which then results is, by definition, the conditional distribution of u given x. Moreover, as we have said, u becomes a monotonic function of the single variable y, although the functional equation relating u and y will contain parameters which depend on x. Therefore, the conditional density function $\phi(u|x)$ can be derived from $f_2(y)$ by the univariate method previously presented. Having done this, we may then construct the joint density function of x and u—say $g(x,u)$—by using the formula

$$g(x,u) = f_1(x)\phi(u|x)$$

Finally, the marginal density of u is obtained by integrating this joint density function with respect to x. The best way to clarify the method is through the consideration of specific examples.

Example 6-8. Let us suppose that we have a random variable x which is rectangularly distributed in the region from $x = 0$ to $x = 1$ and thus $f(x) = 1$ $(0, 1)$. Let us draw two observations at random from this infinite population and call them x_1 and x_2.

The problem is to find the distribution of the sum of x_1 and x_2, say $u = x_1 + x_2$. What is meant by this is that two observations are drawn at random and added together and the sum computed. This process is repeated over and over again, each time obtaining a new value for the sum. We now ask what the probability distribution of all these values of the sum would be if we could carry out this experiment. Since the population is infinite, its probability distribution is not disturbed by sampling. Hence the sample values behave independently, and the sampling process is equivalent to drawing the first observation from one rectangular distribution and the second from another, both of which run from 0 to 1.

FIG. 6-6

As the first step in deriving the distribution of u, we regard x_1 as fixed and change the variable in the distribution of x_2, which is given by $f_2(x_2) = 1$ $(0, 1)$. The derivative of x_2 with respect to u holding x_1 fixed will, of course, be a *partial* derivative. Thus we have

$$x_2 = u - x_1 \qquad \frac{\partial x_2}{\partial u} = 1$$

whence $\quad \phi(u|x_1) = [f_2(u - x_1)]\dfrac{\partial x_2}{\partial u} = (1)(1) = 1 \qquad (x_1 \le u \le 1 + x_1)$

The range of u is obtained by noting that the equation $u = x_1 + x_2$ yields $u = x_1$ when $x_2 = 0$ and $u = x_1 + 1$ when $x_2 = 1$.

The next step is to obtain the joint distribution of x_1 and u. This is given by

$$g(x_1,u) = f_1(x_1)\phi(u|x_1) = 1 \qquad (0 \le x_1 \le 1; x_1 \le u \le 1 + x_1)$$

The bivariate region of definition is obtained merely by supplementing the original range of x_1 with a statement of the conditional limits of u. From the diagram of this region (shaded portion of Fig. 6-6) we see that the integration on x_1 must be performed in two steps, which implies that the marginal density of u requires two functions for its definition.

In the range $0 \le u \le 1$ the values of x_1 run from 0 at the left-hand boundary to u at the right-hand boundary, and the corresponding limits of integration are from 0 to u. In the range $1 \le u \le 2$ the left-hand boundary is the line $x_1 = u - 1$ and the right-hand boundary is the vertical line $x_1 = 1$; thus in this range, the limits are from $u - 1$ to 1. Hence we obtain the marginal distribution of u as follows:

Range I $(0 \le u \le 1)$: $h(u) = \int_0^u dx_1 = u$

Range II $(1 \le u \le 2)$: $h(u) = \int_{u-1}^1 dx_1 = 2 - u$

whereupon,

$$h(u) = u \quad (0 \le u \le 1) \qquad h(u) = 2 - u \quad (1 \le u \le 2)$$

This triangular distribution is shown in Fig. 6-7.

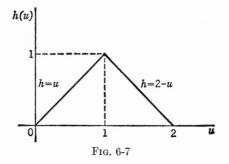

FIG. 6-7

Example 6-9. Two independent random variables x, y are distributed as follows:

$$f_1(x) = \tfrac{1}{2} \quad (1, 3) \quad \text{and} \quad f_2(y) = e^{-(y-2)} \quad (2, \infty)$$

Find the distribution of $z = x/y$.

FIG. 6-8

Since $f_1(x)$ is simpler than $f_2(y)$ it will be easier to determine $\phi(z|y)$ than the alternative. Accordingly, holding y fixed we find the conditional distribution of $z = x/y$ regarded as a function of x alone. Here $x = yz$, $\partial x/\partial z = y$, and

$$[f_1(yz)]y = \tfrac{1}{2}y$$

Now when $x = 1$, $z = 1/y$, and when $x = 3$, $z = 3/y$. Therefore, the conditional distribution of z given y is

$$\phi(z|y) = \tfrac{1}{2}y \quad \left(\frac{1}{y}, \frac{3}{y}\right)$$

and the joint distribution of y and z is

$$g(y,z) = \tfrac{1}{2}ye^{-(y-2)} \quad \left(2 \le y < \infty; \frac{1}{y} \le z \le \frac{3}{y}\right)$$

The admissible region (shaded in Fig. 6-9) consists of that portion of the first quadrant bounded on the left by the vertical line $y = 2$, above by the hyperbola $z = 3/y$, below by $z = 1/y$, and open on the right.

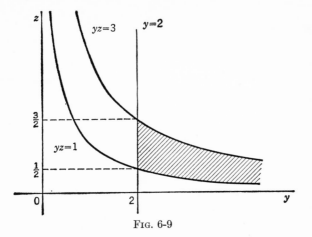

FIG. 6-9

The least possible value of z is 0, which is the limit approached as $y \to \infty$. The greatest possible value of z is $\frac{3}{2}$, which corresponds to the point of intersection of the higher boundary curve $z = 3/y$ and the line $y = 2$. Once again, the integration must be done in two steps. The lower hyperbola cuts the left boundary at $z = \frac{1}{2}$. Below this level, y ranges between the two hyperbolas, the limits being $y = 1/z$ to $y = 3/z$. Above the level $z = \frac{1}{2}$, the left-hand boundary is the line $y = 2$, and the limits are $y = 2$ to $y = 3/z$. Thus the distribution of z must be expressed by two different functions, each of which applies to a stated range.

Range I ($0 \le z \le \frac{1}{2}$):

$$h(z) = \int_{1/z}^{3/z} g(y,z)\, dy = \frac{-e^2}{2}\, [e^{-y}(y + 1)]_{1/z}^{3/z}$$

$$= \frac{e^2}{2z}\, [e^{-1/z}(1 + z) - e^{-3/z}(3 + z)]$$

Range II ($\frac{1}{2} \le z \le \frac{3}{2}$):

$$h(z) = \int_{2}^{3/z} g(y,z)\, dy = \frac{-e^2}{2}\, [e^{-y}(y + 1)]_{2}^{3/z}$$

$$= \frac{3}{2} - \frac{e^2}{2z}\, e^{-3/z}(3 + z)$$

We note that when $z = \frac{1}{2}$ both functions yield the same value

$$h\left(\frac{1}{2}\right) = \frac{3 - 7e^{-4}}{2}$$

As a check let us verify that the density function has unit area. To this end consider, first, the following indefinite integral:

$$I(a) = \int \left(1 + \frac{a}{z}\right) e^{-a/z}\, dz$$

If we set $u = -1/z$, this integral becomes

$$I(a) = \int (1 - au)e^{au} \frac{du}{u^2} = \int \frac{e^{au}}{u^2} du - a \int \frac{e^{au}}{u} du$$

On the other hand,

$$a \int \frac{e^{au}}{u} du = \frac{e^{au}}{u} + \int \frac{e^{au}}{u^2} du$$

From this, we easily get

$$I(a) = \frac{-e^{au}}{u} = ze^{-a/z}$$

Now, integrating $h(z)$,

$$\int_0^{3/2} h(z)\, dz = \frac{e^2}{2} [I(1) - I(3)]_0^{1/2} + \left[\frac{3z}{2} - \frac{e^2}{2} I(3) \right]_{1/2}^{3/2} = 1$$

Example 6-10. Find the distribution of the sum $y = x_1 + x_2$ of two independent gamma variates x_1, x_2, the respective parameters of which are (α_1, β) and (α_2, β); that is, the exponential parameter β is common to both distributions. The distributions of x_1 and x_2 are

$$f_1(x_1) = k_1 x_1^{\alpha_1} e^{-x_1/\beta} \qquad (0, \infty)$$
$$f_2(x_2) = k_2 x_2^{\alpha_2} e^{-x_2/\beta} \qquad (0, \infty)$$

where $\qquad k_1 = \dfrac{1}{\beta^{\alpha_1+1}\Gamma(\alpha_1 + 1)} \qquad k_2 = \dfrac{1}{\beta^{\alpha_2+1}\Gamma(\alpha_2 + 1)}$

and no restrictions are imposed on the parameters α_1, α_2 beyond the fundamental requirement for the existence of the distributions, namely, $\alpha_1 > -1$, $\alpha_2 > -1$.

Holding x_1 fixed in the equation $y = x_1 + x_2$ we put

$$x_2 = y - x_1 \qquad \frac{\partial x_2}{\partial y} = 1$$

and note that y ranges from x_1 to ∞, respectively, as x_2 goes from 0 to ∞. Thus the conditional distribution of y given x_1 is

$$\phi(y|x_1) = [f_2(y - x_1)] \frac{\partial x_2}{\partial y} = k_2(y - x_1)^{\alpha_2} e^{-(y-x_1)/\beta} \qquad (x_1 \leq y < \infty)$$

and as the joint distribution of x_1 and y we obtain

$$g(x_1, y) = k_1 k_2 x_1^{\alpha_1}(y - x_1)^{\alpha_2} e^{-x_1/\beta} e^{-(y-x_1)/\beta}$$
$$= k_1 k_2 e^{-y/\beta} x_1^{\alpha_1}(y - x_1)^{\alpha_2} \qquad (0 \leq x_1 < \infty ; x_1 \leq y < \infty)$$

The admissible region, shown in Fig. 6-10, consists of the second octant of the plane, i.e., that portion of the first quadrant included between the y axis and the line $y = x_1$. As indicated by the figure, the extreme limits of y are 0 to ∞. The limits of integration on x_1 are from 0 to y, and the integration can be performed in one step as a beta function, with the substitution $x_1 = ty$.

$$h(y) = k_1 k_2 e^{-y/\beta} \int_0^y x_1^{\alpha_1}(y - x_1)^{\alpha_2}\, dx_1 = k y^{\alpha_1+\alpha_2+1} e^{-y/\beta} \qquad (0, \infty)$$

where $\qquad k = \dfrac{1}{\beta^{\alpha_1+\alpha_2+2}\Gamma(\alpha_1 + \alpha_2 + 2)}$

Therefore, the sum of two independent gamma variates with common parameter β is another gamma variate with the same β and with $\alpha = \alpha_1 + \alpha_2 + 1$.

We may generalize the result of this example. Suppose we had the sum of three independent gamma variates, $z = x_1 + x_2 + x_3$ with common β. We could rewrite this identically as $z = y + x_3$ and, by applying the proposition we just proved, deduce that the distribution of z is gamma with parameters

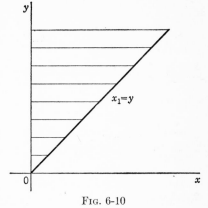

FIG. 6-10

$$\alpha = \alpha_1 + \alpha_2 + \alpha_3 + 2$$

and β. By induction, we obtain the following theorem, a special case of which was proved in Chap. 4:

THEOREM 6-2. If $x_1, x_2, \ldots, x_k$ are independent gamma variates with α parameters $\alpha_1, \alpha_2, \ldots, \alpha_k$ and a common value of β, then their sum $x = x_1 + x_2 + \cdots + x_k$ is a gamma variate with the same β and with $\alpha = \alpha_1 + \alpha_2 + \cdots + \alpha_k + k - 1$.

Example 6-11. The independent variates x, y are normally distributed with parameters (μ_1, σ_1) and (μ_2, σ_2) respectively:

$$f_1(x) = \frac{1}{\sigma_1 \sqrt{2\pi}} e^{-(x-\mu_1)^2/2\sigma_1^2} \qquad (-\infty, \infty)$$

$$f_2(y) = \frac{1}{\sigma_2 \sqrt{2\pi}} e^{-(y-\mu_2)^2/2\sigma_2^2} \qquad (-\infty, \infty)$$

Find the distribution of the sum $z = x + y$.

Holding x fixed, we obtain the conditional distribution of z given x by changing variables in $f_2(y)$. Here $y = z - x$, $\partial y/\partial z = 1$, and so

$$\phi(z|x) = \frac{1}{\sigma_2 \sqrt{2\pi}} e^{-(z-x-\mu_2)^2/2\sigma_2^2} \qquad (-\infty, \infty)$$

The range of z is $(-\infty, \infty)$ because y has this range, and for any fixed value of x the quantity $x + y$ will approach infinity in either direction with y. Now let us put

$$K = \frac{1}{2\pi\sigma_1\sigma_2} \qquad Q = \frac{(x-\mu_1)^2}{2\sigma_1^2} + \frac{(z-x-\mu_2)^2}{2\sigma_2^2}$$

Then the joint distribution of x, z becomes

$$g(x,z) = Ke^{-Q} \qquad (-\infty, \infty \text{ each})$$

and the marginal density function of z will be given by

$$h(z) = K \int_{-\infty}^{\infty} e^{-Q} \, dx$$

To perform the integration, we first complete the square on x obtaining, after simplification,

$$Q \equiv \frac{(\sigma_1{}^2 + \sigma_2{}^2)}{2\sigma_1{}^2\sigma_2{}^2} \left[x - \frac{(\sigma_2{}^2\mu_1 + \sigma_1{}^2 z - \sigma_1{}^2\mu_2)}{\sigma_1{}^2 + \sigma_2{}^2} \right]^2 + \frac{(z - \mu_1 - \mu_2)^2}{2(\sigma_1{}^2 + \sigma_2{}^2)}$$

When we integrate on x, we hold z fixed. Hence for integration purposes, we may change variables, setting

$$v = x - \frac{(\sigma_2{}^2\mu_1 + \sigma_1{}^2 z - \sigma_1{}^2\mu_2)}{\sigma_1{}^2 + \sigma_2{}^2} \qquad dx = dv$$

Also, for convenience let us put

$$\mu = \mu_1 + \mu_2 \qquad \sigma^2 = \sigma_1{}^2 + \sigma_2{}^2$$

Then
$$h(z) = K e^{-(z-\mu)^2/2\sigma^2} \int_{-\infty}^{\infty} e^{-\sigma^2 v^2/2\sigma_1{}^2\sigma_2{}^2} \, dv$$

By use of the gamma function, we find that the latter integral reduces to $(\sigma_1\sigma_2 \sqrt{2\pi})/\sigma$. Hence, multiplying by K we obtain

$$h(z) = \frac{1}{\sigma \sqrt{2\pi}} e^{-(z-\mu)^2/2\sigma^2} \qquad (-\infty, \infty)$$

showing that the sum of any two independent normally distributed variates is again normally distributed.

By induction, this proposition can be extended to any number of independent normal variates. This fact together with Theorem 6-1, yields the following theorem:

THEOREM 6-3. If $x_1, x_2, \ldots, x_n$ are independent, normally distributed variates with respective parameters (μ_1, σ_1), (μ_2, σ_2), $\ldots$, (μ_n, σ_n), then the *weighted* sum $x = a_0 + a_1 x_1 + a_2 x_2 + \cdots + a_n x_n$ (where at least one of the coefficients $a_1, a_2, \ldots, a_n$ is not zero) is normally distributed with parameters (μ, σ) where

$$\mu = a_0 + a_1\mu_1 + a_2\mu_2 + \cdots + a_n\mu_n$$
and
$$\sigma = \sqrt{a_1{}^2\sigma_1{}^2 + a_2{}^2\sigma_2{}^2 + \cdots + a_n{}^2\sigma_n{}^2}$$

A very important special case of Theorem 6-3 arises when a series of independent random observations $x_1, x_2, \ldots, x_n$ of the same normal variate x are taken and averaged to obtain the sample mean $\bar{x} = (x_1 + x_2 + \cdots + x_n)/n$. If the parameters of x are (μ, σ), then the observations can be regarded as particular values of independent normal variates all having the same parameters (μ, σ). The coefficients $a_1, a_2, \ldots, a_n$ are all equal to $1/n$ while $a_0 = 0$. Thus the formula $a_0 + \sum_1^n a_i\mu_i$ reduces to μ and the formula $\sum_1^n a_i{}^2\sigma_i{}^2$ reduces to σ^2/n. Consequently $\bar{x}$, in repeated trials, will be normally distributed with parameters $(\mu, \sigma/\sqrt{n})$. Although a corollary of the latter theorem, this result is important enough to be classed as a theorem itself.

THEOREM 6-4.   In repeated independent trials, the sample mean $\bar{x}$ of n independent random observations of the same normal variate x with parameters (μ, σ) is normally distributed with corresponding parameters $(\mu, \sigma/\sqrt{n})$.

6-8. Some Derived Distributions Used in Statistics.   Three basic distributions are employed over and over again in statistical applications of mathematical probability.   These are known as the chi-square distribution, the t distribution, and the F distribution.   They are used to answer such questions as whether an assumed type of probability distribution fits the observational facts, whether two or more variates are similarly distributed, or more specifically, whether two or more variates have a common average value.   At present, we shall not attempt to show the connection between the formal definitions and the practical applications—this subject is developed later—but we shall derive the distributions of the variates from the definitions we are about to state.   All three distributions are offshoots from the normal.

6-9. The Chi-square Distribution.   Chi-square (χ^2) is defined as the sum of the squares of n independent unit normal variates.   Let x be a unit normal variate.   Then putting $y = x^2$, the distribution of y, already found in Example 6-6, is

$$f(y) = \frac{1}{\sqrt{2\pi}}\, y^{-\frac{1}{2}}e^{-y/2} \qquad (0, \infty) \qquad\qquad (6\text{-}8)$$

This, then, is the distribution of chi-square when $n = 1$.   Noticing that this is merely a gamma distribution with $\alpha = -\frac{1}{2}$, $\beta = 2$ we may apply Theorem 6-2 and state the general distribution of chi-square at once:

$$f(\chi^2) = \frac{1}{2^{n/2}\Gamma(n/2)}\,(\chi^2)^{n/2-1}e^{-\chi^2/2} \qquad (0, \infty) \qquad\qquad (6\text{-}9)$$

Chi-square Distribution
with n Degrees of Freedom

We mention, in passing, that for reasons founded on the effective number of independent variates on which a derived function is based, the parameter n is called the *degrees of freedom* of chi-square.   Thus we say that the equation

$$\chi^2 = x_1{}^2 + x_2{}^2 + \cdots + x_n{}^2$$

where $x_1, x_2, \ldots, x_n$ are independent unit normal variates, or the equivalent equation

$$\chi^2 = y_1 + y_2 + \cdots + y_n$$

where the y's are independently distributed according to Eq. (6-8), defines chi-square with n degrees of freedom, and its distribution is given by Eq.

(6-9).　An obvious deduction from the definition is that the sum of two independent chi-squares with, say, n_1 and n_2 degrees of freedom, respectively, is in turn distributed as chi-square with $n_1 + n_2$ degrees of freedom and, of course, this proposition (which is merely a special case of Theorem 6-2) can be extended to any number of independent chi-squares.　The term "degrees of freedom" is used in several connections, but in the probability sense it nearly always means the maximum number of variates in a given system which are mutually independent under stated conditions.

The t distribution and the F distribution are developed through auxiliary functions based on chi-square, and we shall call these functions the *mean square* and the *root mean square*.　While chi-square is the *sum* of the squares of n independent unit normal variates, the *average* of the squares (usually called the mean square), which we shall denote by w, is equal to the sum of the squares divided by n.　The square root of the average of the squares (usually called the root mean square), which we shall denote by r for the time being, is the positive square root of w.　For simplicity, we shall denote both density functions by the letter f, even though the expressions are different.　By simple changes of variable in Eq. (6-9) with $w = \chi^2/n$ and $r = \sqrt{\chi^2/n}$, we obtain

$$f(w) = \frac{(n/2)^{n/2}}{\Gamma(n/2)} w^{n/2-1} e^{-nw/2} \qquad (0, \infty) \qquad (6\text{-}10)$$

Mean-square Distribution
with n Degrees of Freedom

$$f(r) = \frac{2(n/2)^{n/2}}{\Gamma(n/2)} r^{n-1} e^{-nr^2/2} \qquad (0, \infty) \qquad (6\text{-}11)$$

Root-mean-square Distribution with n Degrees of Freedom

6-10. The t Distribution.　The variate t may be defined as the quotient of two independent variates x and r where x is unit normal and r is the root mean square of n other independent unit normal variates; that is $t = x/r$.　To derive the distribution of t let us hold r fixed and change variables in the distribution of x by setting $x = rt$.　Making this substitution in

$$f_1(x) = \frac{1}{\sqrt{2\pi}} e^{-x^2/2} \qquad (-\infty, \infty)$$

we obtain
$$\phi(t|r) = \frac{r}{\sqrt{2\pi}} e^{-r^2 t^2/2} \qquad (-\infty, \infty)$$

and since the marginal distribution of r is given by Eq. (6-11), the joint distribution of r and t is

$$g(r,t) = \frac{2(n/2)^{n/2}}{(\sqrt{2\pi})\Gamma(n/2)} r^n e^{-r^2(n+t^2)/2} \qquad (0 \leq r < \infty, -\infty < t < \infty)$$

Setting $u = (r\sqrt{n + t^2})/\sqrt{2}$, we may express the marginal distribution of t as follows:

$$h(t) = \int_0^\infty g(r,t)\ dr = \frac{n^{n/2}}{\Gamma(n/2)\ \sqrt{\pi}}\ \frac{1}{(n + t^2)^{(n+1)/2}}\ \int_0^\infty 2u^n e^{-u^2}\ du$$

$$= \frac{n^{n/2}\Gamma\left(\dfrac{n + 1}{2}\right)}{\Gamma(n/2)\ \sqrt{\pi}}\ \frac{1}{(n + t^2)^{(n+1)/2}}\qquad (-\infty,\ \infty)$$

The distribution of t is usually rewritten by expressing $(n + t^2)$ as $n(1 + t^2/n)$. The result is

$$h(t) = \frac{\Gamma[(n + 1)/2]}{\Gamma(n/2)\ \sqrt{n\pi}}\ \frac{1}{(1 + t^2/n)^{(n+1)/2}}\qquad (-\infty,\ \infty)\qquad (6\text{-}12)$$

t Distribution with
n Degrees of Freedom

Equation (6-12) gives the distribution of t with n degrees of freedom.

6-11. The F Distribution. The variate F may be defined as the quotient of the respective mean squares of a and b independent unit normal variates. Thus $f_1(w_1)$ is given by Eq. (6-10) with $n = a$, and $f_2(w_2)$ is given by setting $n = b$. Since $F = w_1/w_2$ we have $w_1 = w_2 F$, and holding w_2 fixed, we obtain the conditional distribution of F from $f_1(w_1)$.

$$\phi(F|w_2) = \frac{(a/2)^{a/2}}{\Gamma(a/2)}\ w_2^{a/2} F^{a/2-1} e^{-aw_2 F_2}\qquad (0,\ \infty)$$

The joint distribution is

$$g(w_2,F) = \frac{(a/2)^{a/2}(b/2)^{b/2}}{\Gamma(a/2)\Gamma(b/2)}\ F^{a/2-1} w_2^{a/2+b/2-1} e^{-w_2(aF+b)/2}\qquad (0,\ \infty\ \text{each})$$

By setting $u = w_2(aF + b)/2$ and $c = a + b$, we may express the marginal distribution of F as follows:

$$h(F) = \frac{a^{a/2} b^{b/2}}{\Gamma(a/2)\Gamma(b/2)}\ \frac{F^{a/2-1}}{(aF + b)^{c/2}}\ \int_0^\infty u^{c/2-1} e^{-u}\ du\qquad (0,\ \infty)$$

whence $\qquad\qquad h(F) = \dfrac{a^{a/2} b^{b/2}}{\beta(a/2, b/2)}\ \dfrac{F^{a/2-1}}{(aF + b)^{c/2}}\qquad (0,\ \infty)\qquad (6\text{-}13)$

F Distribution with a
and b Degrees of Freedom

This can be simplified a little by dividing numerator and denominator by $a^{c/2}$. The result is

$$h(F) = \frac{(b/a)^{b/2}}{\beta(a/2, b/2)}\ \frac{F^{a/2-1}}{(F + b/a)^{c/2}}\qquad (0,\ \infty)\qquad (6\text{-}14)$$

Alternative Form of F Distribution with a and b Degrees of Freedom

The variate F, as here defined, is also known as the *variance ratio* with a and b degrees of freedom.

6-12. The Distribution of a Function of Nonindependent Variates. The general principles discussed in Sec. 6-7 for deriving the distribution of a function of independent variates can be extended to nonindependent variates by substituting conditional distributions for marginal distributions.

Consider a pair of nonindependent variates x, y and a monotonic function of them u. Denote the joint density function of x and y by $f(x,y)$, the marginal density function of x by $f_1(x)$, and the conditional density function of y given x by $\phi(y|x)$. Then

$$f(x,y) = f_1(x)\phi(y|x)$$

Holding x fixed, the conditional density function of u given x, say $\theta(u|x)$, is derived from $\phi(y|x)$ by the regular univariate method. We then have

$$g(x,u) = f_1(x)\theta(u|x)$$

and the remaining steps are the same as before.

This, at any rate, is the logic of the method. In practice it is possible to eliminate some steps, but this is best explained with reference to a specific example.

Example 6-12. Find the distribution of $u = y/\sqrt{x}$ given that x and y are jointly distributed as follows:

$$f(x,y) = 120y(x - y)(1 - x) \qquad (0 \le x \le 1; 0 \le y \le x)$$

The marginal distribution of x is

$$f_1(x) = \int_0^x f(x,y)\, dy = 20x^3(1 - x) \qquad (0, 1)$$

and so the conditional distribution of y given x is

$$\phi(y|x) = \frac{6y}{x^3}(x - y) \qquad (0 \le y \le x)$$

As y goes from 0 to x, the function $u = y/\sqrt{x}$ goes from 0 to $\sqrt{x}$, and to change variables we put

$$y = u\sqrt{x} \qquad \frac{\partial y}{\partial u} = \sqrt{x}$$

Accordingly, $\quad \theta(u|x) = [\phi(u\sqrt{x}|x)]\sqrt{x} = \dfrac{6u}{x^{3/2}}(\sqrt{x} - u) \qquad (0 \le u \le \sqrt{x})$

$$g(x,u) = 120x^{3/2}(1 - x)u(\sqrt{x} - u) \qquad (0 \le x \le 1; 0 \le u \le \sqrt{x})$$

The admissible region is shown in Fig. 6-11.

Integrating the joint density function $g(x,u)$ from $x = u^2$ to 1, we find the marginal distribution of u to be as follows:

$$h(u) = \tfrac{3}{7}u(35 - 48u + 28u^6 - 15u^8) \qquad (0, 1)$$

The fact that a density function cannot be negative implies that this polynomial cannot have any roots inside the range $(0, 1)$ for which it represents the distribution of u. By algebraic factorization we obtain:

$$h(u) = \tfrac{2}{7}u(1 - u)^3(15u^5 + 45u^4 + 62u^3 + 66u^2 + 57u + 35) \qquad (0, 1)$$

From this form, it is evident that there are, in fact, no roots inside the range $(0, 1)$.

With regard to the possibility of saving some steps, we notice that the actual operations are as follows:

1. $\phi(y|x) = f(x,y)/f_1(x)$.

2. $\theta(u|x) = [\phi(y^*|x)]\,\partial y/\partial u$, where y^* denotes the functional expression of y in terms of u and x. In the foregoing example this would mean writing $u\sqrt{x}$ in place of y.

3. $g(x,u) = f_1(x)\theta(u|x)$. At this step, $f_1(x)$ cancels out and we are left with

$$g(x,u) = [f(x,y^*)]\,\frac{\partial y}{\partial u}$$

Fig. 6-11

In other words, we may write down the joint distribution of x and u directly without bothering with the intermediate marginal and conditional distributions. We merely substitute for y in $f(x,y)$ and multiply the result by the partial derivative of y with respect to u. The limits on y are replaced by the corresponding limits on u, which are found directly from the equation by which u is defined. Thus, in the foregoing example we could have written

$$f(x,u\sqrt{x}) = 120(u\sqrt{x})(x - u\sqrt{x})(1 - x)$$
$$= 120x(1 - x)u(\sqrt{x} - u)$$

and when this is multiplied by the partial derivative $\sqrt{x}$ we get the same expression for $g(x,u)$ as before. This technique is especially convenient when the function considered involves more than two variables. A three-variable illustration is given in the following example.

Example 6-13. Given the trivariate distribution

$$f(x_1,x_2,x_3) = (x_2 - x_3)e^{-x_1} \qquad (0 \le x_1 < \infty; 0 \le x_2 \le x_1; 0 \le x_3 \le x_2)$$

find the distribution of the function $y = x_1 - x_2 + x_3$.

Replacing x_3, we substitute $x_3 = y + x_2 - x_1$ and then multiply by $\partial x_3/\partial y = 1$. As x_3 goes from 0 to x_2, the function $y = x_1 - x_2 + x_3$ goes from $x_1 - x_2$ to x_1. Hence the joint distribution of x_1, x_2, y becomes

$$g(x_1,x_2,y) = [x_2 - (y + x_2 - x_1)]e^{-x_1}(1)$$
$$= (x_1 - y)e^{-x_1} \qquad (0 \le x_1 < \infty; 0 \le x_2 \le x_1; x_1 - x_2 \le y \le x_1)$$

An equivalent set of limits, defining exactly the same admissible region, is $(0 \leq y < \infty$; $y \leq x_1 < \infty$; $x_1 - y \leq x_2 \leq x_1)$. Accordingly, the marginal distribution of y is given by

$$h(y) = \int_y^\infty (x_1 - y)e^{-x_1}\, dx_1 \int_{x_1-y}^{x_1} dx_2 = ye^{-y} \qquad (0, \infty)$$

Example 6-14.   Under the topic of ordered statistics in Chap. 5 the joint distribution of the smallest and largest observations in a random sample was derived in Example 5-12 for the particular case of a sample of four observations from an exponential distribution.   The same line of argument is readily generalized to any sample size n and any density function $f(x)$ $(A \leq x \leq B)$.   Denoting the (algebraically) smallest and

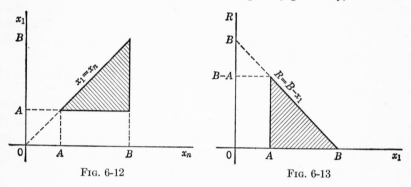

FIG. 6-12   FIG. 6-13

largest observations by x_1 and x_n respectively, and noticing that the permutation factor $n!/1!(n - 2)!1!$ reduces to $n(n - 1)$, we obtain (Fig. 6-12)

$$g(x_1, x_n) = n(n - 1)f(x_1)\left[\int_{x_1}^{x_n} f(x)\, dx\right]^{n-2} f(x_n) \qquad (A \leq x_n \leq B; A \leq x_1 \leq x_n)$$

Now suppose we wished to know the distribution of the range R (i.e., the difference between the largest and smallest observations) in repeated random samples of n observations.   Since x_1 and x_n are not independent, the range $R = x_n - x_1$ provides a simple but important illustration of a function of nonindependent variates.   Replacing x_n by $x_1 + R$ we obtain (Fig. 6-13)

$$h(x_1, R) = n(n - 1)f(x_1)\left[\int_{x_1}^{x_1+R} f(x)\, dx\right]^{n-2} f(x_1 + R)$$
$$(A \leq x_1 \leq B; 0 \leq R \leq B - x_1)$$

Whence, the marginal distribution of R is given by

$$p(R) = n(n - 1) \int_A^{B-R} f(x_1)f(x_1 + R)\left[\int_{x_1}^{x_1+R} f(x)\, dx\right]^{n-2} dx_1$$
$$(0 \leq R \leq B - A)$$

As a specific illustration, let us take the exponential distribution $f(x) = \dfrac{1}{\beta} e^{-x/\beta}$ $(0, \infty)$.   Here the integration can be performed explicitly and yields

$$p(R) = \frac{n-1}{\beta} e^{-R/\beta} (1 - e^{-R/\beta})^{n-2} \qquad (0 \le R < \infty)$$

6-13. Joint Distributions of Multivariate Functions. When two or more quantities are computed from the same data, or, equivalently, when two or more functions are determined from a common set of initial variates, their joint distribution in repeated independent trials may become an important issue in the problem considered. For instance, the question of independence can be settled only by referring to the joint distribution. The methods thus far expounded yield the distribution of a single function of initial variates but do not apply to the joint distribution of two or more functions. The latter comes under the heading of variate transformations, and we shall borrow what we need from the standard material of advanced calculus.

Suppose the initial variates (whether independent or not) are x_1, x_2, x_3 and their joint density function $f(x_1,x_2,x_3)$ is defined over some region of space R_x. Let y_1, y_2, y_3 be single-valued functions of x_1, x_2, x_3 such that the x's can be recovered uniquely if the y's are given. A necessary property of $g(y_1,y_2,y_3)$, the joint density function of the y's, is that its total integral over its own region of definition R_y is unity. Now the theory of transforming integrals has already been developed, and we have only to adapt it to our own purposes. If we begin with the definite integral

$$\iiint_{R_x} f(x_1,x_2,x_3)\ dx_1\ dx_2\ dx_3 = 1 \qquad (6\text{-}15)$$

and decide to change to new variables y_1, y_2, y_3, then the integrand proper $f(x_1,x_2,x_3)$ is transformed by direct substitution, but the differential element $dx_1\ dx_2\ dx_3$ has to be replaced by the correct volume element in the new coordinate system. In advanced calculus, it is proved that the new volume element becomes

$$\left[\text{Absolute value of } \frac{\partial(x_1,x_2,x_3)}{\partial(y_1,y_2,y_3)} \right] dy_1\ dy_2\ dy_3$$

where the expression $\partial(x_1,x_2,x_3)/\partial(y_1,y_2,y_3)$ is called the *Jacobian* of the x system with respect to the y system and is defined as the determinant of first partial derivatives. That is,

$$\frac{\partial(x_1,x_2,x_3)}{\partial(y_1,y_2,y_3)} \equiv \begin{vmatrix} \dfrac{\partial x_1}{\partial y_1} & \dfrac{\partial x_1}{\partial y_2} & \dfrac{\partial x_1}{\partial y_3} \\[2mm] \dfrac{\partial x_2}{\partial y_1} & \dfrac{\partial x_2}{\partial y_2} & \dfrac{\partial x_2}{\partial y_3} \\[2mm] \dfrac{\partial x_3}{\partial y_1} & \dfrac{\partial x_3}{\partial y_2} & \dfrac{\partial x_3}{\partial y_3} \end{vmatrix} \qquad (6\text{-}16)$$

Following accepted engineering usage, we shall represent the Jacobian of the initial variables with respect to the new by the symbol J. Thus $dx_1 \, dx_2 \, dx_3$ is replaced by $|J| \, dy_1 \, dy_2 \, dy_3$ (note *absolute* value) and this absolute value of the Jacobian becomes the analogue of the absolute value of the derivative employed in changing a single variable. Consequently, in order to state that

$$\iiint_{R_x} f(x_1,x_2,x_3) \, dx_1 \, dx_2 \, dx_3 = \iiint_{R_y} g(y_1,y_2,y_3) \, dy_1 \, dy_2 \, dy_3 = 1 \quad (6\text{-}17)$$

we must incorporate the term $|J|$ into the definition of the new density function. Just as dx/dy is the reciprocal of dy/dx, it can be demonstrated also that the Jacobian of the x's with respect to the y's is the reciprocal of the Jacobian of the y's with respect to the x's. Before illustrating the derivation of joint distributions, we shall give an example of the Jacobian itself.

Example 6-15. In changing from rectangular to polar coordinates in two dimensions we have $x = r \cos \theta$, $y = r \sin \theta$ and

$$\frac{\partial(x,y)}{\partial(r,\theta)} = \begin{vmatrix} \dfrac{\partial x}{\partial r} & \dfrac{\partial x}{\partial \theta} \\ \dfrac{\partial y}{\partial r} & \dfrac{\partial y}{\partial \theta} \end{vmatrix} = \begin{vmatrix} \cos \theta & -r \sin \theta \\ \sin \theta & r \cos \theta \end{vmatrix}$$

$$= r \cos^2 \theta + r \sin^2 \theta = r$$

Accordingly, as the student already knows, $dx \, dy$ transforms into $r \, dr \, d\theta$. Again, to go from polar to rectangular coordinates, we put $r = \sqrt{x^2 + y^2}$, $\theta = \tan^{-1}(y/x)$ whence

$$\frac{\partial(r,\theta)}{\partial(x,y)} = \begin{vmatrix} \dfrac{x}{\sqrt{x^2 + y^2}} & \dfrac{y}{\sqrt{x^2 + y^2}} \\ \dfrac{-y}{x^2 + y^2} & \dfrac{x}{x^2 + y^2} \end{vmatrix}$$

$$= \frac{x^2 + y^2}{(x^2 + y^2)^{3/2}} = \frac{1}{r}$$

which is the reciprocal of first Jacobian. Thus from $dx \, dy$ we go to $r \, dr \, d\theta$ and from $r \, dr \, d\theta$ we go to $r \dfrac{1}{r} \, dx \, dy = dx \, dy$.

We are now prepared to derive some joint distributions by variate transformations.

Example 6-16. Given two random observations x_1, x_2 of the variate x, where $f(x) = 1/x^2$ $(1, \infty)$, find the joint and marginal distributions of u and v where $u = x_1 x_2$ and $v = x_1/x_2$.

Since the initial variates are independent, their joint distribution is given by

$$f(x_1,x_2) = f_1(x_1)f_2(x_2) = \frac{1}{x_1^2 x_2^2} \quad (1, \infty \text{ each})$$

Noticing that the denominator of this joint density function is equal to u^2, we may write

$$f(x_1, x_2) = \frac{1}{u^2}$$

Next, we must find the Jacobian. In this case, the labor of differentiation can be shortened by deriving the Jacobian of the new variates with respect to the initial ones and then taking the reciprocal. Hence we put

$$\frac{\partial(u,v)}{\partial(x_1,x_2)} = \begin{vmatrix} x_2 & x_1 \\ \dfrac{1}{x_2} & -\dfrac{x_1}{x_2{}^2} \end{vmatrix} = -2\frac{x_1}{x_2} = -2v$$

whereupon

$$J = -\frac{1}{2v} \qquad |J| = \frac{1}{2v}$$

and

$$g(u,v) = \frac{1}{2vu^2}$$

This gives us the equation for the joint density function, but we have yet to establish the admissible region. The general procedure is to express the initial variates in terms of the new ones and then determine the loci which the boundary curves of the initial region trace out in the new system of coordinates.

From the product of u and v, we get

$$uv = x_1{}^2 \qquad x_1 = \sqrt{uv}$$

and from the quotient we get

$$\frac{u}{v} = x_2{}^2 \qquad x_2 = \frac{\sqrt{u}}{\sqrt{v}}$$

Now the original boundaries were $x_1 = 1$, $x_2 = 1$. Accordingly, the new ones are

$$\sqrt{uv} = 1 \qquad \text{or} \qquad v = \frac{1}{u}$$

$$\frac{\sqrt{u}}{\sqrt{v}} = 1 \qquad \text{or} \qquad v = u$$

These curves, together with the fact that u cannot be less than unity (since this is the product of the minimum values of x_1 and x_2), describe the admissible region, indicated by shading in Fig. 6-14.

The complete statement of the joint distribution, then, is

$$g(u,v) = \frac{1}{2vu^2} \qquad \left(1 \leq u < \infty; \frac{1}{u} \leq v \leq u\right)$$

The marginal distribution of u is

$$g_1(u) = \frac{1}{2u^2} \int_{1/u}^{u} \frac{dv}{v} = \frac{\ln u}{u^2} \qquad (1, \infty)$$

However, the marginal distribution of v has two parts. Thus

Range I ($0 \leq v \leq 1$): $\qquad g_2(v) = \dfrac{1}{2v} \displaystyle\int_{1/v}^{\infty} \frac{du}{u^2} = \frac{1}{2}$

Range II ($1 \leq v < \infty$): $\qquad g_2(v) = \dfrac{1}{2v} \displaystyle\int_{v}^{\infty} \frac{du}{u^2} = \frac{1}{2v^2}$

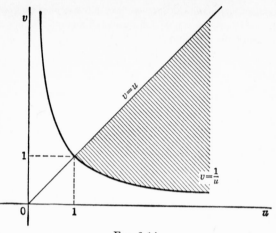

FIG. 6-14

Example 6-17. From a unit normal population, we draw two random observations x_1, x_2 and compute their sum $u = x_1 + x_2$ and their difference $v = x_1 - x_2$. Find the joint distribution of u and v which would be obtained if this experiment could be repeated for an indefinitely large number of independent trials. The initial variates are jointly distributed as follows:

$$f(x_1,x_2) = f_1(x_1)f_2(x_2) = \frac{1}{2\pi}\,e^{-(x_1{}^2+x_2{}^2)/2} \qquad (-\infty,\ \infty\ \text{each})$$

By definition, $x_1 + x_2 = u$; $x_1 - x_2 = v$. Therefore, by addition, $x_1 = (u + v)/2$ and by subtraction, $x_2 = (u - v)/2$. The Jacobian is

$$J = \begin{vmatrix} \tfrac{1}{2} & \tfrac{1}{2} \\ \tfrac{1}{2} & -\tfrac{1}{2} \end{vmatrix} = -\tfrac{1}{2}$$

and $|J| = \tfrac{1}{2}$. Also

$$x_1{}^2 + x_2{}^2 = \frac{u^2 + 2uv + v^2}{4} + \frac{u^2 - 2uv + v^2}{4}$$
$$= \frac{u^2 + v^2}{4}$$

whence the joint distribution of u and v is

$$g(u,v) = \frac{1}{4\pi}\,e^{-(u^2+v^2)/4} \qquad (-\infty,\ \infty\ \text{each})$$

Both variates have a total range of $(-\infty,\ \infty)$ because the original variates have this range, and the new ones can go to infinity in either direction with them. The fact that u and v have this range independently of each other may be seen by fixing the value of one of them, say u, at an arbitrary value c. Then

$$x_1 + x_2 = c \qquad x_2 = c - x_1 \qquad v = x_1 - x_2 = 2x_1 - c$$

and the latter function will vary from minus to plus infinity with x_1 irrespective of c. Similarly, fixing v at an arbitrary value k, we have $u = 2x_2 + k$, which will vary from minus to plus infinity with x_2 irrespective of k.

The marginal density functions can be written down at once by applying Theorem 6-3, or alternatively, by integrating the joint density function. Denoting the marginal densities by $g_1(u)$ and $g_2(v)$, we find

$$g_1(u) = \frac{1}{2\sqrt{\pi}} e^{-u^2/4} \quad (-\infty, \infty) \qquad g_2(v) = \frac{1}{2\sqrt{\pi}} e^{-v^2/4} \quad (-\infty, \infty)$$

Therefore $g(u,v) = g_1(u)g_2(v)$ and the variates are independent, even though constructed from the same data.

Example 6-18. Given x_1, x_2 as in Example 6-17, find the joint and marginal distributions of the sample average $\bar{x} = (x_1 + x_2)/2$ and the sum of squares of deviations from the sample average

$$S = (x_1 - \bar{x})^2 + (x_2 - \bar{x})^2$$

Also find the distribution of the variate $z = \bar{x}\sqrt{2}/\sqrt{S}$.

Here the original variates cannot be recovered uniquely from $\bar{x}$ and S, because the latter is quadratic. We therefore proceed indirectly. To simplify the expression for S, rewrite $x_1 - \bar{x}$ as follows:

$$x_1 - \bar{x} = x_1 - \frac{x_1 + x_2}{2} = \frac{x_1 - x_2}{2}$$

Similarly,

$$x_2 - \bar{x} = \frac{x_2 - x_1}{2} = -\frac{x_1 - x_2}{2}$$

Whence, by squaring and adding, we obtain

$$S = \frac{(x_1 - x_2)^2}{2}$$

Referring now to the constructed variates u, v of the previous example, we recognize that $\bar{x} = u/2$, $S = v^2/2$. But since u and v are independent, it follows that $\bar{x}$ and S, being pure functions of them, are also independent. Hence their marginal distributions, found by changing variables in $g_1(u)$ and $g_2(v)$, are

$$h_1(\bar{x}) = \frac{1}{\sqrt{\pi}} e^{-\bar{x}^2} \quad (-\infty, \infty)$$

and (from the intermediate distribution of v^2)

$$h_2(S) = \frac{1}{\sqrt{2\pi}} S^{-\frac{1}{2}} e^{-S/2} \quad (0, \infty)$$

Their joint distribution, of course, is

$$h(\bar{x},S) = \frac{1}{\pi\sqrt{2}} e^{-\bar{x}^2} S^{-\frac{1}{2}} e^{-S/2} \quad (-\infty < \bar{x} < \infty; 0 \leq S < \infty)$$

By inspection we see that the variate $\bar{x}$ is normally distributed with $\mu = 0$, $\sigma^2 = \frac{1}{2}$ (which checks with Theorem 6-4), while S is independent of $\bar{x}$ and is distributed as chi-square with *one* degree of freedom. Thus a derived variate can be distributed as chi-square even though it is not originally defined as the sum of squares of independent unit normal variates. In this case, of course, S is distributed as chi-square with one degree of freedom precisely because $v/\sqrt{2}$ is unit normal. And although we started with two unit normal variates, x_1 and x_2, we have only one degree of freedom for S. The other degree of freedom was absorbed by $\bar{x}$.

Turning now to z, its numerator $\bar{x}\sqrt{2}$ is readily seen to be a unit normal variate. The denominator, $\sqrt{S}$, is the root-mean-square variate with one degree of freedom.

Therefore, the variate $z = \bar{x}\sqrt{2}/\sqrt{S}$ is distributed as t with one degree of freedom:

$$f(z) = \frac{1}{\pi}\frac{1}{1+z^2} \qquad (-\infty, \infty)$$

Example 6-19. From a general normal population (μ, σ arbitrary), three observations x_1, x_2, x_3 are taken at random, and from them the quantities $u = x_1 - x_3$, $v = x_2 - x_3$ are computed. If an indefinite number of independent trials of this experiment could be made, find the joint distribution of u and v. Also find the distribution of the quotient $z = u/v$.

The distribution of single random observations from this population is

$$f(x) = \frac{1}{\sigma\sqrt{2\pi}}\,e^{-(x-\mu)^2/2\sigma^2} \qquad (-\infty, \infty)$$

Hence, the joint distribution of three random observations is

$$f(x_1,x_2,x_3) = \frac{1}{(\sigma\sqrt{2\pi})^3}\,e^{-Q} \qquad (-\infty, \infty \text{ all variates})$$

where
$$Q = \frac{(x_1 - \mu)^2 + (x_2 - \mu)^2 + (x_3 - \mu)^2}{2\sigma^2}$$

Although the problem prescribes two variates u, v we must introduce a third, say w, in order to make a complete change of variables. Otherwise, the Jacobian is undefined. This third variable can be any function which suits our convenience; for instance, one of the initial variables. The only restriction is that the original variables must be recoverable from the new. In this problem, a simple and convenient choice is

$$w = (x_1 - \mu) + (x_2 - \mu) + (x_3 - \mu)$$

Then, since we may write

$$u = x_1 - x_3 \equiv (x_1 - \mu) - (x_3 - \mu)$$
$$v = x_2 - x_3 \equiv (x_2 - \mu) - (x_3 - \mu)$$

the following results are readily obtained by substitution:

$$x_1 - \mu = \frac{2u - v + w}{3} \qquad x_2 - \mu = \frac{2v - u + w}{3} \qquad x_3 - \mu = \frac{w - u - v}{3}$$

The Jacobian (which we may simplify by adding the first two rows to the third) is

$$J = \begin{vmatrix} \tfrac{2}{3} & -\tfrac{1}{3} & \tfrac{1}{3} \\ -\tfrac{1}{3} & \tfrac{2}{3} & \tfrac{1}{3} \\ -\tfrac{1}{3} & -\tfrac{1}{3} & \tfrac{1}{3} \end{vmatrix} = \begin{vmatrix} \tfrac{2}{3} & -\tfrac{1}{3} & \tfrac{1}{3} \\ -\tfrac{1}{3} & \tfrac{2}{3} & \tfrac{1}{3} \\ 0 & 0 & 1 \end{vmatrix} = \tfrac{1}{3}$$

and the quadratic exponent of e becomes

$$Q = \frac{u^2 - uv + v^2}{3\sigma^2} + \frac{w^2}{6\sigma^2} = Q' + \frac{w^2}{6\sigma^2}$$

where Q' represents that part of Q which depends on u, v. By an argument similar to that used in Example 6-17, we conclude that all three variates range from $-\infty$ to ∞ without restriction. Therefore, their joint distribution is

$$g(u,v,w) = \frac{1}{3(\sigma\sqrt{2\pi})^3}\,e^{-Q'}e^{-w^2/6\sigma^2} \qquad (-\infty, \infty \text{ all})$$

and the joint distribution of u and v is

$$h(u,v) = \int_{-\infty}^{\infty} g(u,v,w)\, dw = \frac{\sqrt{3}}{6\pi\sigma^2} e^{-Q'} \qquad (-\infty,\ \infty \text{ each})$$

This time, we find the rather common result that two variates u, v derived from the same data are not independent but dependent. Nevertheless, the third variate w, as we have defined it, does turn out to be independent of u and v.

Now to obtain the distribution of $z = u/v$ we could follow the method used in previous sections, but to illustrate variate transformations let us choose a second variable $y = v$. Then $u = vz = yz$ and

$$J = \begin{vmatrix} z & y \\ 1 & 0 \end{vmatrix} = -y \qquad |J| = |y|$$

The quantity Q' in $h(u,v)$ becomes

$$Q' = \frac{y^2 z^2 - y^2 z + y^2}{3\sigma^2} = \frac{y^2(z^2 - z + 1)}{3\sigma^2}$$

and the joint distribution of y and z is

$$f(y,z) = \frac{\sqrt{3}}{6\pi\sigma^2} |y| e^{-y^2(z^2-z+1)/3\sigma^2} \qquad (-\infty,\ \infty \text{ each})$$

Since the integrand is symmetrical about zero (a result made possible by the absolute value of the Jacobian), we obtain, for the marginal distribution of z,

$$g(z) = \frac{\sqrt{3}}{6\pi\sigma^2} \int_0^{\infty} 2y e^{-y^2(z^2-z+1)/3\sigma^2}\, dy$$

$$= \frac{\sqrt{3}}{2\pi} \frac{1}{z^2 - z + 1} \qquad (-\infty,\ \infty)$$

Therefore the distribution of z is independent of the values of μ and σ. Because $h(u,v)$ is a symmetrical function of u and v, we would obtain the same distribution for the alternative quotient v/u—a fact which is also verified by changing from z to its reciprocal in $g(z)$.

By completing the square in the density function of z, we obtain the following equivalent expression

$$g(z) = \frac{\sqrt{3}}{2\pi} \frac{1}{(z - \frac{1}{2})^2 + \frac{3}{4}} \qquad (-\infty,\ \infty)$$

which shows that the modal value of z is $\frac{1}{2}$. At first sight this fact is puzzling because it is difficult to see intuitively why the value $\frac{1}{2}$ has any special significance for the variate considered. One way of understanding how this result comes about is to define an analogous quotient

$$q = \frac{x_1 - x_2}{x_3 - x_2}$$

and note the identity

$$z \equiv \frac{x_1 - x_3}{x_2 - x_3} \equiv 1 - \frac{(x_1 - x_2)}{x_3 - x_2} \equiv 1 - q$$

From the formal interchangeability of the variates x_1, x_2, x_3 it is obvious that q has exactly the same distribution as z. Hence, both must have the same modal value m. On the other hand, if the mode of q is m, that of z must be $1 - m$, since $z = 1 - q$.

Therefore

$$m = 1 - m \quad \text{and} \quad m = \tfrac{1}{2}$$

Example 6-20. The variates x_1, x_2 are said to be "normally correlated" when their joint density function is of the form

$$f(x_1,x_2) = ke^{-Q/2} \qquad (-\infty, \ \infty \ \text{each variate}) \qquad (6\text{-}18)$$

where

$$k = \frac{1}{2\pi\sigma_1\sigma_2 \sqrt{1 - \rho^2}}$$

$$Q = \frac{1}{1 - \rho^2} \left[\frac{(x_1 - \mu_1)^2}{\sigma_1{}^2} - \frac{2\rho(x_1 - \mu_1)(x_2 - \mu_2)}{\sigma_1\sigma_2} + \frac{(x_2 - \mu_2)^2}{\sigma_2{}^2} \right]$$

It can be shown that the marginal distribution of x_1 is normal with parameters μ_1, σ_1 while that of x_2 is normal with parameters μ_2, σ_2. The parameter ρ is called the *coefficient of linear correlation*. In the present context, this quantity must be less than unity in absolute value, but in connection with the general theory of correlation, the upper limit unity is theoretically possible. The locus of points having a fixed probability density can be obtained by setting Q equal to a constant. By analytical geometry, it can be shown that this locus is an ellipse. Let us determine the probability P that a random point x_1', x_2' will fall outside of any given contour ellipse corresponding to a fixed value of Q, say $Q = C_1$. While this can be done by geometric considerations, we shall use the method of variate transformations. In either approach, the trick is to notice that the probability in question can be obtained in terms of the distribution function of Q.

Since Q is a function of the variates x_1, x_2 it is a random variable itself. If a random point falls outside of a given contour ellipse $Q = C_1$, then there is another contour ellipse $Q = C_2$, with larger semiaxes, which passes through it. Hence the probability that x_1', x_2' fall outside of $Q = C_1$ is exactly equal to the probability that $Q > C_1$.

To obtain the distribution of Q let us first make the transformation

$$y_1 = \frac{x_1 - \mu_1}{\sigma_1} \qquad y_2 = \frac{x_2 - \mu_2}{\sigma_2}$$

The Jacobian of x_1, x_2 with respect to y_1, y_2 is $\sigma_1\sigma_2$ and the quadratic expression becomes

$$Q = \frac{1}{1 - \rho^2} (y_1{}^2 - 2\rho y_1 y_2 + y_2{}^2)$$

Thus the joint distribution of y_1, y_2 is

$$g(y_1,y_2) = \frac{1}{2\pi \sqrt{1 - \rho^2}} e^{-Q/2} \qquad (-\infty, \ \infty \ \text{each})$$

Next, complete the square in Q by putting

$$z_1 = \frac{y_1 - \rho y_2}{\sqrt{1 - \rho^2}} \qquad z_2 = y_2$$

This gives

$$Q = z_1{}^2 + z_2{}^2$$

and since the Jacobian of the y's with respect to the z's is equal to $\sqrt{1 - \rho^2}$, the joint distribution of the z's reduces to

$$h(z_1,z_2) = \frac{1}{2\pi} e^{-(z_1{}^2 + z_2{}^2)/2} \qquad (-\infty, \ \infty \ \text{each})$$

Therefore, z_1 and z_2 are independent unit normal variates, and Q, being equal to their sum of squares, is distributed as chi-square with two degrees of freedom. Consequently, denoting the density function and distribution function of Q by $\lambda(Q)$ and $\Lambda(Q)$, respectively, we have

$$\lambda(Q) = \tfrac{1}{2}e^{-Q/2} \qquad (0 \leq Q < \infty) \tag{6-19}$$
$$\Lambda(Q) = 1 - e^{-Q/2} \qquad (0 \leq Q < \infty) \tag{6-20}$$

whereupon
$$P = 1 - \Lambda(C_1) = e^{-C_1/2} \tag{6-21}$$

This answers the original question. As far as the marginal distributions of x_1 and x_2 are concerned, the fact that the distribution of $y_2 \equiv z_2$ is unit normal implies immediately that x_2 is normal with parameters μ_2, σ_2. By interchanging subscripts, we also infer that x_1 is normal with parameters μ_1, σ_1.

Example 6-21. As an exercise in establishing a multivariate admissible region, let us derive the joint distribution of y_1, y_2, y_3 where

$$y_1 = x_1 + x_2 \qquad y_2 = x_2 + x_3 \qquad y_3 = x_1 + x_3$$

given that the x's are random observations of the variate x, the distribution of which is $f(x) = e^{-x}$ $(0, \infty)$. Here the problem is almost wholly one of determining the region of definition.

Solving for x_1, x_2, x_3 in terms of y_1, y_2, y_3, we readily obtain

$$x_1 = \frac{y_1 - y_2 + y_3}{2} \qquad x_2 = \frac{y_1 + y_2 - y_3}{2} \qquad x_3 = \frac{y_2 + y_3 - y_1}{2}$$

and the Jacobian of the x's with respect to the y's is $\tfrac{1}{2}$. Since the joint density function of the x's is

$$f(x_1,x_2,x_3) = e^{-(x_1+x_2+x_3)} \qquad (0, \infty \text{ each})$$

and $x_1 + x_2 + x_3 = (y_1 + y_2 + y_3)/2$, the joint density function of the y's is

$$g(y_1,y_2,y_3) = \tfrac{1}{2}e^{-(y_1+y_2+y_3)/2}$$

The boundary of the admissible region in the x system is given by $x_1 = 0$, $x_2 = 0$, $x_3 = 0$. Hence, substituting for the x's, the boundary of the y system will be given by the planes

$$y_1 - y_2 + y_3 = 0 \qquad y_1 + y_2 - y_3 = 0 \qquad y_2 + y_3 - y_1 = 0$$

These planes intersect at the origin and cut out an infinite inclined wedge having semi-infinite rectangular cross sections (Fig. 6-15) when cut by any plane $y_1 = $ constant. Therefore, when y_2 lies in the range $0 \leq y_2 \leq y_1$, the range of y_3 is $y_1 - y_2 \leq y_3 \leq y_1 + y_2$, but when y_2 lies in the range $y_1 \leq y_2 < \infty$, the range of y_3 is $y_2 - y_1 \leq y_3 \leq y_2 + y_1$. Accordingly, we may express the joint distribution as follows:

$$g(y_1,y_2,y_3) = \frac{e^{-(y_1+y_2+y_3)/2}}{2} \qquad \begin{array}{l} (0 \leq y_1 < \infty; 0 \leq y_2 \leq y_1; \\ y_1 - y_2 \leq y_3 \leq y_1 + y_2; y_1 \leq y_2 < \infty; \\ y_2 - y_1 \leq y_3 \leq y_2 + y_1) \end{array}$$

This formulation may be verified by deriving the marginal distribution of y_1. From Theorem 6-2 we know that the correct result is $g_1(y_1) = y_1 e^{-y_1}$ $(0, \infty)$. From the joint distribution we obtain

$$g_1(y_1) = \int_0^{y_1} \left[\int_{y_1-y_2}^{y_1+y_2} g(y_1,y_2,y_3)\, dy_3 \right] dy_2 + \int_{y_1}^{\infty} \left[\int_{y_2-y_1}^{y_2+y_1} g(y_1,y_2,y_3)\, dy_3 \right] dy_2$$
$$(0, \infty)$$

The integration is easy to carry out and the result is

$$g_1(y_1) = y_1 e^{-y_1} \qquad (0, \infty)$$

which checks. The reader is invited to test his own understanding by deriving the marginal distribution of y_2 or y_3 from $g(y_1, y_2, y_3)$.

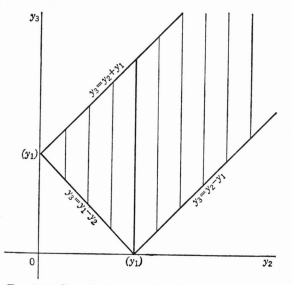

FIG. 6-15. Cross section made by plane $y_1 =$ constant.

6-14. Collective Significance.

The control of extraneous sources of variation in an experiment sometimes imposes such severe restrictions on the sample size that it is necessary to pool the results of several independent samples in order to obtain enough data for a satisfactory test of significance. Under such circumstances, it rarely happens that the samples can be legitimately lumped together, but it is often possible to combine the respective probabilities into a single index of collective significance. Let us see how this can be done for a *continuous variate*.

Suppose that the criterion of significance can be regarded as the deviation (either algebraic or absolute) of a continuous variate x from an appropriate norm and that this variate has a density function $f(x)$. We may assume that the significant values lie toward the right-hand extreme of the distribution of x, for this can be brought about by a change of variable. Associated with any observed value x_1, the measure of significance $S(x_1)$ then consists of the area under the density curved beyond x_1 (Fig. 6-16). It is readily seen that $S(x)$ itself is a random variable, and it follows from Sec. 6-5 that it is rectangular in the interval $(0, 1)$.

If two independent tests yield significance measures S_1 and S_2, respec-

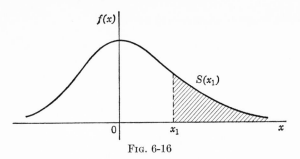

Fig. 6-16

tively, the probability of the joint event is the product S_1S_2, which is the chance of drawing a deviation at least as great as x_1 on the first trial and a deviation at least as great as x_2 on the second trial. What we want, therefore, is the chance that any pair of samples will yield a joint probability less than or equal to the actual product S_1S_2. Construct a rectangular coordinate system as in Fig. 6-17. Under the null hypothesis, the points (S_1, S_2), representing the results of any pair of tests, are uniformly distributed over the unit square in the first quadrant. The rectangular hyperbola $S_1S_2 = \lambda$ defines the locus of all pairs of test results having equal likelihood λ. The combined significance measure of any pair of tests for which $S_1S_2 = \lambda$ is equal to the area of that portion of the unit square which lies below the hyperbola, for this area represents the total

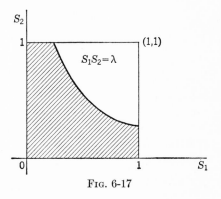

Fig. 6-17

probability of obtaining some pair of values for which the likelihood is equal to or less than λ. Denoting the combined significance by P, we have

$$P = 1 - \int_\lambda^1 \int_{\lambda/S_1}^1 dS_1\, dS_2 = \lambda(1 - \ln \lambda) \qquad (6\text{-}22)$$

Similarly, for three independent tests the sample space is confined to a unit cube, within which all points have unit density. The likelihood contour is the hyperbolic surface $S_1S_2S_3 = \lambda$ and the combined significance measure is

$$P = 1 - \int_\lambda^1 \int_{\lambda/S_1}^1 \int_{\lambda/S_1S_2}^1 dS_1\, dS_2\, dS_3 = \lambda \left[1 - \ln \lambda + \frac{(\ln \lambda)^2}{2} \right] \qquad (6\text{-}23)$$

In general, for n independent tests, it is easy to show that the combined significance measure is

$$P = \lambda \left[1 - \ln \lambda + \frac{(\ln \lambda)^2}{2!} - \frac{(\ln \lambda)^3}{3!} + \cdots + (-1)^{n-1} \frac{(\ln \lambda)^{n-1}}{(n-1)!} \right]$$
(6-24)

where λ equals the product of the S's.

Since very good tables of natural logarithms are available, P can be computed directly from the foregoing equation. However, Eq. (6-24) has a remarkable relationship to the distribution of chi-square with $2n$ degrees of freedom and, as a consequence, most of the arithmetic can be avoided by using tables of the chi-square integral. For $2n$ degrees of freedom [see Eq. (6-9)], the density function of chi-square is

$$g(\chi)^2 = \frac{1}{2^n \Gamma(n)} (\chi^2)^{n-1} e^{-\chi^2/2} \qquad (0, \infty)$$
(6-25)

and it turns out that the corresponding probability integral is

$$\int_A^\infty g(\chi^2) \, d\chi^2 = e^{-A/2} \left[1 + (A/2) + \frac{(A/2)^2}{2!} + \frac{(A/2)^3}{3!} + \cdots \right.$$
$$\left. + \frac{(A/2)^{n-1}}{(n-1)!} \right] \quad (6-26)$$

Accordingly, if we are considering the combined significance of separate tests, we make the substitution $A = -2(\ln \lambda)$, and Eq. (6-26) becomes identical with Eq. (6-24). Therefore, the combined significance measure P can be evaluated from tables of the chi-square integral using $2n$ degrees of freedom and looking up under $-2(\ln \lambda)$. A more sophisticated way of establishing this connection with chi-square is outlined in Exercise 22.

Example 6-22. Suppose that the test variate x is distributed as

$$f(x) = 12(4 + x^2)^{-5/2}$$

$(-\infty, \infty)$ and the significance measure is

$$S(u) = \int_u^\infty f(x) \, dx = \frac{1}{2} \left[1 - \frac{u(6 + u^2)}{(4 + u^2)^{3/2}} \right]$$

Three independent samples yield

$$x_1 = 1.42 \qquad x_2 = 1.61 \qquad x_3 = 1.79$$
$$S_1 = S(x_1) = .114 \qquad S_2 = .091 \qquad S_3 = .074$$

Thus $\lambda = S_1 S_2 S_3 = 7.68 \times 10^{-4}$ $\ln \lambda = -7.172$ $(\ln \lambda)^2 = 51.438$

and the collective significance is

$$P = 7.68 \times 10^{-4}(1 + 7.172 + 25.719)$$
$$= 7.68 \times 10^{-4}(33.891)$$
$$= 2.60 \times 10^{-2} = .026$$

Alternatively, we set chi-square equal to $-2(\ln \lambda) = 14.344$, and referring to standard tables for six degrees of freedom, the nearest tabulated value we find is 14.45, for which $P = .025$.

The formula (6-24) derived for a continuous variate does not hold for a discrete variate. However, the general approach is much the same, as the following example illustrates.

TABLE 6-1. POSSIBLE SAMPLE VALUES YIELDING $S_1S_2 \leq (\tfrac{1}{2})^7$

Values		Probabilities		Joint probabilities
x_1	x_2	x_1	x_2	
0	≥ 7	$f(0)$	$S(7)$	$f(0)S(7) = (\tfrac{1}{2})^8$
1	≥ 6	$f(1)$	$S(6)$	$f(1)S(6) = (\tfrac{1}{2})^8$
2	≥ 5	$f(2)$	$S(5)$	$f(2)S(5) = (\tfrac{1}{2})^8$
3	≥ 4	$f(3)$	$S(4)$	$f(3)S(4) = (\tfrac{1}{2})^8$
4	≥ 3	$f(4)$	$S(3)$	$f(4)S(3) = (\tfrac{1}{2})^8$
5	≥ 2	$f(5)$	$S(2)$	$f(5)S(2) = (\tfrac{1}{2})^8$
6	≥ 1	$f(6)$	$S(1)$	$f(6)S(1) = (\tfrac{1}{2})^8$
≥ 7	≥ 0	$S(7)$	$S(0)$	$S(7)S(0) = (\tfrac{1}{2})^7$

Total probability $P = 7(\tfrac{1}{2})^8 + (\tfrac{1}{2})^7 = \tfrac{9}{256}$

Example 6-23. Suppose a discrete variate x is distributed as $f(x) = (\tfrac{1}{2})^{x+1}$ $(x = 0, 1, 2, \ldots , \infty)$ and the measure of significance is

$$S(u) = \sum_{u}^{\infty} f(x) = (\tfrac{1}{2})^u$$

Two independent samples yield

$$x_1 = 3 \qquad S_1 = S(x_1) = (\tfrac{1}{2})^3$$
$$x_2 = 4 \qquad S_2 = S(x_2) = (\tfrac{1}{2})^4$$
$$\text{Joint probability} = S_1S_2 = (\tfrac{1}{2})^7$$

To evaluate the combined significance of the two samples, we determine the total probability that any pair of samples would yield a joint probability less than or equal to $(\tfrac{1}{2})^7$. The possible situations and corresponding probabilities are exhibited in Table 6-1. From this table we find that the combined significance is

$$P = 7(\tfrac{1}{2})^8 + (\tfrac{1}{2})^7 = \tfrac{9}{256} \approx .035$$

EXERCISES

1. Untanned hides are bought by the pound, but finished leather is sold by the square foot. The following table, showing the distribution of poundage, refers to a particular shipment of 500 hides, which were shaved to a uniform thickness before

x	7	8	9	10	11	12	13	14
$F(x)$	.000	.026	.178	.386	.616	.826	.970	1.000

being weighed.   (a) Given that the shaved hides weighed .75 lb per sq ft, what proportion of the hides had areas not exceeding 12 sq ft?   (b) Areas greater than 16 sq ft?

Ans. (a) .178, (b) .174.

✗   **2.** Expressed in appropriate monetary units, the distribution of yearly income in a certain population is given by $f(x) = \dfrac{3}{2,500} x(10 - x)^2$ (0, 10).   (a) What proportion of the population have incomes below the mode?   (b) What would the distribution be if everybody's income were exactly doubled?

$$Ans. \ (a) \ 11\tfrac{1}{2}7, \ (b) \ g(y) = \frac{3}{40,000} y(20 - y)^2 \ (0, \ 20).$$

In the following three exercises, sketch $f(x)$ and derive and sketch $g(y)$, the corresponding density function of y.

✗   **3.** $f(x) = 1/\pi \ (-\pi/2, \pi/2)$; $y = \sin x$.
    Ans. The distribution of x is rectangular; that of y is U-shaped. $g(y) = 1/\pi \sqrt{1 - y^2}$ $(-1, 1)$.

✗   **4.** $f(x) = 1/\pi(1 + x^2) \ (-\infty, \infty)$; $y = \tan^{-1} x$.
    Ans. The distribution of x is bell-shaped; that of y is rectangular. $g(y) = 1/\pi$ $(-\pi/2, \pi/2)$.

    5. $f(x) = (1/\sqrt{2\pi}) \ x^{-2} e^{-1/(2x^2)} \ (-\infty, \infty)$; $y = 1/x$.
    Ans. The distribution of x is bimodal; that of y is bell-shaped. $g(y) = (1/\sqrt{2\pi})$ $e^{-y^2/2} \ (-\infty, \infty)$.

    6. Find the exact distribution of the variate w derived from a gamma variate x by the Wilson-Hilferty transformation, $w = [x/\beta(\alpha + 1)]^{1/3}$.

$$Ans. \ g(w) = [3(\alpha + 1)^{\alpha+1}/\Gamma(\alpha + 1)]w^{3\alpha+2}e^{-(\alpha+1)w^3} \ (0, \infty).$$

✗   **7.** Find the distribution of $y = x^2$ given that $f(x) = \dfrac{1}{\pi}\dfrac{1}{1 + x^2} \ (-\infty, \infty)$.

$$Ans. \ g(y) = \frac{1}{\pi}\frac{1}{(1 + y) \sqrt{y}} \ (0, \infty).$$

    8. Find the distribution of $y = |x|$ given that $f(x) = \tfrac{1}{3} \ (-1 \le x \le 2)$.
      Ans. $g(y) = \tfrac{2}{3} \ (0 \le y \le 1)$; $g(y) = \tfrac{1}{3} \ (1 < y \le 2)$.

    9. In a circle of radius R a chord AB is drawn (refer to Figs. 2-1a and 2-2a). The tangent CAD is constructed at the point A and the angle ϕ is taken as the angle DAB. Also, the perpendicular bisector OH of the chord is constructed and the point of intersection is denoted by X.   (a) If the angle ϕ is rectangularly distributed over the range $(0, \pi)$, find the distribution of $x = OX$.   (b) If x is rectangularly distributed over the range $(0, R)$, find the distribution of ϕ, given that the two supplementary values of this angle associated with a fixed value of x are equally likely.   (c) Using (a) find $P(x \le R/2)$.   (d) Using (b) find $P(\pi/3 \le \phi \le 2\pi/3)$.

✗   *Ans.* (a) $g(x) = 2/\pi \sqrt{R^2 - x^2}$ (0, R); (b) $h(\phi) = \tfrac{1}{2} \sin \phi(0, \pi)$; (c) $\tfrac{1}{3}$; (d) $\tfrac{1}{2}$.
    10. If two observations x_1, x_2 of the variate x are taken at random and $f(x) = 1$ (0, 1), find the density function and distribution function of the product $y = x_1 x_2$.
      Ans. $h(y) = -\ln y$ (0, 1); $H(y) = y(1 - \ln y)$ (0, 1).

    11. Two random observations x_1, x_2 of the rectangular variate x are taken and their difference $y = x_1 - x_2$ is computed. Assuming that this experiment could be repeated for an infinite number of independent trials, and the range of x is (0, 1), find (a) the distribution of y and (b) from this, the distribution of $z = |y|$.   (c) Sketch both.
      Ans. (a) $g(y) = 1 + y \ (-1 \le y \le 0)$; $g(y) = 1 - y \ (0 \le y \le 1)$.   (b) $h(z) = 2(1 - z)$ (0, 1).   (c) Both are triangular; the former, is an isosceles triangle, the latter, a right triangle.

12. Independent variates x and y are distributed as follows: $f_1(x) = 12x^2(1 - x)$ $(0, 1); f_2(y) = 2y$ $(0, 1)$. Find the distribution of the product $u = xy$.
$$Ans. \ h(u) = 12u(1 - u)^2 \ (0, 1).$$

13. Find the distribution of the quotient of two independent unit normal variates. [CAUTION: Remember the absolute value of the derivative.]
$$Ans. \ h(u) = 1/\pi(1 + u^2) \ (- \infty, \ \infty).$$

14. The variates x and y are jointly distributed as follows: $f(x,y) = 24 \ xy(1 - x)^2$ $(0, 1 \text{ each})$. Show that they are independent and find the distribution of their product $v = xy$.
$$Ans. \ h(v) = 12v(4v - v^2 - 2 \ln v - 3) \ (0, 1).$$

15. From the population corresponding to $f(x) = e^{-x}$ $(0, \infty)$ two random observations are taken. Find the distribution of v, the square root of their sum.
$$Ans. \ g(v) = 2v^3 e^{-v^2} \ (0, \infty).$$

16. Derive the distribution of the product $v = x_1 x_2$ of two random observations of the variate x, where $f(x) = 6x(1 - x)$ $(0, 1)$.
$$Ans. \ g(v) = -36v[(1 + v) \ln v + 2(1 - v)] \ (0, 1).$$

17. Independent variates x, y are exponentially distributed with unequal parameters $f_1(x) = ae^{-ax}$ $(0, \infty); f_2(y) = be^{-by}$ $(0, \infty); (0 < b < a)$. Find the distribution of the sum $z = x + y$.
$$Ans. \ h(z) = [ab/(a - b)](e^{-bz} - e^{-az}) \ (0, \infty).$$

18. Independent gamma variates x, y with unequal values of β are distributed as follows: $f_1(x) = xe^{-x}$ $(0, \infty); f_2(y) = 4 \ ye^{-2y}$ $(0, \infty)$. Find the distribution of their sum $z = x + y$.
$$Ans. \ h(z) = 4(z - 2)e^{-z} + 4(z + 2)e^{-2z} \ (0, \infty).$$

19. Random observations x_1, x_2 are taken on the variate x, the distribution of which is $f(x) = \dfrac{1}{x^2}$ $(1, \infty)$. Find the distribution of their quotient $v = x_1/x_2$.
$$Ans. \ q(v) = \tfrac{1}{2} \ (0 \le v \le 1); \ q(v) = 1/2v^2 \ (1 \le v < \infty).$$

20. Two independent rectangular variates x and y are distributed as follows:

$$f(x) = \tfrac{1}{2} \quad (1, 3) \qquad g(y) = \tfrac{1}{3} \quad (5, 8)$$

Derive the distribution of their sum $z = x + y$.
$$Ans. \ h(z) = (z - 6)/6 \ (6 \le z \le 8); \ h(z) = \tfrac{1}{3} \ (8 \le z \le 9); \ h(z) = (11 - z)/6$$
$(9 \le z \le 11)$.

21. The variate x has the Cauchy distribution $f(x) = 1/\pi(1 + x^2)$ $(- \infty, \infty)$. If two observations x_1, x_2 are taken at random and added together, find the distribution of their sum $u = x_1 + x_2$ and from this deduce the distribution of their average $\bar{x} = u/2$. Integrate as a rational fraction making use of the identity

$$\frac{1}{(1 + x^2)[1 + (u - x)^2]}$$
$$\equiv \frac{1}{u^2(u^2 + 4)} \left[\frac{u^2}{1 + x^2} + \frac{2ux}{1 + x^2} + \frac{u^2}{1 + (x - u)^2} - \frac{2u(x - u)}{1 + (x - u)^2} \right]$$

Indeterminate forms can be avoided by combining logarithms before substituting limits of integration.
$$Ans. \ g(u) = 2/\pi(u^2 + 4) \ (- \infty, \ \infty); \ h(\bar{x}) = 1/\pi(1 + \bar{x}^2) \ (- \infty, \ \infty).$$

22. The variate x is rectangularly distributed over the range $(0, 1)$. (a) Derive the distribution of $y = -2 \ln x$ and relate to chi-square. (b) Let $x_1, x_2, \ldots, x_n$ be random observations of x, define y_i as $-2 \ln x_i$ $(i = 1, 2, \ldots, n)$ and let z denote the sum $y_1 + y_2 + \cdots + y_n$. By immediate deduction from (a) state the distribution of z.
$$Ans. \ (a) \ g(y) = \tfrac{1}{2}e^{-y/2} \ (0, \infty).$$ Hence y is distributed as chi-square with two degrees of freedom. (b) z is distributed as chi-square with $2n$ degrees of freedom.

23. Find the distribution of the quotient $u = x/y$ of the independent variates x and y which are distributed as follows:

$$f_1(x) = \frac{2}{\sqrt{2\pi}} e^{-x^2/2} \quad (0, \infty) \qquad f_2(y) = 2y^3 e^{-y^2} \quad (0, \infty)$$

By comparing distributions, identify u as $|t|/\sqrt{2}$ where t has the t distribution with four degrees of freedom.

Ans. $h(u) = 6/(2 + u^2)^{5/2}$ $(0, \infty)$. The same distribution is obtained with $v = |t|/\sqrt{2}$ if t has four degrees of freedom.

24. A variate x has the F distribution with a and b degrees of freedom and another unrelated variate y has the F distribution with b and a degrees of freedom. (a) If one had a table giving $P(x \geq c)$ for an arbitrary value $c > 0$, how could this be used to find $P(y \leq 1/c)$? (b) As a consequence of this property, show at once that in case $a = b$, the median of the F distribution is unity.

Ans. (a) By a change to reciprocal the two probabilities are found to be identical. (b) In this case x and y have the same distribution, hence $F(1/c) = 1 - F(c)$. But for the median, $1 - F(c) = F(c)$. Therefore $F(c) = F(1/c)$ and $c = 1/c = 1$.

25. The variates x and y are jointly distributed as follows:

$$f(x,y) = 24y(1 - x) \qquad (0 \leq x \leq 1, 0 \leq y \leq x)$$

Find the distribution of the quotient $z = y/x$. *Ans.* $h(z) = 2z$ $(0, 1)$.

26. Derive the distribution of $z = xy$ given that $f(x,y) = xe^{-x(1+y)}$ $(0, \infty$ each).

Ans. $g(z) = e^{-z}$ $(0, \infty)$.

27. Derive the distribution of $u = x/y$, given that $f(x,y) = 120\ x(y - x)(1 - y)$ $(0 \leq x \leq y; 0 \leq y \leq 1)$. *Ans.* $h(u) = 6u(1 - u)$ $(0, 1)$.

28. Derive the distribution of the function $z = y(1 + x)$ given that x and y are jointly distributed as follows: $f(x,y) = \frac{4}{7}(1 + y + xy)$ $(0, 1$ each).

Ans. $h(z) = [(4 \ln 2)/7](1 + z)$ $(0 \leq z \leq 1)$; $h(z) = \frac{4}{7}(1 + z)(\ln 2 - \ln z)$ $(1 \leq z \leq 2)$.

29. Find the distribution of the sum $s = x + y$ given that $f(x,y) = 6xy(2 - x - y)$ $(0, 1$ each). *Ans.* $h(s) = s^3(2 - s)$ $(0, 1)$; $h(s) = (2 - s)^2(s^2 + 2s - 2)$ $(1, 2)$.

30. The variates x, y are jointly distributed as follows: $f(x,y) = (2/\pi)(1 - x^2 - y^2)$ $(0 \leq x^2 + y^2 \leq 1)$. Find the joint distribution of x and r and obtain the marginal distribution of r, where $r = \sqrt{x^2 + y^2}$.

Ans. $g(x,r) = \dfrac{4}{\pi} \dfrac{r(1 - r^2)}{\sqrt{r^2 - x^2}}$ $(-1 \leq x \leq 1; |x| \leq r \leq 1)$; $h(r) = 4r(1 - r^2)$ $(0, 1)$.

31. From an initial pair of variables x, y a new pair u, v is derived by the transformation $u = x + y$, $v = x/y$. Show that the Jacobian of u, v with respect to x, y is $-(x + y)/y^2$. By an independent derivation show that the Jacobian of x, y with respect to u, v is the reciprocal of the first Jacobian and can be expressed as $-u/(1 + v)^2$.

32. Given $u = x + y$, $v = x/(x + y)$ find both Jacobians.

Ans. $\partial(u,v)/\partial(x,y) = -1/(x + y)$; $\partial(x,y)/\partial(u,v) = -u$.

33. Find the joint distribution of r and θ where $r = \sqrt{x^2 + y^2}$, $\theta = \tan^{-1}(y/x)$ given that x and y are jointly distributed as follows:

$$f(x,y) = \frac{2}{\pi}(1 - x^2 - y^2) \qquad (0 \leq x^2 + y^2 \leq 1)$$

Ans. $g(r,\theta) = (2r/\pi)(1 - r^2)$ $(0 \leq r \leq 1; 0 \leq \theta \leq 2\pi)$; $h(r) = 4r(1 - r^2)$ $(0, 1)$.

34. Two observations x_1, x_2 of the variate x, the distribution of which is $f(x) = e^{-x}$ $(0, \infty)$ are taken at random and their sum $u = x_1 + x_2$ and their quotient $v = x_1/x_2$ are computed. Derive the joint and marginal distributions of u and v in repeated independent trials. Are u and v independent?

Ans. $g(u,v) = ue^{-u}/(1 + v)^2$ $(0, \infty$ each); $g_1(u) = ue^{-u}$ $(0, \infty)$; $g_2(v) = 1/(1 + v)^2$ $(0, \infty)$.

35. Independent variates x and y are distributed as chi-square with $2a$ and $2b$ degrees of freedom respectively. Derive the joint distribution of u and v and the marginal distribution of v where $u = x + y$, $v = x/(x + y)$.

Ans. $g(u,v) = [1/2^{a+b}\Gamma(a)\Gamma(b)]u^{a+b-1}e^{-u/2}v^{a-1}(1 - v)^{b-1}$ $(0 \leq u < \infty, \ 0 \leq v \leq 1)$; $h(v) = [1/\beta(a,b)]v^{a-1}(1 - v)^{b-1}$ $(0, 1)$.

36. Independent variates x, y are distributed as follows:

$$f_1(x) = \frac{1}{\sqrt{2\pi}}\, x^{\frac{1}{2}}e^{-x/2} \qquad (0, \infty) \qquad\qquad f_2(y) = \frac{1}{\sqrt{2\pi}}\, y^{-\frac{1}{2}}e^{-y/2} \qquad (0, \infty)$$

Derive the joint distribution of their sum $u = x + y$ and their difference $v = x - y$.

$$Ans. \ g(u,v) = \frac{1}{4\pi}\sqrt{\frac{u + v}{u - v}}\, e^{-u/2} \ (0 \leq u < \infty; \ -u \leq v \leq u).$$

37. The variates $u = x_1 + x_2$, $v = x_1 - x_2$ are constructed from two random observations x_1, x_2 of the variate x, distributed as $f(x) = e^{-x}$ $(0, \infty)$. Find the joint distribution of u and v in repeated independent trials and find the marginal distribution of v.

Ans. $g(u,v) = \frac{1}{2}e^{-u}$ $(0 \leq u < \infty; \ -u \leq v \leq u)$, $h(v) = \frac{1}{2}e^{-|v|}$ $(-\infty, \infty)$.

38. Given random observations x_1, x_2, x_3 from a unit normal population. Find (a) the joint distribution of y_1, y_2, y_3, (b) the marginal distribution of each, and (c) the distribution of $z = y_1^2 + y_2^2 + y_3^2$ where

$$y_1 = \frac{x_1 + x_2 + x_3}{\sqrt{3}} \qquad y_2 = \frac{x_1 - x_2}{\sqrt{2}} \qquad y_3 = \frac{2x_3 - x_1 - x_2}{\sqrt{6}}$$

Make free use of inspection and of results proved in the text.

Ans. (a) $g(y_1,y_2,y_3) = [1/(\sqrt{2\pi})^3]e^{-Q/2}$ $(-\infty, \infty$ each) where $Q = y_1^2 + y_2^2 + y_3^2$; (b) marginal distributions are unit normal; (c) hence z is distributed as chi-square with three degrees of freedom, that is, $h(z) = (1/\sqrt{2\pi})\, z^{\frac{1}{2}}e^{-z/2}$ $(0, \infty)$.

39. Establish the following properties of special cases of the chi-square, t, and F distributions:

(a) If x is distributed as chi-square with an even number of degrees of freedom $2n$, then the density function can be integrated explicitly to yield the closed expression

$$P(x \geq 2u) = e^{-u}\left[1 + u + \frac{u^2}{2!} + \frac{u^3}{3!} + \cdots + \frac{u^{n-1}}{(n - 1)!} \right]$$

(b) If x is distributed as t with n degrees of freedom, then x^2 is distributed as F with 1 and n degrees of freedom.

(c) If x is distributed as F with two and n degrees of freedom, then the density function can be integrated explicitly to yield

$$P(x \geq k) = \left(1 + \frac{2k}{n} \right)^{-n/2}$$

40. The variate x is rectangularly distributed over the interval $(0, 1)$. (a) Find the distribution of the range R in repeated random samples of n observations. (b) Determine the probability that the range of a sample of five will exceed .5.

Ans. (a) $p(R) = n(n - 1)R^{n-2}(1 - R)$ $(0, 1)$; (b) .8125.

41. Find the distribution of the range R of four random observations of the triangular variate x, where $f(x) = 2x$ $(0, 1)$.

         Ans. $p(R) = \frac{8}{5}R^2(1 - R)^2(24 - 12R + 2R^2 + R^3)$ $(0, 1)$.

42. Derive the distribution of the range R for random samples of three observations of the beta variate x where $f(x) = 6x(1 - x)$ $(0, 1)$.

         Ans. $p(R) = \frac{36}{35}R(1 - R)^3(9 + 27R + 19R^2 - 15R^3 - 5R^4)$ $(0, 1)$.

43. In most applications of the F test the appropriate critical region occupies the right-hand portion of the distribution. With 2 and 4 degrees of freedom it is easy to show that under the null hypothesis the probability of attaining or exceeding any particular value of F, say $F = A$, is given by

$$S(A) \equiv \int_A^\infty f(F)\, dF = \frac{4}{(2 + A)^2}$$

Two independent samples using this test variate (F with 2 and 4 degrees of freedom) gave $F = 4$ and $F = 6$ respectively. Determine whether or not the combined result is significant at the 5 per cent level.   *Ans.* Yes, $P \approx .04$.

44. With the test variate $z = x_i{}^3/y_i{}^3$ in the fiber problem (Example 5-9), show that the significance measure under the working hypothesis that synthetic fiber is stronger than natural $(a < b)$ is $S(z) = (z + 1)^{-1}$. Test the collective significance of the data in Exercise 21, chap. 3, given that with 10 degrees of freedom and $\alpha = .05$ the critical value of chi-square is 18.307. Actually the parameters a, b in the respective distributions of x_i and y_i should be multiplied by a common factor k_i which adjusts for local conditions; a common factor, however, would not affect the distribution of z.

Ans. Collectively significant, although no comparison is individually significant.

45. The object of the series of exercises on the fiber problem is to illustrate the increase of power which can be gained by narrowing the specification of the distribution either through direct information or by reducing the number of distinct parameters. Under the conditions of Exercise 22, Chap. 3, the parameter k_i can be incorporated with a and b, yielding $f(x) = 3ax^2e^{-ax^3}$ $(0, \infty)$ and $g(y) = 3by^2e^{-by^3}$ $(0, \infty)$. Still assuming two independent samples of five observations, show that the test variate $\Sigma x^3/\Sigma y^3$ is distributed as F with 10 and 10 degrees of freedom under the null hypothesis. Compute this ratio for the data in question and judge the comparative power of the latter test from the following fractiles: $\alpha = .05$, $F = 2.97$, $\alpha = .025$, $F = 3.72$; $\alpha = .01$, $F = 4.85$.

         Ans. $F = 4.46$; hence this test is the most powerful of the series considered.

CHAPTER 7

MATHEMATICAL EXPECTATION

7-1. Definition. The concept of mathematical expectation is of paramount importance both in the mathematical development and practical use of probability theory. The term "mathematical expectation" dates back to the pioneer work in the theory of probability, which received impetus from games of chance. The common experience of fortuitous variations in luck prompted gamblers to pose the question as to how much, in the long run, one might expect to win per game under stated rules of play, and mathematicians answered the question by defining "expected value."

Consider the distribution function $F(x)$ of any variate x, which may be either discrete or continuous or, in fact, such that its distribution function is continuous over part of its range but discontinuous at a series of discrete values, such as x_1 and x_2 in Fig. 7-1a. Simultaneously, consider a function $\phi(x)$ which is continuous over the entire region of definition of $F(x)$ (see Fig. 7-1b).

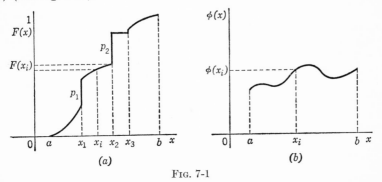

$$(a) \qquad\qquad (b)$$
$$\text{FIG. 7-1}$$

As one of the first steps in building the concept of the definite integral in the calculus, one divides the range of definition of the function into a series of parts Δx_i where the sum of the Δx_i equals the range of x. In this case, however, remembering that $F(x)$ is monotonic, let us divide the ordinate range from 0 to 1 into n divisions where each part is $\Delta F(x_i)$. These divisions may be equal or not, as we please, but the sum of the $\Delta F(x_i)$ must again equal the range, which in this case is unity. Lines parallel to the

x axis from two consecutive points on the vertical axis will ordinarily intersect the curve $F(x)$ in two points (see Fig. 7-1a). The abscissas of these two points may be the same or different, as one may see by examining the figure. However, if a point x_i is chosen anywhere between the two abscissas, it will determine a value of $\phi(x)$, say $\phi(x_i)$. Under very general restrictions placed on $F(x)$, including the fact that it must be monotonic, the sum $\Sigma\Delta(x_i)\,\Delta F(x_i)$ (where the summation goes from $i = 1$ to $i = n$) can be shown to approach a definite limit as the number of divisions $\Delta F(x_i)$ become infinite, irrespective of the choice of the size of each $\Delta F(x_i)$, provided they all approach zero as n becomes infinite. This unique limit is defined as the expected value of $\phi(x)$ and is denoted as the Stieltjes integral,

$$E[\phi(x)] = \int_a^b \phi(x)\,dF(x) \tag{7-1}$$

It should be noted that in the case of the vertical jumps in the function $F(x)$, (such as at x_1 and x_2 in Fig. 7-1a) the function $\phi(x)$ remains constant along those jumps and the $\Delta F(x_i)$ sum to give the total rise in each case. The contributions to the integral at the points x_1 and x_2 would be $\phi(x_1)p_1 + \phi(x_2)p_2$. Thus, in the case of the distribution function of a discrete random variable, which must consist of a series of these jumps, the incremental value of the integral is different from zero only at the jump points, since that portion of $F(x)$ which is parallel to the x axis, such as between x_2 and x_3 in Fig. 7-1a, will contribute nothing to the integral, as $\Delta F(x_i) = 0$ in such a case. Thus, the expected value can be represented by a pure summation as

$$E[\phi(x)] = \sum_{i=1}^n \phi(x_i)f(x_i) \tag{7-2}$$

where the x_i's are the values of x for which the probability is defined.

In the case wherein $F(x)$ is differentiable, which implies a continuous variate having a density function $f(x)$, we have

$$E[\phi(x)] = \int_a^b \phi(x)f(x)\,dx \tag{7-3}$$

The case shown in Fig. 7-1a is a combination of these two concepts, so that (except at two points) we have a function which is differentiable and, therefore, the integral can be computed as in Eq. (7-3), while at the two points x_1 and x_2 the integral must be evaluated as in Eq. (7-2). The sum of these two integrals, of course, gives the expected value, and it must be remembered that $\int_a^b f(x)\,dx$ plus the heights p_1 and p_2 will give a value equal to unity.

7-2. Averages. By the ordinary rule, the average of a set of N numbers is obtained by computing their sum, then dividing by N. Now since it is not necessary that these numbers all be different, let us suppose that there are n distinct values, $x_1, x_2, \ldots, x_n$, respectively, occurring N_1, $N_2, \ldots, N_n$ times, where $N_1 + N_2 + \cdots + N_n = N$. The average would then be given by

$$\text{Average} = \frac{\sum_{i=1}^{n} N_i x_i}{N} = \sum_{i=1}^{n} R_i x_i$$

where $R_i = N_i/N$. Recognizing R_i as the relative frequency of x_i, it may be seen that the average of a random variable could be defined in exactly the same way but with the relative frequency replaced by a probability in each case. Hence, we arrive at the following definitions:

1. For a discrete variate x with an exhaustive set of admissible values $x_i(i = 1, 2, \ldots, n)$ and corresponding probabilities $f(x_i)$ we have

$$\text{Average of } x = \sum_{i=1}^{n} x_i f(x_i) \tag{7-4}$$

2. For a continuous variate x with density function $f(x)$ defined in the range (a,b) we have

$$\text{Average of } x = \int_a^b x f(x) \, dx \tag{7-5}$$

3. For a random variate x with a distribution function $F(x)$ defined over the region (a,b) we have in general, because of the definition of the Stieltjes integral defined in Sec. 7-1,

$$\text{Average of } x = \int_a^b x \, dF(x) \tag{7-6}$$

where, of course, Eq. (7-6) includes (7-5) and (7-4) as special cases. In statistical terminology, the average as defined by Eqs. (7-4) to (7-6) is called the arithmetic mean, or briefly, the *mean*, and is often denoted by the Greek letter μ.

By comparing Eq. (7-6) with the definition of expected value [Eq. (7-1)] we see that for the special case of $\phi(x) = x$ the two are equivalent and, therefore,

$$E(x) = \int_a^b x \, dF(x) = \text{average of } x \tag{7-7}$$

Actually, the expected value can always be thought of as some kind of average. Although the following specialization is not essential to the argument, it very well illustrates this concept. Let $\phi(x)$ be a continuous monotonic function and $f(x)$ the density function of the variable x over the range (a, b). In this case, the expected value is given by Eq. (7-3). Let y be a new variable equal to $\phi(x)$ so that it is now possible to compute the probability density of y as

$$g(y) = f[\phi^{-1}(y)] \left| \frac{d}{dy} [\phi^{-1}(y)] \right|$$

Therefore, if we substitute $y = \phi(x)$ in Eq. (7-3), replace $f(x)\,dx$ by its equal $g(y)\,dy$, and revise the limits of integration accordingly, we have

$$E[\phi(x)] = E(y) = \int_{\phi(a)}^{\phi(b)} yg(y)\,dy \tag{7-8}$$

Equation (7-8) thus indicates that the expected value of $\phi(x)$ is the average value of $\phi(x)$ taken with respect to its own probability density.

Now let us return to an application of the idea which originally motivated the concept of expected value. From the probability standpoint, a game of chance can be regarded as a process of making a random draw x_i from a possible set of n distinct scores or n distinct payoffs $x_1, x_2, \ldots, x_n$. If the probability of any particular score (payoff) x_i is $f(x_i)$, where $\Sigma_i f(x_i) = 1$, then the *expected value* $E(x)$ of the scores (payoffs) is defined as the sum of products obtained by weighting each score (payoff) by its own chance of occurrence:

$$E(x) = \sum_1^n x_i f(x_i)$$

Example 7-1. A player tosses a die, and if the numbers 1, 2, or 3 appear, he will receive two cents. If, however, a 4 or 5 turns up, he will receive one cent, while the occurrence of a 6 will cost him two cents. Thus, in ascending order, the payoffs are $-2, 1, 2$, and their respective probabilities are $\frac{1}{6}, \frac{1}{3}, \frac{1}{2}$. The expected value of the game is obtained by multiplying each payoff by its chance of occurrence and then adding these products over all possibilities. Hence

$$E(x) = (-2)(\tfrac{1}{6}) + (1)(\tfrac{1}{3}) + (2)(\tfrac{1}{2}) = 1 \text{ cent}$$

If our gambler plays this game over and over, we should expect him to average one cent for each individual toss.

Example 7-2. The profit realized by the utilization of a particular power-generating plant during August is a function of the rainfall during that month. The value of the profit is approximately $5(1 - e^{-x})$ million dollars, where x (itself a pure number) represents the total number of inches of rainfall during the month. Assuming the distribution of x is $f(x) = e^{-x}$ $(0, \infty)$, what is the expected value of rain for the power company?

Denoting the value of rain by $\phi(x)$, we have

$$E[\phi(x)] = \int_0^\infty 5(1 - e^{-x})e^{-x}\,dx = 5\int_0^\infty e^{-x}\,dx - 5\int_0^\infty e^{-2x}\,dx$$
$$= 5(1 - \tfrac{1}{2}) = 2\tfrac{1}{2} \text{ million dollars}$$

The leveling off of the profit function as indicated in Fig. 7-2 is due to the spilling of water over the dam in periods of heavy rainfall. The $2\frac{1}{2}$ million dollars is the amount that the company would receive on the average for the month of August if the average were to be computed for that month for a large number of years.

FIG. 7-2

Example 7-3. Find the expected value, hence the average, of the geometric variate x, distributed as follows:

$$f(x) = (1 - \alpha)\alpha^x \qquad (0 < \alpha < 1; x = 0, 1, 2, \ldots, \infty)$$

By definition of the expected value

$$E(x) = \sum_0^\infty x(1 - \alpha)\alpha^x = (1 - \alpha) \sum_0^\infty x\alpha^x$$

To evaluate this summation, put

$$S_n = \sum_0^n x\alpha^x$$

Multiply by α and subtract:

$$S_n - \alpha S_n = \sum_0^n x\alpha^x - \sum_0^n x\alpha^{x+1} = \sum_1^n \alpha^i - n\alpha^{n+1}$$

whence
$$(1 - \alpha)S_n = \frac{\alpha(1 - \alpha^n)}{1 - \alpha} - n\alpha^{n+1}$$

Now
$$\lim_{n \to \infty} n\alpha^{n+1} = 0$$

and so
$$E(x) = \lim_{n \to \infty} (1 - \alpha)S_n = \frac{\alpha}{1 - \alpha}$$

Example 7-4. The discrete variate x has the Poisson distribution:

$$f(x) = e^{-\mu} \frac{\mu^x}{x!} \qquad (\mu > 0; x = 0, 1, 2, \ldots, \infty)$$

Find the average value of x.

Since $0f(0) = 0$, we may write

$$E(x) \equiv \sum_0^\infty xf(x) = \sum_1^\infty xf(x)$$

Now if $x > 0$ we have

$$xf(x) = e^{-\mu} \frac{\mu^x}{(x - 1)!} = \mu e^{-\mu} \frac{\mu^{x-1}}{(x - 1)!}$$

Setting $t = x - 1$ and noting that the Maclaurin expansion for e^μ is $\sum_0^\infty \mu^t/t!$ we obtain

$$E(x) = \mu e^{-\mu} \sum_0^\infty \frac{\mu^t}{t!} = \mu e^{-\mu} e^\mu = \mu$$

As an aid in the geometric interpretation of the mean, this distribution is plotted for $\mu = 9$ in Fig. 7-3.

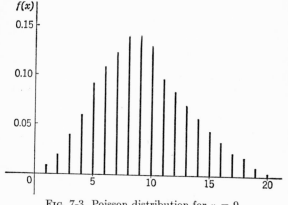

FIG. 7-3. Poisson distribution for $\mu = 9$.

Example 7-5. Find the average value of the continuous variate x, where

$$f(x) = 6x(1 - x) \qquad (0, 1)$$

It follows from the definition that

$$E(x) = \int_0^1 xf(x) = \int_0^1 6x^2(1 - x)\, dx = \tfrac{1}{2}$$

Example 7-6. Find the average value of the function $y = x^2$ given that x is unit normal. Using the distribution of x we have

$$E(y) = E(x^2) = \int_{-\infty}^\infty x^2 \frac{1}{\sqrt{2\pi}} e^{-x^2/2}\, dx$$
$$= \frac{2\sqrt{2}}{\sqrt{2\pi}} \Gamma(\tfrac{3}{2}) = 1$$

Alternatively, we may evaluate the expected value of y from its own distribution, namely,

$$g(y) = \frac{1}{\sqrt{2\pi}} y^{-\frac{1}{2}} e^{-y/2} \qquad (0, \infty)$$

Thus
$$E(y) = \int_0^\infty y g(y)\, dy = \frac{1}{\sqrt{2\pi}} \int_0^\infty y^{\frac{1}{2}} e^{-y/2}\, dy$$

$$= \frac{2\sqrt{2}}{\sqrt{2\pi}} \Gamma(\tfrac{3}{2}) = 1$$

7-3. Some Additional Properties of the Mean. Two rather obvious properties of the mean are worthy of explicit statement.

Property 1. If $A \le x \le B$, then $A \le E(x) \le B$.

Property 2. If $\alpha(x) = a_0 + a_1\alpha_1(x) + \cdots + a_n\alpha_n(x)$, then

$$E[\alpha(x)] = a_0 + a_1E[\alpha_1(x)] + \cdots + a_nE[\alpha_n(x)]$$

The first property guarantees that the mean cannot fall outside of the limits for which the variate is defined. By way of proof, we notice that $\int_A^B A\, dF(x) \le \int_A^B x\, dF(x) \le \int_A^B B\, dF(x)$, hence $A \le E(x) \le B$. The verbal translation of the second property is that if $\alpha(x)$ is a linear function of any number of components, then its expected value is given by the same linear function of the expected values of those components. To prove this fact, we substitute $\alpha(x) = a_0 + \Sigma a_i\alpha_i(x)$ into the equation

$$E[\alpha(x)] = \int_A^B \alpha(x)\, dF(x)$$

and integrate term by term.

For some purposes it is convenient to consider an average value of a function $\alpha(x)$ over a portion of the total range of x. Thus, if $A \le x < P$ we define a *submean* $M(a,b)$ over the range a, b as

$$M(a,b) = \frac{\int_a^b \alpha(x)\, dF(x)}{\int_a^b dF(x)} \tag{7-9}$$

From this definition, it follows that a submean may be interpreted as an average taken with respect to a conditional distribution. It is readily seen that Properties 1 and 2 of regular means hold also for submeans. As an application, suppose we divide the total range of x into n arbitrary intervals by marking off $n+1$ points, $(x_0 \equiv A)$, x_1, x_2, . . . , x_{n-1}, $(x_n \equiv B)$. Putting $P_i = \int_{x_{i-1}}^{x_i} dF(x)$ and $M_i = \frac{1}{P_i}\int_{x_{i-1}}^{x_i} \alpha(x)\, dF(x)$, we then have the identity

$$E[\alpha(n)] \equiv \sum_1^n P_iM_i \tag{7-10}$$

Formulas of this type have long been used in mechanics in connection with center of gravity.

Example 7-7. Find the submean of a normal variate x over the range $\mu + \sigma \le x < \infty$. Consider, first, a unit normal variate u. The corresponding range of u is

1, ∞ and the submean m is given by

$$m = \frac{\displaystyle\int_1^\infty (1/\sqrt{2\pi})\, u e^{-u^2/2}\, du}{\displaystyle\int_1^\infty (1/\sqrt{2\pi})\, e^{-u^2/2}\, du} = \frac{[-(1/\sqrt{2\pi})\, e^{-u^2/2}]_1^\infty}{R(1)}$$

$$= \frac{f(1)}{R(1)} = \frac{.2420}{.1587} = 1.525$$

Now applying Property 2 we have $x = \mu + \sigma u$ whence

$$M = \mu + \sigma m = \mu + 1.525\sigma$$

More generally, if t is any positive number, the submean $m(t, \infty)$ of a unit normal variate in the range t, ∞ is

$$m(t, \infty) = \frac{f(t)}{R(t)}$$

and the corresponding submean $M(\mu + t\sigma,\ \infty)$ of any normal variate is

$$M(\mu + t\sigma,\ \infty) = \mu + \frac{\sigma f(t)}{R(t)}$$

where $f(t)$ and $R(t)$ refer to the unit normal distribution.

7-4. Applications of Expected Value Theory.

Applications of probability to small- and large-scale military and industrial operations often involve the consideration of pertinent random variables. As the appropriate mathematical models contain more and more of these random variables, the actual solutions become very complicated. It is the purpose of this section to illustrate the use of "expected value" in a group of problems for which the mathematical models are relatively simple, so that the manipulations can be easily performed. It must be remembered that the point of departure between the method of using the distribution functions to compute an average and the elementary technique of addition and division is very important and is worth considerable thought on the part of the student.

Example 7-8. A seasonal article which must be ordered in advance and stocked by a department store sells for \$100 per unit and costs the store \$50 per unit irrespective of disposal; however, any article not sold during the season must be sold at a sacrifice to a special dealer for \$35 per unit. Given that the distribution of customer orders for the item is $f(z) = e^{-9}9^z/z!$ $(z = 0, 1, 2, \ldots, \infty)$ and that the number of orders during any season is a random draw from this distribution, how many units should be stocked in order to maximize the expected value of the profit?

Letting x denote an arbitrary number of units stocked, we shall express the expected value of the profit as a function of x, say $\bar{P}(x)$, and then determine x so as to maximize this function. Depending on the magnitude of the number of orders z relative to x, the profit function assumes two distinct forms. In range A $(0 \le z \le x)$, we have the profit function P_A based on the analysis that we sell z units at \$100 each, sell the remaining $x - z$ units at \$35 each, and at the same time we have to pay for x units at

$50 each. In range B $(z > x)$, we have the profit function P_B based on the fact that we have only x units available for sale regardless of the actual demand, where each unit is sold for $100 but costs the store $50. Hence the two profit functions are

$$P_A = 100z + 35(x - z) - 50x = 65z - 15x \qquad (0 \leq z \leq x)$$
$$P_B = 50x \qquad (z > x)$$

The over-all expected value of the profit $\bar{P}(x)$, for any value of x, is given by

$$\bar{P}(x) = \sum_{z=0}^{\infty} P(x)f(z) = \sum_{z=0}^{x} P_A f(z) + \sum_{z=x+1}^{\infty} P_B f(z)$$
$$= \sum_{0}^{x} (65z - 15x)f(z) + \sum_{x+1}^{\infty} 50x f(z)$$

Now
$$\sum_{x+1}^{\infty} f(z) = 1 - \sum_{0}^{x} f(z)$$

Hence

$$\bar{P}(x) = \sum_{0}^{x} (65z - 15x)f(z) + 50x \left[1 - \sum_{0}^{x} f(z) \right] = 50x + 65 \sum_{0}^{x} (z - x)f(z)$$

An obvious method of arriving at the maximum profit would be to evaluate this function at successive points until the maximum is located. For illustrative purposes we have carried out this calculation, with the results shown in Fig. 7-4; the maximum

FIG. 7-4. Expected profit $\bar{P}(x)$ versus amount stocked x.

is reached $x = 11$. On the other hand, a method of solution which relies so heavily on computation is both time-consuming and inflexible. Therefore, we present the following method of analysis because of its greater efficiency and mathematical generality.

To determine the optimum value of x, let us investigate whether we would increase or decrease the expected profit by increasing x by one unit. By substitution,

$$\bar{P}(x+1) = 50(x+1) + 65 \sum_0^{x+1} (z - x - 1)f(z) = 50(x+1) + 65 \sum_0^{x} (z - x - 1)f(z)$$

since $(z - x - 1) = 0$ when $z = x + 1$. Subtracting $\bar{P}(x)$ from $\bar{P}(x+1)$, we find that the difference is

$$\Delta\bar{P}(x) = \bar{P}(x+1) - \bar{P}(x) = 50 + 65 \sum_0^{x} [(z - x - 1) - (z - x)]f(z)$$

$$= 50 - 65 \sum_0^{x} f(z) = 50 - 65F(x)$$

where $F(x)$ is the value of the distribution function of z at $z = x$. From the latter equation it is clear that $\Delta\bar{P}(x)$ will be positive as long as $F(x) < {}^{50}\!/_{65}$ and will be nega-

TABLE 7-1

x	9	10	11
$F(x)$	.587	.706	.803
$\Delta\bar{P}(x)$	11.8	4.1	-2.2

tive when $F(x) > {}^{50}\!/_{65}$, while if $F(x) = {}^{50}\!/_{65}$, $\bar{P}(x) = \bar{P}(x+1)$. Therefore, the *maximum value* of the *profit* will be obtained if we choose x to be the *smallest* value for which $\Delta\bar{P}(x)$ is zero or negative. For in case $F(x) = {}^{50}\!/_{65}$ for an integral value of x, we get the same expected profit with x as with $x + 1$, and the smaller number has the advantage of smaller investment. Moreover, in case $F(x)$ cannot equal ${}^{50}\!/_{65}$ for an integral value of x, the smallest value of x such that $\Delta\bar{P}(x)$ is negative has the property that the next larger value of x would yield a smaller profit, in view of this negative difference, while the next smaller value would also yield a smaller profit, because for the latter the difference is positive.

In the particular case considered here, the distribution is the well known Poisson distribution, and extensive tables have been prepared by E. C. Molina of the Bell Telephone Laboratories. Adapting Molina's tables, we find the following values (Table 7-1) near ${}^{50}\!/_{65} \approx .769$. Thus, the maximum value of the expected profit will be obtained by choosing $x = 11$. This solution, of course, agrees with Fig. 7-4.

We know, however, from the solution of Example 7-4 that the average number of orders is 9, and from experience the manager would be aware of this fact even though he might not know the form of the distribution. Thus, he might pick 9 as the appropriate number to stock. The expected profit would be in that case \$373 as opposed to the maximum of \$389, and the difference is about 4 per cent of the smaller figure. It happens that there are four values of x (10, 11, 12, 13) which would yield a higher profit than $x = 9$ even though the curve is fairly flat near the average order level. The 4 per cent additional profit in most businesses is well worth going after, but it brings out a point which must be considered carefully. What is the company's policy or what is its object in being in business? In this case we have maximized the profit; but obviously one might wish to maximize the return on investment, which would give a different answer, and one certainly cannot maximize both at the same time. A mathematical model of the operation, therefore, is not the only part of a statistical problem which is important; there is also the formulation of the objective to be accomplished by the operation. Thus if one is going to pick the best strategy to use against a set of random causes, one has to have a measure of effectiveness which, if maximized, will convince one that the procedure is correct.

Example 7-9. A company has a sole purchaser for its product. If this purchaser on a particular day does not obtain the number of items which he requests, he will merely buy them on the open market; but his failure to obtain the necessary number from this company does not effect his future course of action. The margin of profit on the item is m dollars and, since the item is perishable, the loss is n dollars for any items not sold to this single purchaser. This purchaser will buy either 100, 200, or 300 items on a given day, with probabilities p_1, p_2, $1 - p_1 - p_2$ respectively. What should be the strategy of the company in order to maximize its profits?

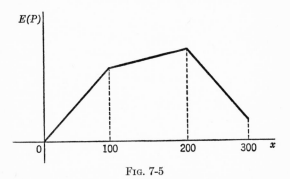

FIG. 7-5

Let x be the number of items the company produces. It is clear that x will not be greater than 300, since this is the maximum number which can be sold. The profit will be given by different mathematical expressions, depending on whether x is less than 100, between 100 and 200, or between 200 and 300. The following is the expected value of the profit (P) for each of these ranges of x.

$$0 \leq x \leq 100 \qquad E(P) = mx$$

$$100 < x \leq 200 \qquad E(P) = p_1[100m - n(x - 100)] + (1 - p_1)mx = 100m$$
$$+ (x - 100)[m - p_1(m + n)]$$

$$200 < x \leq 300 \qquad E(P) = p_1[100m - n(x - 100)] + p_2[200m - n(x - 200)]$$
$$+ (1 - p_1 - p_2)mx$$

$$= 200m - 100(m + n)p_1$$
$$+ (x - 200)[m - (m + n)(p_1 + p_2)]$$

In a simple case like this, one would guess without any analysis that there are only three strategies capable of maximizing the profit. The company would produce 100, 200, or 300 items. This is clearly shown in Fig. 7-5, where the expected value of the profit is plotted against x. The straight line running from $x = 0$ to $x = 100$ always has a positive slope, but the slopes of the other two segments may be negative. Therefore, at least 100 items should be produced. In examining the equation for the expected value of the profit in the range from $x = 100$ to $x = 200$ we see that the slope is positive if $p_1 < m/(m + n)$ which means that if this inequality holds, 200 items should be produced as the profit increases continuously from $x = 100$ to $x = 200$. If, however, the slope is negative, the company would, of course, make only the 100 items.

If we now examine the equation for the expected profit in the final range, that is, from 200 to 300, we find that the slope is positive for this segment if $p_1 + p_2 < m/(m + n)$, which again gives the condition that the company should move to the 300-item level. It is obviously impossible for the slope to be negative in the middle range and positive in the final range. Therefore, the best strategy out of a theoretically infinite number of possible strategies is determined by comparing the probabilities p_1 and $p_1 + p_2$ with the ratio $m/(m + n)$ of marginal profit per item to the sum of marginal profit per item and loss per item.

Example 7-10. An item to be sold during the Christmas season brings a net profit of m dollars for each unit sold and a net loss of n dollars for each unit left unsold when the season ends. If the distribution of order volume v may be approximated by the density function $f(v)$ $(0 < v < V)$, determine the optimum number of units x to be stocked in order to maximize the expected value $\bar{P}$ of the profit P.

Two forms of the profit function exist, depending upon whether v is less than x or greater than x. Thus

$$P(x) = mv - n(x - v) = (m + n)v - nx \qquad (v \leq x)$$
$$P(x) = mx \qquad (v > x)$$

Hence, the expected value of the profit is

$$\bar{P}(x) = \int_0^x [(m + n)v - nx]f(v)\ dv + \int_x^V mxf(v)\ dv$$

or, rewriting $\displaystyle\int_x^V mxf(v)\ dv$ as $mx\left[1 - \displaystyle\int_0^x f(v)\ dv\right]$, the expected value becomes

$$\bar{P}(x) = mx + (m + n)\int_0^x (v - x)f(v)\ dv$$

Differentiating this function with respect to x we obtain

$$\frac{\partial \bar{P}(x)}{\partial x} = m + (m + n)(x - x)f(x) - (m + n)\int_0^x f(v)\ dv = m - (m + n)F(x)$$

Hence, the maximum average profit is reached if x is so chosen that

$$F(x) = \frac{m}{m + n} = \frac{\text{unit profit}}{\text{unit profit} + \text{unit loss}}$$

If $m = \$1$ and $n = \$2$, then x must be chosen so that the area under $f(v)$ to its left will equal $\frac{1}{3}$.

It might be interesting to ask the question, at this point, as to what would happen if the loss of sales due to lack of the item might also produce a loss to the company because of a goodwill factor. This loss of future profit could be taken into account during the current year by assigning a net loss to the company for each item for which there is a demand that cannot be supplied. From a practical viewpoint, the loss per item might be proportionately greater in case there were many items which could not be supplied. However, for illustrative purposes, let us consider that the loss to the company is a constant for each item that cannot be supplied. The integral for the expected value of the profit would then be

$$\bar{P}(x) = \int_0^x [(m + n)v - nx]f(v)\ dv + \int_x^V [mx - a(v - x)]f(v)\ dv$$

where a is the loss to the company for each item not available to a customer. Differentiating this function with respect to x we obtain

$$F(x) = \frac{m + a}{m + a + n}$$

Therefore, the effect of the goodwill factor in determining the value of x for the best strategy is to add the loss per item due to goodwill to the margin of profit per item in order to determine an effective margin of profit. It is clear from this that as a increases, it tends to move x farther and farther towards its upper limit. If we had applied a goodwill factor to the previous problem (Example 7-8) the effect would be exactly the same, that is, the margin of profit would be augmented by the numerical value of the goodwill factor.

Example 7-11. In Example 7-10 let us suppose that the probability density of sales can be represented by

$$f(v) = \frac{1}{2b} \qquad (s - b \leq v \leq s + b)$$

This is a situation in which a sales forecast indicates that the amount to be sold is s, but previous history indicates that there is an error in estimating the sales and that this error is equally likely to assume any value from $-b$ to b. What is the additional profit that would be realized by stocking the number which maximizes the profit rather than stocking the amount s which is the estimated sale of the item?

The expected value of the profit (P), if we stock s, is given by

$$E(P_s) = \frac{1}{2b} \int_{s-b}^{s} [(m + n)x - ns]\, dx + \frac{1}{2b} \int_{s}^{s+b} ms\, dx$$

By carrying out the indicated integration and substituting the appropriate limits, we obtain for the expected value of the profit

$$E(Ps) = ms - \frac{b(m + n)}{4}$$

By choosing n sufficiently large in this formula, it is seen that the expected profit may become negative. The possibility of this situation is enhanced when b is almost as large as s. The expression for the maximum expected value of the profit is given by

$$E(P_{\max}) = \frac{1}{2b} \int_{s-b}^{y} [mx - n(s - x)]\, dx + \frac{1}{2b} \int_{y}^{s+b} ms\, dx$$

where y is the solution (see Example 7-10) of the equation

$$\frac{1}{2b} \int_{s-b}^{y} dx = \frac{m}{m + n}$$

By carrying out the indicated integration and solving the result for y, we have

$$y = \frac{m(s + b) + n(s - b)}{m + n}$$

Evaluating the maximum expected value of the profit by substituting the correct value of y in the integral for $E(P_{\max})$, we obtain

$$E(P_{\max}) = ms - \frac{bmn}{m + n}$$

Even for $b = s$, this expression still remains positive for any n.   The net gain in profit by stocking the value y rather than the value s is now obtained by subtracting the two expected profits as

$$E(P_{max}) - E(P_s) = \frac{b}{4} \frac{(m-n)^2}{m+n}$$

This expression is equal to zero when $m = n$ but for $m \neq n$ the gain is always positive. The numerical unit of this calculated difference is necessarily the total gain in dollars, since b has the unit of number of items and both m and n are in dollars.   This calculated difference is independent of s but, of course, in most practical cases the range of error of forecasting is a function of the value forecasted.   If we assume a constant percentage error of estimate in the sales, then $b = ks$ (where k, in this case, must lie between 0 and 1) and the percentage gain in profit would be given by

$$\frac{100(ks/4)(m-n)^2/(m+n)}{sm - ks(m+n)/4} = \frac{100k(m-n)^2}{(m+n)[4m - k(m+n)]} \approx 25k \frac{(1-K)^2}{1+K}$$

The last approximate value is obtained under the assumption that $k(m+n)$ is small compared to $4m$ and with the notation that K is the ratio of n to m.   As an illustration, if we lose \$2 for every \$1 (the margin of profit) so that $K = 2$ and the range of error of the estimate of the sales forecast is ± 25 per cent, then the percentage gain in profit is approximately 2 per cent.   If, however, $K = 3$ in this instance, the gain is about 6 per cent.

Example 7-12.   Raw material must be ordered in the spring for sale in a finished product in the fall.   The cost of raw material is c_1 dollars per item.   If this raw material is not used, it has a scrap value which is c_2 dollars where $c_2 < c_1$.   The raw material may be processed during the summer at a cost of $g_1(x)$ dollars per item (that is, the unit cost) where x is the number to be manufactured.   The loss that is incurred on those completed products which are not sold can be again expressed as the fact that the scrap value is c_3 dollars per item.   It is here assumed that the scrap value is less than the cost incurred to produce the item.   On the other hand, it is possible to produce W items during the fall season (thus at the time that the demand is known) at a higher rate of $g_2(W)$ dollars per item so that one never has to suffer the loss on manufactured goods not sold but merely on the raw material.   There is, however, a maximum total number (A) which can be produced during the season of sale itself because of limited plant capacity.   With a selling price of s dollars per item, what is the maximum amount of raw material to be ordered and how much should be processed during the summer in order to maximize the profit, assuming the probability of sales can be represented by a density function $f(v)$ $(0 < v < \infty)$?

Assuming that the total number of pieces of raw material is made up of the x pieces which are to be manufactured during the summer and y pieces which are to be produced during the season if the demand is demonstrated, we have for the expected value of the profit the following expression, where it must be remembered that the function representing the profit differs in the three ranges of the volume of sales, namely, $0 < v < x$, $x < v < x + y$, and $x + y < v < \infty$.

$$\text{Expected profit} = E(P) = \int_0^x [sv - c_1(x+y) - xg_1(x) + c_2y + c_3(x-v)]f(v)\,dv$$
$$+ \int_x^{x+y} [sv - c_1(x+y) - xg_1(x) - (v-x)g_2(v-x) + c_2(x+y-v)]f(v)\,dv$$
$$+ \int_{x+y}^\infty [s(x+y) - c_1(x+y) - xg_1(x) - yg_2(y)]f(v)\,dv$$

It is tentatively assumed at this point in the analysis that there is no restriction on the amount y which can be manufactured during the season, and the integral for this expected profit can be differentiated first with respect to x and then with respect to y.

For this situation, the derivatives with respect to the limits on the integrals cancel each other in both equations because of the continuity conditions that exist from one range of v to the next. The only time that differentiation with respect to the limits produces nonvanishing terms is when a setup charge or its equivalent is introduced at a particular volume of sales so that it occurs in one integral and not the other, which is not true here. Therefore we have

$$\frac{\partial E(P)}{\partial x} = \int_0^x \left[-c_1 - \frac{d}{dx}[xg_1(x)] + c_3 \right] f(v) \, dv$$
$$+ \int_x^{x+y} \left\{ -c_1 - \frac{d}{dx}[xg_1(x)] - \frac{d}{dx}[(v-x)g_2(v-x)] + c_2 \right\} f(v) \, dv$$
$$+ \int_{x+y}^\infty \left\{ s - c_1 - \frac{d}{dx}[xg_1(x)] \right\} f(v) \, dv$$

and

$$\frac{\partial E(P)}{\partial y} = \int_0^x [-c_1 + c_2] f(v) \, dv + \int_x^{x+y} [-c_1 + c_2] f(v) \, dv$$
$$+ \int_{x+y}^\infty \left\{ s - c_1 - \frac{d}{dy}[yg_2(y)] \right\} f(v) \, dv$$

These equations can now be simplified by considering the integral from 0 to x of $f(v) \, dv$ in $\partial E(P)/\partial x$ as $1 - $ (integral from x to $x + y$ plus the integral from $x + y$ to ∞) and the integral from 0 to x plus the integral from x to $x + y$ of $f(v) \, dv$ as $1 - $ (integral from $x + y$ to ∞) in $\partial E(P)/\partial y$ to give

$$\frac{\partial E(P)}{\partial x} = -c_1 + c_3 - \frac{d}{dx}[xg_1(x)] + (c_2 - c_3) \int_x^{x+y} f(v) \, dv$$
$$- \int_x^{x+y} \frac{d}{dx}[(v-x)g_2(v-x)] f(v) \, dv + (s - c_3) \int_{x+y}^\infty f(v) \, dv$$
$$\frac{\partial E(P)}{\partial y} = -c_1 + c_2 + \left\{ s - c_2 - \frac{d}{dy}[yg_2(y)] \right\} \int_{x+y}^\infty f(v) \, dv$$

The integral involving $d[(v - x)g_2(v - x)]/dx$ must be kept intact, since this term involves v which is the variable of integration, whereas the other coefficients of $f(v)$ in the several integrals are constants.

Following the usual technique, one would set these two derivatives equal to zero in order to obtain a stationary point as the minimum. This would generate two equations in the two unknowns x and y, which could then be solved by any of several methods of successive approximations.

It must be noted that in this problem there are very definite restrictions which have to be satisfied, and a stationary point may not occur within these limitations. The total area under the probability density $f(v)$ must equal unity, x and y must each be equal to or greater than zero, and y cannot be greater than A. Such minimization with lateral restrictions is, of course, often found in practical applications. In order to analyze the difficulties and to illustrate the solution of a problem in this category, we now simplify the above expressions by assuming $g_1(x)$ and $g_2(W)$ to be constants c_4 and c_5 respectively. Then

$$\frac{\partial E(P)}{\partial x} = (-c_1 + c_3 + c_4) + (c_2 - c_3 + c_5) \int_x^{x+y} f(v) \, dv + (s - c_3) \int_{x+y}^\infty f(v) \, dv$$
$$\frac{\partial E(P)}{\partial y} = -c_1 + c_2 + [s - c_2 - c_5] \int_{x+y}^\infty f(v) \, dv$$

If the expression for $\partial E(P)/\partial y$ is set equal to zero we have

$$\int_{x+y}^{\infty} f(v)\, dv = \frac{c_1 - c_2}{s - c_2 - c_5}$$

Since $c_1 > c_2$ and $s > c_1 + c_5$ by the conditions imposed upon the problem, this integral is always positive and less than unity. It therefore always uniquely determines the value of $x + y$ if the function $f(v)$ is given, and thus the stationary point, as far as $\partial E(P)/\partial y$ is concerned, is also uniquely determined.

Substituting this value for the integral in $\partial E(P)/\partial y$, we have

$$\frac{\partial E(P)}{\partial x} = (-c_1 + c_3 + c_4) + (c_2 - c_3 + c_5) \int_{x}^{x+y} f(v)\, dv + \frac{(s - c_3)(c_1 - c_2)}{s - c_2 - c_5}$$

which gives the slope of the $E(P)$ surface in the x direction.

For a stationary point to exist, it is necessary that $\partial E(P)/\partial x$ change sign. This is not always the case, as one can see by letting $c_3 = c_5$ and $c_2 = 0$, which are possible values of these constants. The sign of the derivative is then always positive, which indicates that the profit is increasing with x, so that we should not plan to produce any of the product after the season starts. Since the value of $x + y$ is known from the integral and $y = 0$, we have determined the amount of x to order. The exact opposite conclusion would be the case if, for some values of the constants, the derivative were always negative with, therefore, $x = 0$ and thus $y = x + y$. This, of course, neglects the limitation on the total amount of y possible. More generally, the fact that $\int_{x}^{x+y} f(v)\, dv$ is restricted to lie between 0 and $1 - \int_{x+y}^{\infty} f(v)\, dv$ means that there are many situations where $\partial E(P)/\partial x$ will not change sign in the possible region of the integral, and the above argument will again necessarily follow. For some ranges of the constants, the partial derivative $\partial E(P)/\partial x$ can be set equal to zero and a value for $\int_{x}^{x+y} f(v)\, dv$ determined which is within its range of possibility. In this case, we have a unique stationary point and can calculate the values of x and y.

After x and y are determined, we must consider the restriction that $y \leq A$. If y comes out less than or equal to A, we have the final solution to the problem. If, however, y is greater than A, it indicates that y should be as large as possible, namely, A. We cannot, however, assign the excess of y over A to x, since this may not produce a maximum profit, but $E(P)$ must be again set up as a function of x alone as

$$E(P) = \int_{0}^{x} [sv - c_1(x + A) - xg_1(x) + c_2 A + c_3(x - v)]f(v)\, dv$$
$$+ \int_{x}^{x+A} [sv - c_1(x + A) - xg_1(x) - (v - x)g_2(v - x) + c_2(x + A - v)]f(v)\, dv$$
$$+ \int_{x+A}^{\infty} [s(x + A) - c_1(x + A) - xg_1(x) - Ag_2(A)]f(v)\, dv$$

This function can now be differentiated with respect to x and the derivative set equal to zero. Since the conditions of the problem were such that a profit is possible, and the range of x is between 0 and ∞, this process will yield a stationary point and therefore constitute a solution to the problem.

Example 7-13. In a building with n lamps lighted at the same time daily a bulb is replaced immediately when it burns out. The costs for replacing one bulb consist of the purchasing cost a_1, the cost a_2 of changing the bulb (i.e., taking out the old and putting a new one in the lamp), and all the costs a_3 for bringing the bulb, ladder, and other necessary things to the required place. Another alternative is to change all the bulbs at the same time periodically with time period T, but still change a bulb when it burns out. When all the bulbs are to be changed together, the costs a_1 and a_2 are the same per bulb, but instead of a_3, we now have a total cost a_4 for bringing all the bulbs and other materials to the place. Determine T such that the average cost per unit of time the bulbs are lit becomes a minimum. The lifetime of a bulb is unknown, but we shall assume that its probability density is $f(t) = 1/K$ $(0 < t < K)$.

Given the probability density, it is possible to compute the expected number of burnouts per socket between $t = 0$ and $t = T$ where T is arbitrary and is to be determined later. Obviously, when a bulb fails and is replaced by another this new replacement bulb has the same rectangular distribution for its life as the burned-out bulb, but starting with the moment of replacement. By reference to Fig. 7-6, the proba-

FIG. 7-6

bilities $P(0)$, $P(1)$, and $P(2)$ of exactly 0, 1, 2 burnouts respectively before time T is reached are as follows:

$$P(0) = 1 - \int_0^T \frac{dt}{K} = 1 - \frac{T}{K}$$

$$P(1) = \int_0^T \frac{dt_1}{K}\left(1 - \int_{t_1}^T \frac{dt}{K}\right) = \int_0^T \frac{dt_1}{K} - \int_0^T \frac{T - t_1}{K^2}\, dt_1 = \frac{T}{K} - \frac{T^2}{2K^2}$$

$$P(2) = \int_0^T \frac{dt_1}{K} \int_{t_1}^T \frac{dt_2}{K}\left(1 - \int_{t_2}^T \frac{dt}{K}\right) = \int_0^T \frac{dt_1}{K}\left(\int_{t_1}^T \frac{dt_2}{K} - \int_{t_1}^T \frac{T - t_2}{K^2}\, dt_2\right)$$

$$= \frac{T^2}{2K^2} - \frac{T^3}{6K^3} = \frac{T^2}{K^2 \times 2!} - \frac{T^3}{K^3 \times 3!}$$

An examination of the form of these integrals indicates that the probability of exactly n burnouts in any one socket would be

$$P(n) = \frac{T^n}{K^n n!} - \frac{T^{n+1}}{K^{n+1}(n + 1)!}$$

From the definition of expected value, the average number of burnouts per socket is

$$E(n) = \sum_{n=0}^{n=\infty} nP(n) = \sum_0^\infty n\left(\frac{T^n}{K^n n!} - \frac{T^{n+1}}{K^{n+1}(n + 1)!}\right)$$

$$= \frac{T}{K}\sum_1^\infty \frac{T^{n-1}}{K^{n-1}(n - 1)!} - \sum_0^\infty \frac{[(n + 1) - 1]T^{n+1}}{K^{n+1}(n + 1)!}$$

$$= \frac{T}{K} e^{T/K} - \frac{T}{K}\sum_0^\infty \frac{T^n}{K^n n!} + \sum_0^\infty \frac{T^{n+1}}{K^{n+1}(n + 1)!}$$

$$E(n) = \frac{T}{K} e^{T/K} - \frac{T}{K} e^{T/K} + (e^{T/K} - 1) = e^{T/K} - 1$$

It is interesting to note that the average number of burnouts per socket over the entire range K of the bulb life obtained by setting $T = K$ is $(e - 1) \approx 1.72$. Referring to the costs given in the statement of the problem, the average cost per unit of time the bulbs are lighted is

$$\text{Cost} = C = \frac{n(a_1 + a_2 + a_3)(e^{T/K} - 1) + n(a_1 + a_2) + a_4}{T}$$

assuming that they were all changed at the specific cycle time T. The derivative of this cost with respect to T is equal to zero if a stationary point exists and thus

$$\frac{dC}{dT}$$

$$= \frac{(T/K)n(a_1 + a_2 + a_3)e^{T/K} - [n(a_1 + a_2 + a_3)(e^{T/K} - 1) + n(a_1 + a_2) + a_4]}{T^2} = 0$$

If $T/K = x$ and $[n(a_1 + a_2) + a_4]/n(a_1 + a_2 + a_3) = A$, then the equation for this stationary point becomes

$$xe^x - (e^x - 1) - A = 0$$

or

$$e^x(1 - x) = 1 - A$$

Since A is less than 1 (in order for this problem to have any meaning the cost of replacing the bulbs all at one time must be less than changing them one at a time), this transcendental equation has a solution for $x < 1$ which determines the period T at which they should all be replaced in order to make this cost a minimum.

7-5. Variance.

The expected value is one of several possible measures (called norms) commonly employed to indicate the general location of a distribution along the coordinate axis of the variate considered. Two other measures often used for the same purpose are the median and the mode. Once a suitable norm (measure of central tendency) is chosen, there arises the question of concentration, that is, the degree to which the norm represents the distribution as a whole. Intuitively we feel that a measure of concentration should indicate how much area there is in the neighborhood of the norm; but upon reflection, it becomes obvious that unless a definite range about the norm is specified, more or less arbitrarily, what we are really considering is a probability function akin to $W(x)$, as defined for the unit normal distribution. Because an arbitrarily chosen range is of dubious merit, let us propose a measure which is itself an average derived from the entire distribution. As the intuitive concept of concentration applies equally to both sides of the norm, the function to be averaged should depend upon the magnitude of the difference between the norm and an individual value; moreover, since it should put a penalty upon large deviations in order to distinguish the immediate from the remote, the function should increase with the magnitude of the deviation. We thus arrive at a measure of departure from the norm, or a measure of variability, rather than a direct measure of concentration, but it will serve the same purpose. Initially we might consider using merely the average absolute deviation from the norm, and, in fact, this measure has gained a limited acceptance; but its exceedingly poor combinative properties render it useless for most purposes, practical and theoretical alike. The simplest measure which satisfies both intuitive and analytical requirements is the mean square deviation from the norm; and when the mean μ is chosen as the norm, this measure of departure is called the *variance* and is denoted by the symbol σ^2. The positive square root of the variance is known as the *standard deviation* and is denoted by the symbol σ. Thus,

$$\text{Variance} \equiv \sigma^2 \equiv E[(x - \mu)^2] \qquad \text{Standard deviation} \equiv \sigma \equiv \sqrt{\sigma^2} \quad (7\text{-}11)$$

By expanding the quadratic $(x - \mu)^2$ and making use of Property 2 (Sec. 7-3), with $E(x)$ replaced by its equal μ, we obtain the following identity, which often simplifies the determination of σ^2:

$$\sigma^2 \equiv E(x^2) - \mu^2 \qquad\qquad (7\text{-}12)$$

Example 7-14. Find the mean, variance, and standard deviation of the variate x where $f(x) = \dfrac{x}{\beta^2}\, e^{-x/\beta}$ $(0,\ \infty\,;\ \beta > 0)$. The mean is given by

$$\mu = \int_0^\infty x f(x)\, dx = \beta\Gamma(3) = 2\beta$$

and the variance is

$$\sigma^2 = E(x^2) - \mu^2 = \int_0^\infty x^2 f(x)\, dx - 4\beta^2$$
$$= \beta^2\Gamma(4) - 4\beta^2 = 2\beta^2$$

Thus the standard deviation is $\sigma = \beta\sqrt{2}$.

Example 7-15. The variance of the Poisson distribution: Use the identity $x^2 \equiv x(x-1) + x$. Then

$$E(x^2) = e^{-\mu} \sum_{x=0}^\infty x(x-1)\frac{\mu^x}{x!} + e^{-\mu}\sum_{x=0}^\infty x\frac{\mu^x}{x!} = e^{-\mu}\left(\mu^2\sum_{u=0}^\infty \frac{\mu^u}{u!} + \mu\sum_{v=0}^\infty \frac{\mu^v}{v!}\right)$$
$$= e^{-\mu}(\mu^2 e^\mu + \mu e^\mu) = \mu^2 + \mu$$
$$\sigma^2 = E(x^2) - [E(x)]^2 = (\mu^2 + \mu) - \mu^2 = \mu$$

Thus the mean and variance of a Poisson distribution are both equal to μ.

Example 7-16. The mean and variance of the binomial distribution: Put $m = n - 1$; then

$$\mu = E(x) = \sum_{x=0}^n \frac{xn!}{x!(n-x)!}\, p^x q^{n-x} = np\sum_{u=0}^m \frac{m!}{u!(m-u)!}\, p^u q^{m-u} = np$$

Put $x^2 \equiv x(x-1) + x$; $L = n - 2$; then

$$E(x^2) = \sum_{x=0}^n \frac{x(x-1)n!}{x!(n-x)!}\, p^x q^{n-x} + \sum_{x=0}^n \frac{xn!}{x!(n-x)!}\, p^x q^{n-x}$$
$$= n(n-1)p^2 \sum_{v=0}^L \frac{L!}{v!(L-v)!}\, p^v q^{L-v} + np$$
$$= n(n-1)p^2 + np = n^2 p^2 + np - np^2$$
$$\sigma^2 = E(x^2) - \mu^2 = np - np^2 = np(1 - p) = npq$$

Therefore, $\mu = np$ and $\sigma^2 = npq$.

Example 7-17. The mean and variance of the normal distribution: For the present write the normal distribution as

$$f(x) = \frac{1}{\beta \sqrt{2\pi}} e^{-(x-\alpha)^2/2\beta^2} \qquad (-\infty, \infty; \beta > 0)$$

Also, put $u = x - \alpha$; then,

$$\mu = E(x) = \int_{-\infty}^{\infty} xf(x)\, dx = \int_{-\infty}^{\infty} (u + \alpha)f(x)\, dx$$

$$= \frac{1}{\beta \sqrt{2\pi}} \int_{-\infty}^{\infty} ue^{-u^2/2\beta^2}\, du + \alpha \int_{-\infty}^{\infty} f(x)\, dx = 0 + \alpha = \alpha$$

Thus $\mu = \alpha$. The variance is

$$\sigma^2 = \int_{-\infty}^{\infty} (x - \mu)^2 f(x)\, dx = \frac{2}{\beta \sqrt{2\pi}} \int_0^{\infty} u^2 e^{-u^2/2\beta^2}\, du = \frac{2\beta^2}{\sqrt{\pi}} \Gamma(3\!/\!2) = \beta^2$$

Since the parameters α, β of the normal distribution are respectively equal to the mean μ and standardd eviation σ, the conventional notation for these parameters is appropriately chosen.

Often the zero point and unit of measurement of a variate are chosen arbitrarily; hence it is useful to establish general formulas for the mean and variance of a linear function $y = a + bx\ (b \neq 0)$. Denote the respective means of x, y by μ_x, μ_y and the variances by σ_x^2, σ_y^2. By Property 2, we have at once

$$\mu_y = E(a + bx) = a + b\mu_x \qquad (7\text{-}13)$$

Thus $y - \mu_y = b(x - \mu_x)$ whence (again by Property 2)

$$\sigma_y^2 = b^2 E[(x - \mu_x)^2] = b^2 \sigma_x^2 \qquad \sigma_y = |b|\sigma_x \qquad (7\text{-}14)$$

The special transformation $z = (x - \mu)/\sigma$ is known as a reduction to *standard scores;* the mean of any such transformed variate is zero and its standard deviation is unity. When this process is applied to a normal variate, the result is a unit normal variate.

Example 7-18. While most of us are aware of the difficulty of forecasting the weather, comparatively few people are familiar with the problem of devising a scoring scheme for weather forecasts. Limiting attention to the simplest case, let us consider the two-category forecast of rain or no rain during a 24-hr period at a given observation station and assume that trial dates are far enough apart to be regarded as independent. As a point of departure, let us examine a scheme wherein a forecaster will score one point if the trial date is correctly classified as to rain or no rain, and zero otherwise; no distinction being made as to relative importance, the total score will equal the total number of correct forecasts. In the utter absence of skill, if r days out of N trials were selected at random and arbitrarily labeled rain, while the remaining $N\text{-}r$ days were labeled no rain, what would be the expected value of the score? Let $p < 1\!/\!2$ denote the probability of rain, and indicate forecast and observed events by the respective subscripts f, 0. From the following table, which refers to repeated independent samples, we find that the expected score on a single trial is $q - r(q - p)/N$

and the expected total score is $Nq - r(q - p)$. Hence, if a pessimistic individual felt that his skill were negligible but still wanted to maximize his score, he could do this by setting $r = 0$, thus obtaining an expected total score of Nq by forecasting no rain on every trial. This way of beating the system can be thwarted by a more judicious choice of scores. Assigning weights w, $-x$, $-y$, z to the four possible events (in the order tabulated), we obtain, as the expected score under the same conditions of randomness,

$$r(wp + yp - zq - xq) + N(zq - yp)$$

Since we want this to vanish for all choices of r, we set the coefficients of r and N equal to zero, obtaining $x = wp/q$, $y = zq/p$.

TABLE 7-2

Event	(R_f, R_0)	$(R_f, \bar{R}_0)$	$(\bar{R}_f, R_0)$	$(\bar{R}_f, \bar{R}_0)$
Probability	pr/N	qr/N	$p(N - r)/N$	$q(N - r)/N$

On the other hand, consider a skilled forecaster; let $\lambda = P(R_0|R_f)$ and $\rho = P(R_f)$. Then we readily find that the respective joint probabilities are $\rho\lambda$, $\rho(1 - \lambda)$, $p - \rho\lambda$, $q - \rho(1 - \lambda)$, and the expected score on a single trial is

$$S = (\lambda - p)\rho \left(\frac{w}{q} + \frac{z}{p} \right)$$

showing that a competent forecaster's score is jointly proportional to his marginal probability of giving a forecast of rain and the excess of the conditional probability of the occurrence of rain when forecast over the unconditional probability of rain. In case of perfect accuracy, $\lambda = 1$ and $\rho = p$, whence $S = pw + qz$.

We have yet to specify w and z. To this end, consider the variance of the score per trial of a random forecast having the same marginal distribution as the actual rain; that is, $\lambda = p = \rho$. This variance is

$$\sigma^2 = \frac{p^2 w^2}{q} + \frac{q^2 z^2}{p}$$

We now propose to choose w and z in such a way that the expected score per trial will be unity in the case of perfect prediction and further that the variance of the scores will be as small as possible in the random case. We thus put $pw + qz = 1$ and minimize σ^2 subject to this restriction:

$$\sigma^2 = \frac{p^2 w^2}{q} + \frac{(1 - pw)^2}{p}$$

$$\frac{d\sigma^2}{dw} = 0 \text{ when } w = \frac{q}{p(p + q)} = \frac{q}{p} \quad \text{Min } \sigma^2 = q + p = 1$$

Correspondingly, $z = (1 - pw)/q = p/q$; $x = wp/q = 1$; $y = zq/p = 1$. Our scoring scheme thus becomes:

TABLE 7-3

Event	(R_f, R_0)	$(R_f, \bar{R}_0)$	$(\bar{R}_f, R_0)$	$(\bar{R}_f, \bar{R}_0)$
Score	q/p	-1	-1	p/q

The skilled forecaster's expected score per trial is $S = (\lambda - p)\rho/pq$; this becomes unity in the case of perfect skill, and the random forecast will have zero mean and unit variance.

7-6. Unbiased Estimator of Variance. A statistic b is said to be an unbiased estimator of a parameter β if $E(b) = \beta$. Let us explore this notion in connection with the problem of estimating the population variance from a sample.

In addition to matters directly related to variability, the variance enters into several questions of fairly general interest which concern the sample mean—what confidence limits can be attached to it, whether an observed sample mean supports a prior hypothesis as to the population mean, or whether two or more sample means could be considered representative of a common population mean. Even assuming a normal distribution for the sample means, numerical values of the probabilities in question can not be obtained so long as they involve the unknown parameter σ^2. However, introducing a suitable estimate s^2 for σ^2 and making a simple change of variables, it turns out, in the normal case, that a parameter-free variate results, and the questions can be answered. As a consequence of the approximate normality of sample means from ordinary non-normal populations, the sampling distributions derived from the normal population are sufficiently close to the true distributions for most practical purposes. Both by theoretical and empirical methods, the effects of non-normality on the standard tests have been investigated by top-notch men in the field, and although the conclusions are necessarily limited to the general classes of non-normality actually examined, the results indicate surprisingly little disturbance of the conventional significance levels.

In devising an estimator for σ^2, we are confronted with choosing between conflicting principles. Applying the method of maximum likelihood to a random sample $x_1, x_2, \ldots, x_n$ from a normal population with both parameters μ, σ unknown, we find that the estimator for μ is the sample mean $\bar{x}$, the estimator for σ^2 is $\Sigma_i(x_i - \bar{x})^2/n$, and that for σ is the square root of the latter quantity. On the other hand, it is readily shown that this maximum likelihood estimator for σ^2 is biased, for taking expectations of both sides of the identity,

$$\Sigma_i(x_i - \mu)^2 \equiv \Sigma_i(x_i - \bar{x})^2 + n(\bar{x} - \mu)^2 \tag{7-15}$$

and using a result which will be proved in Sec. 7-11, we obtain

$$n\sigma^2 = E[\Sigma_i(x_i - \bar{x})^2] + \sigma^2$$
whence $\qquad E[\Sigma_i(x_i - \bar{x})^2] = (n - 1)\sigma^2 \tag{7-16}$

Consequently, the expected value of the maximum likelihood estimator is $\sigma^2(n - 1)/n$ rather than σ^2. If we were sure we had a normal population in a particular instance, we might be influenced more strongly in favor of the maximum likelihood estimator, despite its bias. But we have at our immediate disposal the alternative estimator,

$$s^2 \equiv \frac{\Sigma_i(x_i - \bar{x})^2}{n - 1} \qquad (7\text{-}17)$$

which is unbiased for all populations such that the variance itself is definable. Therefore, in the interests of generality, and also because standard tests have already been developed from this point of view, we adopt $s^2 \equiv \Sigma_i(x_i - \bar{x})^2/(n - 1)$ as our estimator of σ^2, and its square root s as our estimator of σ. It should be pointed out, however, that there is no general rule for obtaining an unbiased estimator of the standard deviation, for the mean of a square root is not in general equal to the square root of the mean of the initial variate. Thus s is usually a biased estimator of σ, and here again our choice between conflicting aims is dictated by the relative breadth of applicability of our options.

By fairly heavy algebra, which we omit, it can be shown that the variance of s^2 in repeated random samples of size n from an infinite population is

$$\text{Variance } (s^2) \equiv E(s^2 - \sigma^2)^2 = \frac{1}{n}\left[\mu_4 - \frac{(n - 3)\sigma^4}{n - 1}\right] \qquad (7\text{-}18)$$

where $\mu_4 \equiv E(x - \mu)^4$. For a normal variate, $\mu_4 = 3\sigma^4$, whence the variance of s^2 in random samples from a normal population is $2\sigma^4/(n - 1)$.

Assuming an adequate reason for hypothesizing a normal distribution, the actual process of fitting a normal curve to a particular sample of n independent observations consists of estimating the two parameters μ and σ from the data. The fitted density function then becomes

$$f(x) = \frac{1}{s\sqrt{2\pi}} e^{-(x-\bar{x})^2/2s^2} \qquad (-\infty, \infty)$$

The extent to which this density function actually agrees with the observed relative frequencies depends upon how well the sample itself is typical of the normal distribution. In this connection, it is important to remember that if the sample were in fact drawn at random from a normal universe, the relative frequencies would exhibit this randomness in the form of irregular deviations about the fitted curve. We shall presently see how to decide whether the normal hypothesis is tenable.

Example 7-19. The annual amounts of rainfall in the Susquehanna valley during the years 1860–1951 are recorded to the nearest hundredth of an inch in Table 7-4. Fit a normal curve to this sample.

Assuming that the annual amounts of rainfall are independently distributed, which is in fact fairly close to the truth, we compute the two statistics $\bar{x}$ and s^2. Here

TABLE 7-4. SUSQUEHANNA ANNUAL RAINFALL, 1860–1951†

Amount (x)	Freq.	Cum. freq.	Amount (x)	Freq.	Cum. freq.	Amount (x)	Freq.	Cum. freq.
28.04	1	1	38.08	1	33	40.75	1	64
31.21	1	2	38.15	1	34	40.78	1	65
31.63	1	3	38.18	1	35	41.12	1	66
32.11	1	4	38.43	1	36	41.18	1	67
33.02	1	5	38.51	1	37	41.23	1	68
34.25	1	6	38.65	1	38	41.45	1	69
34.34	1	7	38.81	1	39	41.72	1	70
34.59	1	8	38.86	1	40	41.80	1	71
35.11	1	9	38.89	1	41	41.85	1	72
35.43	1	10	38.91	1	42	41.90	1	73
35.76	1	11	39.08	1	43	41.96	1	74
36.35	1	12	39.13	1	44	42.03	1	75
36.39	1	13	39.55	1	45	42.09	1	76
36.62	2	15	39.56	1	46	42.26	1	77
36.63	1	16	39.74	1	47	42.85	1	78
36.65	1	17	39.82	1	48	43.17	1	79
36.68	1	18	39.99	1	49	43.38	1	80
36.70	1	19	40.06	1	50	43.44	1	81
36.86	1	20	40.08	1	51	44.34	1	82
37.00	1	21	40.14	2	53	44.46	1	83
37.13	1	22	40.15	1	54	44.56	1	84
37.15	1	23	40.23	1	55	44.76	1	85
37.33	1	24	40.40	1	56	44.82	1	86
37.57	1	25	40.41	1	57	45.06	1	87
37.72	1	26	40.48	1	58	45.89	1	88
37.77	1	27	40.54	1	59	46.51	1	89
37.79	2	29	40.57	1	60	47.31	1	90
37.96	1	30	40.60	1	61	48.22	1	91
38.04	1	31	40.62	1	62	48.61	1	92
38.07	1	32	40.67	1	63			

† Courtesy of the Pennsylvania Water and Power Company.

we have

$$N = 92 \qquad \Sigma x = 3633.24 \qquad \Sigma x^2 = 144700.7034$$
$$\bar{x} = 39.492 \qquad \Sigma(x - \bar{x})^2 = \Sigma x^2 - \bar{x}\Sigma x = 1216.7893$$
$$s^2 = \frac{\Sigma(x - \bar{x})^2}{N - 1} = \frac{1216.7893}{91} = 13.3713$$
$$s = 3.657$$

Therefore the fitted normal distribution is

$$f(x) = \frac{1}{s\sqrt{2\pi}}\, e^{-(x-\bar{x})^2/2s^2} \qquad (-\infty,\ \infty)$$

$$= \frac{1}{(3.657)\sqrt{2\pi}}\, e^{-(x-39.492)^2/26.743} \qquad (-\infty,\ \infty)$$

7-7. Probability of Extreme Values. The intimate connection between the standard deviation and the intuitive concept of concentration is brought out by the fact that, in terms of standard deviation, an upper bound can be set on the probability of extreme deviations from the mean. A very general relation of this sort, applicable to any distribution for which μ and σ are definable, is known as the Tchebysheff inequality, while a stronger inequality, but one restricted to unimodal distributions, was previously established by Gauss.

The Tchebysheff Inequality. For any distribution with finite mean and variance,

$$P(|x - \mu| \geq t\sigma) \leq \frac{1}{t^2} \qquad (7\text{-}19)$$

Tchebysheff Inequality

where $t > 0$.

Proof. Let P denote the probability that $|x - \mu| \geq t\sigma$. Let A represent the class of values of x for which $|x - \mu| \geq t\sigma$ and B, the complementary class, for which $|x - \mu| < t\sigma$. Denote the submean of $(x - \mu)^2$ by α^2 in class A and by β^2 in class B; thus $\alpha^2 \geq t^2\sigma^2$. By definition, $\sigma^2 = P\alpha^2 + (1 - P)\beta^2$ whence

$$P = \frac{\sigma^2 - (1 - P)\beta^2}{\alpha^2} \leq \frac{\sigma^2 - (1 - P)\beta^2}{t^2\sigma^2} \leq \frac{1}{t^2}$$

Note that this proposition yields no information unless $t > 1$, for $P \leq 1$ in any event. Note further that P is definitely less than $1/t^2$ if the probability of class B is other than zero; also P is less than $1/t^2$ if class A contains any area beyond its inside limit $|x - \mu| = t\sigma$. Hence $P < 1/t^2$ for all variates having a density function, and the same is true for most discrete variates as well.

The Gauss Inequality. For a unimodal density function, let m denote the mode, and put $\lambda = (\mu - m)/\sigma$. Then when $t > |\lambda|$,

$$P(|x - \mu| \geq t\sigma) \leq \frac{4(1 + \lambda^2)}{9(t - |\lambda|)^2} \qquad (7\text{-}20)$$

Gauss Inequality

Thus if $\lambda = 0$,

$$P \leq \frac{1}{2.25t^2} \qquad (7\text{-}21)$$

Camp-Meidell Inequality

The latter relation is commonly called the *Camp-Meidell* inequality.   For an indication of the proof of the Gauss inequality, the reader is referred to H. Cramer.[1]   The probability P is represented graphically as the shaded portion of Fig. 7-7.

From the quantity $(|x - \mu|)/\sigma$ in these inequalities, it is seen that the probability of exceeding a stated magnitude of deviation from the mean tends to decrease as σ decreases, or what amounts to the same thing, the

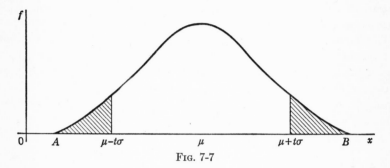

FIG. 7-7

probability of keeping within preassigned limits tends to increase with decreasing σ; accordingly, in a general way (but not a unique way, since the precise relationship depends upon the distribution considered) concentration is inversely related to the standard deviation.   Whereas the Tchebysheff inequality guarantees that no more than one-ninth of any distribution with finite μ and σ lies beyond 3σ from its mean, we learn from the Camp-Meidell inequality that this region includes less than 5 per cent of any distribution to which that inequality applies.   It should be kept in mind, however, that because of their generality, these inequalities cannot specify the true probabilities very precisely; and as they yield only upper bounds, the actual probabilities are often much lower.   With reference to significance tests, such overestimates of the tail areas (outlying portions of the curve) ordinarily would be on the conservative side, inasmuch as the evidence in support of an innovation would then be deemed inconclusive.   Even when the mean and mode do not coincide, the Camp-Meidell inequality frequently leads to an overestimate of tail areas of unimodal distributions.   In Example 7-14, for instance, where the mean is exactly twice the mode, the true probability is .039 that a random point will deviate from μ by as much as 2σ, and .014 that it will deviate by as much as 3σ, whereas the corresponding bounds, as given by the Camp-Meidell inequality, are .111 and .049 respectively.

7-8. Moment-generating Functions.   The expected value of a variate has the same formal definition as the x centroid of the area under the curve

[1] H. Cramer, "Mathematical Methods of Statistics," pp. 183, 256, Princeton University Press, Princeton, N.J., 1946.

$f(x)$. The expected value, therefore, is called the first moment of the distribution, and by analogy, the quantity $E(x^n)$ is called the nth moment. Moments were originally introduced into the field of probability in order to characterize an arbitrary distribution by a series of numbers in somewhat the same way that an ordinary mathematical function is characterized by a series expansion. In the past a great deal of profound mathematical research has been devoted to moments, but present-day interest in the subject is due largely to the moment-generating function, which incorporates the most valuable properties of the moments themselves.

The moment-generating function may be defined as the expected value of the function $e^{\theta x}$, where θ is an arbitrary (real) parameter. Since this expected value is clearly dependent upon both the value of θ and the nature of the distribution of x, we shall employ the symbol $M(\theta:x)$ to represent the moment-generating function derived from the variate x when the arbitrary parameter is θ. Thus, if the distribution of x is given by $f(x)$ $(A \leq x \leq B)$, then

$$M(\theta:x) \equiv E(e^{\theta x}) = \int_A^B e^{\theta x} f(x) \, dx$$

or, if x is discrete,

$$M(\theta:x) = \sum_x e^{\theta x} f(x)$$

(7-22)

The moment-generating function is a type of Laplace transform, a discussion of which is contained in many of the recent textbooks on advanced calculus. If the moment-generating function exists for all values of θ in the arbitrarily small interval $(-h, h)$ where $h > 0$, then the distribution of x is uniquely determined by it; also, in that case, all of the moments exist. The reason for the name may be seen from the series expansion $e^{\theta x} = \sum_{n=0}^{\infty} (\theta x)^n / n!$, whence

$$M(\theta:x) = 1 + \theta E(x) + \frac{\theta^2}{2!} E(x^2) + \cdots + \frac{\theta^n}{n!} E(x^n) + \cdots \quad (7\text{-}23)$$

and

$$\left. \frac{d^n M(\theta:x)}{d\theta^n} \right|_{\theta=0} = E(x^n) \quad (7\text{-}24)$$

In mathematical terminology, a function which yields a given system of constants when operated upon in a prescribed manner is called a "generating function" for that system of constants.

Example 7-20. The moment-generating function of the gamma variate x (parameters α, β) is

$$M(\theta:x) = \int_0^{\infty} e^{\theta x} f(x) \, dx = \frac{1}{\beta^{\alpha+1} \Gamma(\alpha + 1)} \int_0^{\infty} x^{\alpha} e^{-(1-\theta\beta)x/\beta} \, dx$$

$$= \frac{1}{(1 - \theta\beta)^{\alpha+1}}$$

The series expansion of this function exists for every value of θ in the interval $(-h, h)$ provided that $h < 1/\beta$; hence the moment-generating function uniquely determines the distribution.

Example 7-21. Given that $M(\theta:x) = (1 - \theta\beta)^{-(\alpha+1)}$ find the distribution of x. Since the moment-generating function uniquely determines the distribution, this must be a gamma distribution with parameters (α, β). Hence

$$f(x) = \frac{1}{\beta^{\alpha+1}\Gamma(\alpha + 1)} x^\alpha e^{-x/\beta} \qquad (0, \infty)$$

Example 7-22. From the moment-generating function find $E(x)$ where

$$f(x) = (1 - \alpha)\alpha^x \qquad (x = 0, 1, 2, \ldots \infty; 0 < \alpha < 1)$$

The moment-generating function of this geometric distribution is

$$M(\theta:x) = \sum_{x=0}^\infty e^{\theta x} f(x) = (1 - \alpha) \sum_{x=0}^\infty (\alpha e^\theta)^x = \frac{1 - \alpha}{1 - \alpha e^\theta}$$

From this function, we obtain $E(x)$ by differentiation:

$$E(x) = \frac{dM(\theta:x)}{d\theta}\bigg|_{\theta=0} = \frac{(1 - \alpha)\alpha e^\theta}{(1 - \alpha e^\theta)^2}\bigg|_0 = \frac{\alpha}{1 - \alpha}$$

This result checks with Example 7-3.

Example 7-23. Given that $M(\theta:x) = (1 - \alpha)/(1 - \alpha e^\theta)$ and $x = 0, 1, 2, \ldots, \infty$ find $f(x)$. This could be done by direct comparison with Example 7-22, but the information that x is confined to integral values is sufficient to determine $f(x)$ from $M(\theta:x)$ without reference to the previous result. Expanding $M(\theta:x)$ in a series, we have

$$M(\theta:x) = (1 - \alpha) \sum_{x=0}^\infty \alpha^x e^{x\theta}$$

But by definition

$$M(\theta:x) = \sum_{x=0}^\infty f(x) e^{x\theta}$$

Therefore, equating general terms,

$$f(x) = (1 - \alpha)\alpha^x \qquad (x = 0, 1, 2, \ldots, \infty)$$

The major application of the moment-generating function lies in the convenient treatment of derived variates. If u is a continuous function of x, the moment-generating function of u can be found from the distribution of x without first deriving the distribution of u proper. For example, if the distribution of x is given by $f(x)$ $(A \le x \le B)$, then

$$M(\theta:u) \equiv E(e^{\theta u}) = \int_A^B e^{\theta u} f(x)\, dx \qquad (7\text{-}25)$$

Once $M(\theta:u)$ is known, it is often possible to identify the distribution of u by an appeal to the uniqueness property.

Example 7-24. Given $f(x) = 1$ $(0, 1)$ determine the distribution of $u = -2 \ln x$ from its moment-generating function. Here $\theta u = \ln x^{-2\theta}$ and $e^{\theta u} = x^{-2\theta}$, whence

$$M(\theta : u) = \int_0^1 x^{-2\theta} \, dx = \frac{1}{1 - 2\theta}$$

Referring to Example 7-20 we recognize this as a special case of the moment-generating function of the gamma distribution with $\alpha = 0$, $\beta = 2$. Hence u is distributed as chi-square with two degrees of freedom.

From Eq. 7-25 we deduce that the effect of a linear transformation $u = a + bx$ $(b \neq 0)$ is to replace θ by $b\theta$ and multiply the resulting function by $e^{a\theta}$. For, in the case considered,

$$M(\theta : a + bx) = \int_A^B e^{\theta(a+bx)} f(x) \, dx = e^{a\theta} \int_A^B e^{b\theta x} f(x) \, dx = e^{a\theta} M(b\theta : x)$$

$$(7\text{-}26)$$

This same result holds in general. An interesting special case of Eq. (7-26) is obtained by setting $a = -\mu$, $b = 1$, where $\mu = E(x)$. Since u then becomes $x - \mu$, this transformation yields the generating function of the so-called *central* moments, i.e., moments taken about the mean as opposed to *raw* moments, which are the regular ones taken about the origin. The result is

$$M(\theta : x - \mu) = e^{-\mu\theta} M(\theta : x) \qquad (7\text{-}27)$$

Conventional symbols for the raw and central moments are μ_n' and μ_n respectively. That is,

$$\mu_n' \equiv E(x^n) \qquad \mu_n \equiv E[(x - \mu)^n] \qquad (7\text{-}28)$$

In terms of this notation, therefore,

$$\mu = \mu_1' \qquad \mu_1 \equiv 0 \qquad \sigma^2 = \mu_2 = \mu_2' - (\mu_1')^2 \qquad (7\text{-}29)$$

For future reference, we state the moment-generating functions of the binomial, Poisson, and normal distributions. The student is invited to establish these himself; for the binomial, the main point of the derivation is to recognize the binomial expansion; for the Poisson, the series expansion of the exponential; for the normal, one must complete the square.

Binomial distribution: $\qquad M(\theta : x) = (q + pe^\theta)^n$

Poisson distribution: $\qquad M(\theta : x) = e^{-\mu} e^{\mu e^\theta} \qquad\qquad (7\text{-}30)$

Normal distribution: $\qquad M(\theta : x) = e^{\mu\theta} e^{\sigma^2 \theta^2 / 2}$

It will be noted that the moment-generating function of the unit normal distribution is simply $e^{\theta^2/2}$.

Closely allied with the moment-generating function are the characteristic function and the cumulant function. Although we shall not develop these concepts at length, we introduce them as interesting and powerful tools. The characteristic function is defined as the expected value of $e^{i\theta x}$ (θ real, $i = \sqrt{-1}$) and is otherwise known as the Fourier transform of $f(x)$. Whereas the integral by which the moment-generating function is defined may diverge for certain distributions, the characteristic function exists for all distributions, because $|e^{i\theta x}| \equiv 1$. A further analytic advantage of the characteristic function is that it satisfies the Fourier inversion theorem

$$f(x) = \frac{1}{2\pi} \int_{-\infty}^{\infty} e^{-i\theta x} M(i\theta : x) \, d\theta \qquad (7\text{-}31)$$

Thus, in principle, $f(x)$ can be determined directly from the characteristic function; in practice, however, this advantage is more nominal than realizable. The *cumulant* function $K(\theta : x)$ is simply the natural logarithm of the moment-generating function; the coefficients (κ_1, κ_2, . . . , κ_r . . .) of $\theta^r/r!$ ($r = 1, 2, \ldots$) in the series expansion of this function are called *cumulants*. Thus, for the normal distribution the cumulants are $\kappa_1 = \mu$, $\kappa_2 = \sigma^2$, $\kappa_r = 0$ ($r > 2$). All of the cumulants of the Poisson distribution have the common value μ, for $K(\theta : x) = -\mu + \mu e^\theta$, whence $\kappa_r = \mu$ ($r = 1, 2, \ldots$). In general, the cumulants can be related to the mean and the central moments. These relations become complicated with increasing r, but for the first four they are as follows:

$$\kappa_1 = \mu \qquad \kappa_2 = \sigma^2 \qquad \kappa_3 = \mu_3 \qquad \kappa_4 = \mu_4 - 3\sigma^4 \qquad (7\text{-}32)$$

From the fact that $M(\theta : a + bx) = e^{a\theta} M(b\theta : x)$, it is readily shown that if $u = a + bx$ ($b \neq 0$) and κ_r, κ_r' denote the respective rth cumulants of x and u, then

$$\kappa_1' = a + b\kappa_1 \qquad \kappa_r' = b^r \kappa_r \qquad (r > 1) \qquad (7\text{-}33)$$

On account of this simple behavior under a linear transformation of variables, the cumulants are also known as *semi-invariants*.

7-9. Multivariate Functions. The rule for finding the expected value of a function $\phi(x)$ can be extended to continuous functions of any number of variables. Thus, if the joint-distribution function $F(x_1, x_2, \ldots , x_n)$ of several random variables x_1, x_2, . . . , x_n is defined over the region of space R_x, and $\phi(x_1, x_2, \ldots , x_n)$ is any continuous function of the x's, then the expected value of this function is given by

$$E[\phi(x_1, x_2, \ldots , x_n)] = \int \int \cdots \int_{R_x} \phi(x_1, x_2, \ldots , x_n) \, dF$$
$$(x_1, x_2, \ldots , x_n) \qquad (7\text{-}34)$$

For a set of discrete variates, this reduces to a multiple summation, while for continuous variates having a joint density function, the equation becomes

$$E[\phi(x_1, x_2, \ldots, x_n)] = \int \int \cdots \int_{R_x} \phi(x_1, x_2, \ldots, x_n) f(x_1, x_2, \ldots, x_n)$$
$$dx_1 \, dx_2 \cdots dx_n \quad (7\text{-}35)$$

Example 7-25. Find the expected value of the function $z = xy$ given that x and y are jointly distributed as follows:

$$f(x,y) = xe^{-x(1+y)} \qquad (0, \infty \text{ each})$$

By Eq. (7-35) we have

$$E(z) = \int_0^\infty \int_0^\infty xy f(x,y) \, dx \, dy = \int_0^\infty e^{-x} \left(\int_0^\infty x^2 y e^{-xy} \, dy \right) dx$$
$$= \int_0^\infty e^{-x} \, dx = 1$$

Now, in Exercise 26 of Chap. 6, the distribution of z was given as $g(z) = e^{-z}$ $(0, \infty)$. Hence we may check our result from the distribution of z itself. Thus, alternatively,

$$E(z) = \int_0^\infty z e^{-z} \, dz = 1$$

As an important special case of Eq. (7-34) we notice that the expected value of any one of the variates x_i of a multivariate system $x_1, x_2, \ldots, x_n$ can be evaluated directly from the joint distribution without first obtaining the marginal distribution. Thus,

$$E(x_i) = \int \int \cdots \int_{R_x} x_i \, dF(x_1, x_2, \ldots, x_n) \qquad (7\text{-}36)$$

Two consequences of the equation for the expected value of a function are sufficiently important to be stated as theorems. The first concerns the sum of any number of variates, whether dependent or independent, while the second concerns the product of independent variates only.

THEOREM 7-1. If $y = x_1 + x_2 + \cdots + x_n$, then

$$E(y) = E(x_1) + E(x_2) + \cdots + E(x_n)$$

Proof. From the equation

$$E(y) = \int \int \cdots \int_{R_x} (x_1 + x_2 + \cdots + x_n) \, dF(x_1, x_2, \ldots, x_n)$$

we obtain by expansion

$$E(y) = \sum_{i=1}^n \int \int \cdots \int_{R_x} x_i \, dF(x_1, x_2, \ldots, x_n) = \sum_{i=1}^n E(x_i)$$

COROLLARY. If $z = a_0 + a_1 x_1 + a_2 x_2 + \cdots + a_n x_n$ where the a's are constants, then

$$E(z) = a_0 + a_1 E(x_1) + a_2 E(x_2) + \cdots + a_n E(x_n)$$

The proof is similar to that of Theorem 7-1.

THEOREM 7-2.   If $y = x_1 x_2 \cdots x_n$ where $x_1, x_2, \ldots, x_n$ are *independent*, then

$$E(y) = E(x_1)E(x_2) \cdots E(x_n)$$

Proof. If the variates are independent, their joint-probability increment $dF(x_1, x_2, \ldots, x_n)$ factors into the product of the increments of their respective distribution functions

$$dF(x_1, x_2, \ldots, x_n) = dF_1(x_1) \, dF_2(x_2) \cdots dF_n(x_n)$$

Also, the respective regions of integration are independent. Consequently, the whole expression defining $E(y)$ may be factored, and the result is

$$
\begin{aligned}
E(y) &= \int_{R_1} x_1 \, dF_1(x_1) \int_{R_2} x_2 \, dF_2(x_2) \cdots \int_{R_n} x_n \, dF_n(x_n) \\
&= E(x_1)E(x_2) \cdots E(x_n)
\end{aligned}
$$

where, of course, R_i represents the region of definition of $dF_i(x_i)$.

COROLLARY.   If y is the product of pure functions of *independent* variates, for instance $y = \phi_1(x_1)\phi_2(x_2) \cdots \phi_n(x_n)$, then

$$E(y) = E[\phi_1(x_1)]E[\phi_2(x_2)] \cdots E[\phi_n(x_n)]$$

The proof is similar to that of Theorem 7-2.

Example 7-26.   If $z = (x + y)^2$ then

$$E(z) = E[(x + y)^2] = E(x^2 + 2xy + y^2)$$

Hence, by Theorem 7-1

$$E(z) = E(x^2) + 2E(xy) + E(y^2)$$

This result holds for any variates whatever. If the variates x and y are *independent*, the cross-product term can be factored by virtue of Theorem 7-2 to yield $E(xy) = E(x)E(y)$. Hence, for independent variates,

$$E(z) = E(x^2) + 2E(x)E(y) + E(y^2)$$

The student's attention is called to the fact that, for brevity, an expression like $E[(x + y)^2]$ is usually written as $E(x + y)^2$.

Example 7-27.   From an infinite population in which the mean value of x is μ, a random sample of n observations $x_1, x_2, \ldots, x_n$ is drawn and the sample average $\bar{x} = (x_1 + x_2 + \cdots + x_n)/n$ is computed. If this experiment could be repeated for an indefinitely large number of independent trials, find the mean value of $\bar{x}$. From the corollary to Theorem 7-1, the mean value of $\bar{x}$ in repeated trials is

$$E(\bar{x}) = \frac{1}{n} E(x_1) + \frac{1}{n} E(x_2) + \cdots + \frac{1}{n} E(x_n)$$

By construction, $x_1, x_2, \ldots, x_n$ constitute independent random variables all having the same distribution as x, the variate being sampled. Hence, they all have the same expected value μ, and

$$E(\bar{x}) = \frac{n\mu}{n} = \mu \tag{7-37}$$

From the foregoing propositions, we may deduce that the variance is a more comprehensive modulus of variability than its definition at first suggests, for it actually measures the squared difference of all possible pairs of values. Now the mean square difference of all possible pairs x_1, x_2 can be obtained by regarding x_1, x_2 as independent variates, each distributed as x. Then

$$E(x_1 - x_2)^2 = E(x_1^2) - 2E(x_1 x_2) + E(x_2^2) = 2[E(x^2) - \mu^2] = 2\sigma^2$$

showing that the variance is equal to half the mean square of all possible differences.

7-10. Covariance and Correlation. Two or more variates are dependent when their joint-distribution function is not simply the product of their marginal-distribution functions. Dependence in this sense is so loosely defined that it can range from the borderline of utter independence to the opposite limit, which is strict mathematical determinism. Except when the latter extreme is approached, the existence of useful relationships between variates is often difficult to detect observationally, and the mathematical representation of the relationship, once demonstrated to exist, is an art in itself.

Standard methods of studying the interrelationships between variates make constant use of the average value of a cross-product of the type $(x_1 - \xi_1)(x_2 - \xi_2)$ where $\xi_1 = E(x_1)$, $\xi_2 = E(x_2)$. This quantity

$$E[(x_1 - \xi_1)(x_2 - \xi_2)]$$

denoted by the symbol σ_{12}, is called the *covariance* of (or between) x_1 and x_2:

$$\sigma_{12} \equiv E[(x_1 - \xi_1)(x_2 - \xi_2)] \equiv E(x_1 x_2) - \xi_1 \xi_2 \tag{7-38}$$
$$\text{Covariance}$$

As a special case of this notation, σ_{11} would represent the variance of x_1, although the symbol σ_1^2 would ordinarily be employed. If x_1 and x_2 are independent, $\sigma_{12} = \xi_1 \xi_2 - \xi_1 \xi_2 = 0$, but the converse does not hold; two variates with zero covariance need not be independent.

Dimensionally, the covariance involves the product of the units of the two variates, while the variance involves the square of the unit of one of them. Therefore, a dimensionless parameter ρ_{12} could be constructed thus:

$$\rho_{12} \equiv \frac{\sigma_{12}}{\sqrt{\sigma_{11}\sigma_{22}}} \equiv \frac{\sigma_{12}}{\sigma_1 \sigma_2} \tag{7-39}$$
$$\text{Coefficient of Correlation}$$

Such a parameter is, in fact, widely used, and it is called the *coefficient of linear correlation* between x_1 and x_2. The linear correlation between two variates is simply the covariance of their corresponding standard scores, and ρ ranges from -1 to $+1$ (see Exercise 43).

7-11. The Variance of a Linear Function. From the viewpoint of general use, an important type of statistical function is a linear function of several variates. The variance of such a function can be expressed in terms of the variances and covariances of the component variates. Consider the linear function

$$y = a_0 + a_1 x_1 + a_2 x_2 + \cdots + a_n x_n$$

where the a's are constants, and put $\xi_i = E(x_i)$, $\mu = E(y)$. Then

$$\mu = a_0 + \sum_1^n a_i \xi_i \qquad y - \mu = \sum_1^n a_i(x_i - \xi_i)$$

and the variance σ^2 of y is

$$\sigma^2 = E(y - \mu)^2 = E\left[\sum_1^n a_i(x_i - \xi_i)\right]^2$$

But $\qquad \left[\sum_1^n a_i(x_i - \xi_i)\right]^2 \equiv \sum_{i=1}^n \sum_{j=1}^n a_i a_j(x_i - \xi_i)(x_j - \xi_j)$

Therefore $\quad \sigma^2 = \sum_1^n \sum_1^n a_i a_j E[(x_i - \xi_i)(x_j - \xi_j)] = \sum_1^n \sum_1^n a_i a_j \sigma_{ij}$ (7-40)

$$\text{Variance of a Linear Function}$$

If the x's are independent, their covariances vanish, and the variance of y reduces to $\sum_1^n a_i^2 \sigma_{ii}$, which is usually written as

$$\sigma^2 = \sum_1^n a_i^2 \sigma_i^2 \qquad (7\text{-}41)$$

$$\text{Variance of a Linear}$$
$$\text{Function of Independent Variates}$$

since $\sigma_{ii} \equiv \sigma_i^2$.

Example 7-28. A sample of n independent observations $x_1, x_2, \ldots, x_n$ of the same variate x is drawn at random, and the sample mean $\bar{x} = (x_1 + x_2 + \cdots + x_n)/n$ is computed. Find the variance of $\bar{x}$ in repeated independent trials of this experiment, if the variance of x is σ^2. In repeated independent trials the observations $x_1, x_2, \ldots, x_n$ may be regarded as independent variates, all distributed as x. Hence, denoting the variance of $\bar{x}$ by $\sigma_{\bar{x}}^2$, we have

$$\sigma_{\bar{x}}^2 = \sum_{1}^{n} a_i^2 \sigma_i^2 = \frac{n\sigma^2}{n^2} = \frac{\sigma^2}{n} \qquad (7\text{-}42)$$

Variance of $\bar{x}$

Therefore, once the mean and variance μ, σ^2 are given for any variate x, the mean and variance μ, σ^2/n of $\bar{x}$ may be inferred directly.

7-12. Multivariate Moment-Generating Functions. A joint multivariate moment-generating function, $M(\theta_1,\theta_2, \ldots ,\theta_n; x_1,x_2, \ldots ,x_n)$ may be defined as the expected value of the exponential function $\exp (\theta_1 x_1 + \theta_2 x_2 + \cdots + \theta_n x_n)$. Joint functions of this type are treated in advanced works on mathematical statistics, but our exposition of the multivariate situation will be limited to the simple moment-generating function of a composite variate involving two or more random variables. If u is a continuous function of several variates $x_1, x_2, \ldots , x_n$, its moment-generating function $M(\theta:u)$, being the expected value of $e^{\theta u}$, can be found from the joint distribution of the x's as a special case of Eq. 7-34. Thus, if the admissible region is R_x,

$$M(\theta:u) = \int \int \cdots \int_{R_x} e^{\theta u} \, dF(x_1,x_2, \ldots ,x_n) \qquad (7\text{-}43)$$

In particular, if a joint density function exists over R_x, then

$$M(\theta:u) = \int \int \cdots \int_{R_x} e^{\theta u} f(x_1,x_2, \ldots ,x_n) \, dx_1 \, dx_2 \cdots dx_n \qquad (7\text{-}44)$$

Example 7-29. By the method of moment-generating functions, find the distribution of $u = xy$ where

$$f(x,y) = xe^{-x(1+y)} \qquad (0, \infty \text{ each})$$

Here the moment-generating function is

$$M(\theta:u) = \int_0^\infty \int_0^\infty e^{\theta xy} xe^{-x-xy} \, dx \, dy = \int_0^\infty e^{-x} \left[\int_0^\infty xe^{-xy(1-\theta)} \, dy \right] dx$$

$$= \int_0^\infty \frac{e^{-x}}{1-\theta} \, dx = \frac{1}{1-\theta} \int_0^\infty e^{-x} \, dx = (1-\theta)^{-1}$$

This is a special case of the function $(1 - \beta\theta)^{-(\alpha+1)}$ with $\alpha = 0$, $\beta = 1$. Hence by Example 7-20 $f(u) = e^{-u}$ $(0, \infty)$ which agrees with previous results.

By direct application of Eq. 7-43 we establish two theorems of considerable importance. The first concerns the sum of independent variates, and the second, the mean values derived from random samples of size n from the same infinite population.

THEOREM 7-3. The moment-generating function of the sum of independent variates is equal to the product of their respective moment-generating functions.

Proof. Let $u = x_1 + x_2 + \cdots + x_n$ where the x's are independent. If $F_i(x_i)$ represents the marginal-distribution function of x_i and R_i its range of definition, the product $e^{\theta u} \, dF(x_1, x_2, \ldots, x_n)$ factors, yielding

$$M(\theta:u) = \int_{R_1} e^{\theta x_1} \, dF_1(x_1) \int_{R_2} e^{\theta x_2} \, dF_2(x_2) \cdots \int_{R_n} e^{\theta x_n} \, dF_n(x_n)$$
$$= M(\theta:x_1) M(\theta:x_2) \cdots M(\theta:x_n)$$

THEOREM 7-4. If $\bar{x}$ is the mean of a random sample of n observations from a population for which the moment-generating function is $M(\theta:x)$, the moment-generating function of $\bar{x}$ in repeated independent trials is

$$M(\theta:\bar{x}) = \left[M\left(\frac{\theta}{n} : x \right) \right]^n$$

Proof. Denoting the independent observations by $x_1, x_2, \ldots, x_n$ we can regard the x's as independent variates having the same distribution, whence each has the same moment-generating function, $M(\theta:x)$. Putting $u = x_1 + x_2 + \cdots + x_n$, it follows from Theorem 7-3 that

$$M(\theta:u) = [M(\theta:x)]^n$$

Now $\bar{x} = u/n$ and from Eq. 7-26

$$M(\theta:\bar{x}) = M\left(\frac{\theta}{n} : u \right) = \left[M\left(\frac{\theta}{n} : x \right) \right]^n$$

Example 7-30. The length of time t required to accumulate a fixed number of counts c of radiational particles impinging upon the counting meter at an average rate r per unit time is distributed as follows: $f(t) = [r^c/\Gamma(c)]t^{c-1}e^{-rt}$ $(0, \infty; c \geq 1)$. If n independent tests are made under similar conditions and the average waiting time τ is computed, find the distribution of τ from its moment-generating function. Since t is a gamma variate with $\alpha = c - 1$, $\beta = 1/r$, its moment-generating function by Example 7-20 is $M(\theta:t) = (1 - \theta/r)^{-c}$. Therefore, by Theorem 7-4,

$$M(\theta:\tau) = (1 - \theta/nr)^{-nc}$$

This is the moment-generating function of a gamma variate with $\alpha = nc - 1$, $\beta = 1/nr$. Therefore, the distribution of τ is

$$g(\tau) = \frac{(nr)^{nc}}{\Gamma(nc)} \tau^{nc-1} e^{-nr\tau} \qquad (0, \infty)$$

This result may be checked by applying Theorem 6-2.

7-13. Asymptotic Distributions.
In Chap. 4 it was shown by specific examples that the normal distribution provides a useful approximation to several other distributions for sufficiently large values of their appropriate parameters. The normal distribution is said to be the *asymptotic* form of any distribution which tends toward it as a limit. In this section, we shall prove the central limit theorem under restricted conditions

and establish the asymptotic forms of the binomial and multinomial distributions.

An elementary form of the central limit theorem asserts that the asymptotic distribution of the sample mean $\bar{x}$ of n independent observations of a variate x having finite mean and variance is normal as n tends to infinity. We shall prove this theorem under the restriction that the moment-generating function exists. This class includes all distributions with finite range and many with infinite range. For convenience, assume tentatively that x has zero mean and unit variance. Its cumulant function $K(\theta:x)$ can then be written as

$$K(\theta:x) = \frac{\theta^2}{2} + \sum_{r=3}^{\infty} c_r \theta^r$$

where $c_r = \kappa_r/r!$. Making the change of variable $y = \bar{x}\sqrt{n}$ in Theorem 7-4, we have

$$M(\theta:y) = \left[M\left(\frac{\theta}{\sqrt{n}}:x\right) \right]^n$$

whence, putting $k_r = c_r/(\sqrt{n})^{r-3}$ we obtain

$$K(\theta:y) = nK\left(\frac{\theta}{\sqrt{n}}:x\right) = \frac{\theta^2}{2} + \frac{1}{\sqrt{n}} \sum_{r=3}^{\infty} k_r \theta^r$$

Now the convergence of the series $c_r \theta^r$ for sufficiently small θ implies the convergence of the series $k_r \theta^r$. Hence, the sum $L(n) \equiv \sum_{3}^{\infty} k_r \theta^r$ is finite for all $n \geq 1$, and we may put

$$K(\theta:y) = \frac{\theta^2}{2} + \frac{1}{\sqrt{n}} L(n)$$

Therefore, in the limit as $n \to \infty$ we obtain

$$\lim_{n \to \infty} K(\theta:y) = \frac{\theta^2}{2}$$

showing that the asymptotic distribution of y is unit normal. Likewise, for any variate x with finite mean and variance μ, σ^2 the asymptotic distribution of the variate $y = [(\bar{x} - \mu)\sqrt{n}]/\sigma$ will be unit normal. Accordingly, for large n the distribution of $\bar{x}$ will be approximately normal with mean $= \mu$ and standard deviation $= \sigma/\sqrt{n}$.

Consider, next, the asymptotic distribution of the binomial. The moment-generating function is $(q + pe^\theta)^n$ and that of the standardized variate $u = \dfrac{x - \mu}{\sigma} = (x - np)/\sqrt{npq}$ is given by

$$M(\theta:u) = e^{-np\theta/\sqrt{npq}}(q + pe^{\theta/\sqrt{npq}})^n$$
$$\equiv (qe^{-p\theta/\sqrt{npq}} + pe^{p\theta/\sqrt{npq}})^n$$

The cumulant function of u can be expressed as

$$K(\theta:u) = \frac{\ln\,(qe^{-p\theta/\sqrt{npq}} + pe^{q\theta/\sqrt{npq}})}{1/n}$$

a form to which L'Hôpital's rule applies. Differentiating twice, we obtain

$$\lim_{n \to \infty} K(\theta:u) = \frac{\theta^2}{2}$$

showing that the asymptotic distribution of u is unit normal. Therefore, with large n, the distribution of the binomial variate x tends toward normality with $\mu = np$, $\sigma^2 = npq$.

The labor entailed in calculating exact probabilities from the multinomial distribution for large n is so heavy that, in the absence of some feasible approximation, practical uses of this distribution would be nonexistent. Therefore, we shall consider a normal approximation and from it derive a variate which is distributed asymptotically as chi-square. The latter has many important applications, but we shall defer their study to Chap. 8.

Let us begin with the simplest multinomial situation—that of three categories. Substituting $x_3 \equiv n - x_1 - x_2$ we may write the joint distribution in bivariate form as

$$f(x_1, x_2) = \frac{n!\,p_1^{x_1}p_2^{x_2}p_3^{n-x_1-x_2}}{x_1!x_2!(n - x_1 - x_2)!}$$

where $p_1 + p_2 + p_3 = 1$; $x_1 = 0, 1, \ldots, n$; $x_2 = 0, 1, \ldots, n - x_1$. Since we have previously noticed that the marginal distribution of x_1 is binomial with parameters (n, p_1), let us revamp the joint distribution as

$$f(x_1, x_2) = f_1(x_1)\phi(x_2|x_1)$$

where

$$f_1(x_1) = C(n, x_1)p_1^{x_1}q_1^{n-x_1} \qquad \phi(x_2|x_1) = C(n - x_1, x_2)(p_2')^{x_2}(q_2')^{n-x_1-x_2}$$

in which

$$q_1 = 1 - p_1 = p_2 + p_3 \qquad p_2' = \frac{p_2}{q_1} \qquad q_2' = 1 - p_2' = \frac{p_3}{q_1}$$

The validity of this substitution may be appreciated by reviewing Example 3-8. Since the conditional distribution of x_2 given x_1 is binomial in form, we may write down the conditional mean and variance by inspection. These are

$$\text{Mean } (x_2|x_1) = (n - x_1)p_2'$$

$$\text{Variance } (x_2|x_1) = (n - x_1)p_2'q_2' = \left(1 - \frac{x_1}{n}\right) np_2'q_2'$$

Now the expected value of the quantity $(1 - x_1/n)$ is equal to q_1 and the variance of it is p_1q_1/n. Accordingly, with a relative error on the order of $1/\sqrt{n}$ (by Tchebysheff's inequality, large multiples of this are improbable), we may write

$$\text{Variance } (x_2|x_1) \approx q_1 np_2'q_2' = \frac{np_2p_3}{q_1}$$

Introducing the normal approximations with $\sigma_1{}^2 = np_1q_1$, $\sigma_2{}^2 = np_2p_3/q_1$, we then have

$$f(x_1,x_2) \approx \frac{1}{\sigma_1 \sqrt{2\pi}} e^{-(x_1-np_1)^2/\sigma_1{}^2} \frac{1}{\sigma_2 \sqrt{2\pi}} e^{-[x_2-(n-x_1)p_2']^2/2\sigma_2{}^2}$$

If we now substitute $u = (x_1 - np_1)/\sigma_1$, $v = [x_2 - (n - x_1)p_2']/\sigma_2$ we find, to the same approximation, that u and v are independent unit normal variates. Consequently, their sum of squares $X^2 = u^2 + v^2$ is asymptotically distributed as chi-square with two degrees of freedom.

By straightforward, though fairly lengthy algebra, we may express this same X^2 in the following symmetrical form (note absence of q's):

$$X^2 = \frac{(x_1 - np_1)^2}{np_1} + \frac{(x_2 - np_2)^2}{np_2} + \frac{(x_3 - np_3)^2}{np_3} = \sum_{i=1}^{3} \frac{(x_i - E_i)^2}{E_i} \quad (7\text{-}45)$$

where E_i is an abbreviation for $E(x_i) = np_i$ $(i = 1, 2, 3)$. We shall omit the steps, but the student needs only patience and moderate manipulative skill to fill them in. The outcome is that the function defined by Eq. 7-45 is distributed asymptotically as chi-square with two degrees of freedom. Now any multinomial probability function can be revamped into a continued product of binomial factors and the same line of argument applied. If there are k categories, we shall arrive at $k - 1$ variates which, asymptotically, are independent and unit normal. Their sum of squares can be expressed in the symmetrical form

$$X^2 = \sum_{i=1}^{k} \frac{(x_i - np_i)^2}{np_i} = \sum_{i=1}^{k} \frac{(x_i - E_i)^2}{E_i} \quad (7\text{-}46)$$

and this variate is distributed asymptotically as chi-square with $k - 1$ degrees of freedom.

EXERCISES

1. The team for a certain game of skill is made up of four players, each of whom has a chance of scoring 0, 1, or 2 points, and the score for the team is the sum of the scores made by the individual players. Assuming independence, derive the distribution of scores for the team of players A, B, C, D whose individual score distributions are shown below.

Score	Players			
	A	B	C	D
0	.5	.2	.3	.2
1	.3	.3	.5	.5
2	.2	.5	.2	.3

From the distribution of team scores find the expected value of the score t for the team and compare this result with the sum of the expected values of the scores of the individual players. Use results of Exercise 5, Chap. 5.

Ans.

t	0	1	2	3	4	5	6	7	8	$E(t)$
$f(t)$	.0060	.0376	.1133	.2124	.2614	.2124	.1133	.0376	.0060	4.0000

Player	A	B	C	D	Sum
Expt. score	.7	1.3	.9	1.1	4.0

2. An insurance company writes a policy for an amount of money A which must be paid if an event E occurs. If the probability of E is p, what should the company charge the customer in order that the expected profit to the company be 10 per cent of A?   *Ans. $A(p + .1)$.*

3. Determine the median of x and investigate whether or not the mean exists if $f(x) = 1/(1 + x)^2$ $(0, \infty)$.   *Ans.* Median = 1. Mean does not exist.

4. For any variate for which the mean μ is finite, prove the identities (a) $E(x - \mu) = 0$, (b) $E(x - a)^2 = E(x - \mu)^2 + (\mu - a)^2$ where a = constant. Use the substitution $(x - a) \equiv (x - \mu) + (\mu - a)$. For any sample of N observations $x_1, x_2, \ldots, x_N$ put $\bar{x} = (1/N) \sum_i x_i$ and prove analogous properties of $\bar{x}$: (c) $\sum_i (x_i - \bar{x}) = 0$, (d) $\sum_i (x_i - a)^2 = \sum_i (x_i - \bar{x})^2 + N(\bar{x} - a)^2$. As a special case of (d) notice that

$$\sum_i (x_i - \mu)^2 = \sum_i (x_i - \bar{x})^2 + N(\bar{x} - \mu)^2.$$

5. By adapting Example 7-3 with the aid of Property 2, find $E(x)$ where $f(x) = pq^{x-1}$ $(x = 1, 2, \ldots; p + q = 1)$ *Ans. $1/p$.*

6. Given $y = x^3$ and $v = (x - \mu)^4$, find $E(y)$ and $E(v)$ where x is normal.   *Ans. $E(y) = 3\sigma^2\mu + \mu^3$; $E(v) = 3\sigma^4$.*

7. Given $f(x) = 6x(1 - x)$ $(0, 1)$ find $E(y)$ where $y = 1/x$ and check by using the distribution of y.   *Ans. 3.*

8. Given $f(x) = e^{-x}$ $(0, \infty)$ find $E(y)$ where $y = e^{x/2}$ and check by applying the distribution of y. *Ans.* 2.

9. Maxwell demonstrated that for a fixed absolute temperature the speed x of individual molecules of a given gas is distributed as follows:

$$f(x) = kx^2e^{-3x^2/2w^2} \qquad (0 < x < \infty)$$

where w is a physical parameter and k is a mathematical parameter so adjusted that the area is unity. Determine k in terms of w, and then find the mean molecular kinetic energy of the gas, letting m represent the mass of an individual molecule. *Ans.* $k = 3\sqrt{6}/w^3\sqrt{\pi}$; $E(x^2) = w^2$; mean KE $= mw^2/2$.

10. (a) If c is an arbitrary constant, show that the quantity $E[(x - c)^2]$ is minimized by choosing $c = \mu$. (b) If x has a density function, show that the quantity $E(|x - c|)$ is minimized by choosing c as the median.

11. The average number of rainy days for a specific period at a certain station is five, and the number of rainy days for this same period is a Poisson distribution. The value of a certain relative index in dollars to the crops in that area increases exponentially in its value as the number of rainy days x increase according to the expression $(e^{2x} - 1)$. What is the expected monetary value of the rain? *Ans.* $e^{5(e^2-1)} - 1$.

12. The cost of operating a hydroelectric plant for a specific period consists of a fixed charge of K_1 dollars independent of the amount of electricity generated and a cost of K_2 dollars per kilowatthour for generation. All of the power generated can be sold at a price which is K_3 dollars per kilowatthour. The possible amount of generation is related to the rainfall in the area, which has a certain probability density, thus permitting the computation of the probability density of the distribution of kilowatthours generated as $f(x) = \alpha^2xe^{-\alpha x}$ $(0 < x < \infty)$. What is the expected value of the profit? By finding the probability density of the profit, determine the probability of going into bankruptcy at the end of the period if only K_4 dollars are available as reserves at the beginning of the period with no borrowing capacity $(K_4 < K_1)$. Plot the distribution of the profit.
Ans. $(2/\alpha)(K_3 - K_2) - K_1$; $1 - [1 + \alpha(K_1 - K_4)/(K_3 - K_2)] e^{-\alpha(K_1-K_4)/(K_3-K_2)}$.

13. The cost to a company for a given manufactured piece consists of a fixed cost which is k_1 dollars irrespective of the volume, a variable manufacturing cost which depends upon volume and is k_2 dollars per piece, and another variable cost which goes down with the volume and can be approximated by k_3/V dollars per piece. The selling price is a variable depending upon the number sold and can be approximated by $k_4(V + 2 \times 10^4)/V$ dollars per piece. What is the expected value of the profit if the probability density of sales is $f(x) = (\frac{4}{625})x^3(5 - x)$ $0 < x < 5$ where the units of x in $f(x)$ are in 10,000 units of volume? *Ans.* $(10^5/3)(k_4 - k_2) + (2 \times 10^4 k_4 - k_3 - k_1)$.

14. The probability of a certain sales volume during a given period is $f(V) = \frac{3}{2,500} V^2(10 - V)$ $0 < V < 10$ and the units are in hundreds of pieces. The cost of the raw material is \$3 per item with an added cost of \$2 per item for manufacturing cost. The raw material is made up only as orders are received, and that raw material which is not used will be sold for scrap at \$1 per piece. Find an expression for the number of items of raw material we should order at the beginning of the period as a function of the mark-up price m per item, under the restriction that the expected value of the profit will be a maximum. The raw material must be on hand at the beginning of the period for fulfillment of orders. *Ans.* $x^3(40 - 3x) = 10^4m/(m + 2)$, where x is in hundreds of pieces.

15. The sales volume of a given concern is given by the following probability density function:

$$f(v|\bar{V}) = \frac{4}{\bar{V}^2} v e^{-2v/\bar{V}} \qquad 0 < v < \infty$$

which has an expected value of $\bar{V}$, that is, $\int_0^\infty v f(v|\bar{V})\, dv = \bar{V}$. This expected value $\bar{V}$

depends upon the selling price per unit s and also upon the total amount of money spent on advertising t. Assume that in the range of application, the relation is

$$\bar{V} = M \frac{1 + bt}{1 + t} e^{-as}$$

where M, a, and b are constant. Also assume that the cost c per item is independent of the volume, since this item is purely one of assembly. The margin of profit m per item is, of course, reduced by the amount spent on production and advertising, so that $m = s - c - (t/v)$. Find the expected value of the product of m times v and then maximize this with respect to t and s in order to determine the best selling price and amount of money to be spent in advertising.

Ans. $E(mv) = (s - c)\bar{V} - t$; $s = c + \dfrac{1}{a}$; $t = -1 + \sqrt{\dfrac{(M)(b - 1)}{a}}\, e^{-ac-1}$.

16. A business consists of renting out the use of 10 washing machines. Assume that, under present conditions, any given machine is likely to be out of commission one day out of five and also that breakdowns occur at random. What is the probability of more than one machine being out of order on a given day? Assuming the average loss is c dollars per day for a machine out of order, write down an expression for the expected loss due to having machines out of service and evaluate by making the substitution $u = k - 1$ and recognizing the binomial expansion.

Ans. $1 - 1\frac{4}{5}(\frac{4}{5})^9$; $\displaystyle\sum_{k=0}^{10} ckC(10,k)(\frac{4}{5})^{10-k}(\frac{1}{5})^k = 2c$.

17. A manufacturer wishes to estimate the mean μ of a certain attribute x of his product by computing the sample mean $\bar{x}$ of a set of n independent observations of x. The cost C of the sampling process is composed of one part proportional to the sample size and one part proportional to the magnitude of the error of the estimate:

$$C = \sqrt{\frac{2}{\pi}}\, n + 16|\bar{x} - \mu|$$

If x is assumed to be normally distributed with unit variance, find the value of n which minimizes the expected value of the cost. *Ans.* $n = 4$.

18. A seasonal item which must be stocked in advance by a retailer costs \$1 per unit and sells for \$2 per unit. Unsold items at the end of the season are a complete loss. The probability of k customer orders is $(\frac{1}{2})^{k+1}$, $k = 0, 1, \ldots$. Find the expected profit as a function of the number of items stocked. Note that

$$K\binom{10}{K} = 10\binom{9}{K-1}$$

$$K\binom{n}{K} = n\binom{n-1}{K-1}$$

$$\sum_{k=0}^{\infty} (\tfrac{1}{2})^k = 2 \qquad \sum_{k=0}^{n} (\tfrac{1}{2})^k = 2[1 - (\tfrac{1}{2})^{n+1}]$$

$$\sum_{k=0}^{n} k(\tfrac{1}{2})^k = 2[1 - (\tfrac{1}{2})^n] - n(\tfrac{1}{2})^n$$

Ans. $2 - x - (\tfrac{1}{2})^{x-1}$.

19. Given a random sample of two observations x_1 and x_2 from any population for which the variance is finite, show that the statistic

$$\tfrac{1}{2}(x_1 - x_2)^2$$

is an unbiased estimate of the population variance.

20. Find the mean and variance of x where

$$f(x) = \frac{1}{b - a} \qquad (a, b)$$

Ans. $\mu = (a + b)/2,\ \sigma^2 = (b - a)^2/12$.

21. Find the mean and variance of the following distributions: (a) gamma, (b) beta, (c) F distribution. (d) Give an approximate formula for the variance of the F distribution for large values of both parameters.

Ans.

(a) $\qquad \mu = \beta(1 + \alpha) \qquad \sigma^2 = \beta^2(1 + \alpha)$

(b) $\qquad \mu = \dfrac{a + 1}{\alpha + \lambda + 2} \qquad \sigma^2 = \dfrac{(\alpha + 1)(\lambda + 1)}{(\alpha + \lambda + 2)^2(\alpha + \lambda + 3)}$

(c) $\qquad \mu = \dfrac{b}{b - 2} \qquad \sigma^2 = \dfrac{2b^2(a + b - 2)}{a(b - 2)^2(b - 4)}$

(d) $\qquad \sigma^2 \approx \dfrac{2(a + b)}{ab} = 2\left(\dfrac{1}{a} + \dfrac{1}{b}\right)$

22. Test the Camp-Meidell inequality with $t = 1, 2, 3$ for the distribution

$$f(x) = 20x^3(1 - x) \qquad (0, 1)$$

23. The variate x is distributed as follows:

$$f(x) = k[1 - (x/c)^2]^{(c^2-3)/2} \qquad (-c, c)$$

where $c > 1$. (a) Determine the value of k and find the mean and variance of x. (b) Sketch the curve for $c^2 < 3$, $c^2 = 3$, and $c^2 = 9$. (c) Using an appropriate inequality give an upper limit for $P(|x| > 3)$ when $c^2 > 9$.

Ans. (a) $k = \Gamma(c^2/2)/(c\sqrt{\pi})\Gamma[(c^2 - 1)/2]$, $\mu = 0$, $\sigma^2 = 1$. (b) U-shaped if $c^2 < 3$, rectangular if $c^2 = 3$, bell-shaped if $c^2 = 9$. (c) From Camp-Meidell inequality, $P(|x| > 3) < 1/20.25 < .0494$.

24. Establish the following formulas expressing central moments in terms of raw moments. (a) $\mu_3 = \mu_3' - 3\mu\mu_2' + 2\mu^3$; (b) $\mu_4 = \mu_4' - 4\mu\mu_3' + 6\mu^2\mu_2' - 3\mu^4$.

25. Derive general expressions for the nth central moments of the following distributions: (a) The rectangular distribution $f(x) = 1$ $(0, 1)$; (b) the normal distribution.

Ans. (a) $\mu_n = 0$ if n is odd, $\mu_n = (2^{-n})/(n + 1)$ if n is even. (b) $\mu_n = 0$ if n is odd, but if n is even, $\mu_n = (n - 1)(n - 3)(n - 5) \cdots (5)(3)(1)\sigma^n$.

26. Given that $\mu = np$, derive the following recursion formula for the central moments of the binomial distribution: $\mu_{k+1} = pq[nk\mu_{k-1} + (d\mu_k/dp)]$ where $k \geq 1$ and $\mu_0 \equiv 1$, $\mu_1 \equiv 0$.

27. Find the moment-generating function of chi-square from its own distribution and check your result against Example 7-20 with $\alpha = (n/2) - 1$, $\beta = 2$.

Ans. $(1 - 2\theta)^{-n/2}$.

28. From the moment-generating functions, determine the variances of the following distributions: (a) binomial, (b) Poisson, (c) geometric with $f(x) = (1 - \alpha)\alpha^x$ $(x = 0, 1, \ldots; 0 < \alpha < 1)$. *Ans.* (a) npq, (b) μ, (c) $\alpha/(1 - \alpha)^2$.

29. From the result of Exercise 28(c) state the variance of the geometric variate with $f(x) = pq^{x-1}$ ($x = 1, 2, \ldots ; p + q = 1$). What general principle is applied? *Ans.* q/p^2. Variance of a linear function.

30. The admissible values of a certain discrete variate x are $0, 1, 2, \ldots, \infty$ and all of the cumulants of x have the same value μ. From this information, derive the distribution of x.   *Ans.* Poisson.

31. Show that $K(\theta : x) = \mu\theta + \ln M(\theta : x - \mu)$. By the Maclaurin expansion, derive the coefficients of $\ln M(\theta : x - \mu)$ as far as θ^4. Thus derive the expressions for the first four cumulants in terms of μ and the central moments.

32. Four independent observations x_1, x_2, x_3, x_4 are taken on the discrete variate x where $f(x) = \frac{1}{2}$ ($x = -1, 1$). (a) State the mean and variance of $y = (x_1 + x_2 + x_3 + x_4)/2$. (b) Check by obtaining the distribution of y and computing the mean and variance from it.   *Ans.* $\mu = 0, \sigma = 1$.

33. Find the expected value of $(x + y)^2$ where x and y are independent unit normal variates.
                                                                                 Ans. 2.

34. Independent variates x, y are distributed as follows:

$$f_1(x) = 12x^2(1 - x) \quad (0, 1) \qquad f_2(y) = 2y \quad (0, 1)$$

Find the expected value of the function $y/x^2 + x/y$.   *Ans.* 5.2.

35. The independent variates x_1, x_2 are normally distributed with respective means $3, -2$ and variances $4, 3$. Write down the distribution of the function $y = 1 + x_1 + 2x_2$.   *Ans.* $f(y) = (1/4 \sqrt{2\pi}) e^{-y^2/32} (-\infty, \infty)$.

36. Derive a formula for the covariance of two linear functions $y_1 = a_0 + a_1x_1 + \cdots + a_nx_n$, $y_2 = b_0 + b_1x_1 + \cdots + b_nx_n$ of the same variates $x_1, x_2, \ldots, x_n$.

$$Ans. \sum_{i=1}^{n} \sum_{j=1}^{n} a_i b_j \sigma_{ij}.$$

37. In any sample of N independent observations from an infinite population with mean μ and variance σ^2, let x_i, x_j denote any pair of observations in the same sample and $\bar{x}$, the corresponding mean of the sample. Prove the following statements by expanding the expressions algebraically and taking expected values term by term.

(a)
$$E[(x_i - \bar{x})(x_j - \bar{x})] = \frac{-\sigma^2}{N} \quad (i \neq j)$$

(b)
$$E\left[\sum_1^N (x_i - \bar{x})^2\right] = (N - 1)\sigma^2$$

38. The covariance of x and y is σ_{xy} and the respective means are μ_x and μ_y. From the bivariate distribution, a random sample of N independent pairs of observations (x_1,y_1), (x_2,y_2), $\ldots$, (x_N,y_N) is drawn, and the corresponding sample means $\bar{x} = \Sigma x_i/N$, $\bar{y} = \Sigma y_i/N$ are computed. Prove that (a) $E(\bar{x}\bar{y}) = (1/N)\sigma_{xy} + \mu_x\mu_y$; (b) $E[\Sigma_i(x_i - \bar{x})(y_i - \bar{y})] = (N - 1)\sigma_{xy}$.

39. From an infinite population with mean μ and variance σ^2, k random samples are drawn. These contain, respectively, $n_1, n_2, \ldots, n_k$ observations. A record of the corresponding sample means $\bar{x}_1, \bar{x}_2, \ldots, \bar{x}_k$ is kept, but the individual observations are not put on record. At a later date, there arises the problem of estimating μ and σ^2 from the available information. Show that the statistics $\bar{x}$ and s^2 have the properties that $E(\bar{x}) = \mu$, $E(s^2) = \sigma^2$, where $\bar{x}$ and s^2 are defined as follows:

$$\bar{x} = \frac{\sum_1^k n_i \bar{x}_i}{\sum_1^k n_i} \qquad s^2 = \frac{\sum_1^k n_i (\bar{x}_i - \bar{x})^2}{k - 1}$$

40. From independent normal variates x_1, x_2 (respective means ξ_1, ξ_2; variances $\sigma_1{}^2$, $\sigma_2{}^2$) two linear functions $u_1 = c_0 + c_1 x_1 + c_2 x_2$ and $u_2 = k_0 + k_1 x_1 + k_2 x_2$ are derived. (a) Show that u_1 and u_2 will be independent if and only if their covariance is zero. (b) Express this condition as a relation between the coefficients.
Ans. (a) HINT: Solve for $x_1 - \xi_1$ and $x_2 - \xi_2$ in terms of $u_1 - m_1$ and $u_2 - m_2$ where $m_1 = E(u_1)$, $m_2 = E(u_2)$; then consider the quadratic. (b) $\sigma_1{}^2 c_1 k_1 + \sigma_2{}^2 c_2 k_2 = 0$.

41. The respective means of independent normal variates x_1, x_2 are $N_1 p$, $N_2 p$ and the variances are $N_1 pq$, $N_2 pq$. Show that the variates $u_1 = (x_1 + x_2)/(N_1 + N_2)$, $u_2 = (x_1/N_1 - x_2/N_2)/\sqrt{pq(1/N_1 + 1/N_2)}$ are independent and that u_2 is unit normal.

42. Given n independent normal variates x_1, x_2, . . . , x_n with common mean and variance, set $\bar{x} = \Sigma_i x_i/n$ and $v_i = x_i - \bar{x}$. The general term of a variable change known as MacMahon's canonical transformation is

$$z_k = \frac{(k + 1)v_k + v_{k+1} + v_{k+2} + \cdots + v_{n-1}}{\sigma \sqrt{k(k + 1)}}$$

From what general proposition does it follow that z_k is normally distributed? By taking expected values, prove that z_k has zero mean and unit variance, and hence is unit normal.

43. Let a, b denote arbitrary real constants and x_1, x_2 any pair of variates for which $E(x_1 - a)^2$ and $E(x_2 - b)^2$ exist. Observing that $E[(x_1 - a) - \lambda(x_2 - b)]^2 \geq 0$ for all real λ show that $[E(x_1 - a)(x_2 - b)]^2 \leq [E(x_1 - a)^2][E(x_2 - b)^2]$. Hence, deduce that $-1 \leq \rho \leq 1$. Also infer that $\rho^2 = 1$ when and only when one variate is an exact linear function of the other. [HINT: Put $\lambda = [E(x_1 - a)(x_2 - b)]/E(x_2 - b)^2$.]

44. The variates x_1, x_2, . . . , x_{2n} all have a common variance σ^2, and for any pair of variates x_i, x_j ($i \neq j$) the correlation coefficient has the same value ρ. Determine the correlation between the two sums $S_1 = x_1 + x_2 + \cdots + x_n$; $S_2 = x_{n+1} + x_{n+2} + \cdots + x_{2n}$. *Ans.* $n\rho/(1 + (n - 1)\rho)$.

45. Expressed as deviations from the curve of seasonal trend, the daily means of temperature at a certain locality may be regarded as identically distributed over a period of a month, with mean and variance 0 and σ^2 respectively. The covariance of any pair of daily mean deviations is given by $\sigma^2 \phi_k$ where ϕ_k is known as the auto-correlation coefficient and depends only on the number of days k between the two dates considered ($\phi_0 \equiv 1$; $|\phi_k| \leq 1$). If τ represents the average of n consecutive daily mean deviations t_1, t_2, . . . , t_n find the variance of τ.

$$\textit{Ans. } \sigma_\tau{}^2 = \sigma^2/n + (\sigma^2/n^2) \sum_1^{n-1} 2(n - k)\phi_k.$$

46. The discrete variate u has two admissible values 0, 1 such that $f(0) = q$, $f(1) = p$ and, of course, $q + p = 1$. (a) Find the mean and variance of u and thereby obtain the mean and variance of the variate $x = u_1 + u_2 \cdots + u_n$ where u_1, . . . , u_n are independently distributed as u. (b) Find the moment-generating function of u and thereby derive the moment-generating function of x. (c) By expanding the latter and equating terms prove that x is binomially distributed.

47. Given that x is unit normal, find the moment-generating function of x^2 directly from the distribution of x. Then deduce at once the moment-generating function of chi-square with n degrees of freedom. From this, infer the distribution.

48. The moment-generating function of the variate x is

$$M(\theta:x) = \cosh \theta = \tfrac{1}{2}(e^\theta + e^{-\theta})$$

Find the moment-generating function of $\bar{x}$, the sample mean of n independent observations. Also find the mean and variance of $\bar{x}$.

$$Ans. \ M(\theta:\bar{x}) = [\cosh (\theta/n)]^n; \ E(\bar{x}) = 0, \ \sigma_{\bar{x}}^2 = 1/n.$$

49. Prove that the rth cumulant of the sum of independent variates is equal to the sum of their respective rth cumulants. Deduce at once that the sum of independent Poisson variates is Poisson distributed. Why cannot the same be said of any linear combination rather than just the sum?

50. Prove that the sum of two correlated Poisson variates does not have the Poisson distribution. [HINT: Show that the variance does not equal the mean.]

51. Given that $M(\theta:x + y) \equiv M(\theta:x)M(\theta:y)$, prove that x and y are independent. [By subtraction, arrive at the equation $E([M(\theta:y) - M(\theta:y|x)]e^{\theta x}) = 0$ for all θ. Hence $M(\theta:y|x) \equiv M(\theta:y)$, whereupon $\phi(y|x) = f(y)$.]

52. The joint distribution of n variates is said to be multivariate-normal if the joint density function is of the form

$$f(x_1, x_2, \ldots, x_n) = Ke^{-\frac{1}{2}Q} \qquad (-\infty, \ \infty \ \text{each variate})$$

where

$$Q = \sum_{i=1}^{n} \sum_{j=1}^{n} a_{ij}(x_i - \xi_i)(x_j - \xi_j)$$

in which (1) the ξ's are constants, (2) the a's are constants having the property that $Q > 0$ for all selections of the x's other than $x_i = \xi_i$ (all i), and (3) K is a positive constant such that the total integral of the joint density function is unity. Prove that the quadratic function Q is distributed as chi-square with n degrees of freedom by deriving the moment-generating function of Q and comparing it with that of chi-square. [To obtain the moment-generating function of Q, substitute $y_i = (x_i - \xi_i)$ $\sqrt{1 - 2\theta}$, remembering the Jacobian, and make use of the condition on K.]

53. In the moment-generating function of the binomial distribution, determine the limiting form as $n \to \infty$ and $p \to 0$ in such a way that $np \to \mu$. Then expanding and equating terms, derive the Poisson distribution as an asymptotic form of the binomial.

54. Show that a Poisson variate is asymptotically normal as μ becomes indefinitely large.

CHAPTER 8

SOME STATISTICAL USES OF PROBABILITY

8-1. Introduction. This chapter presents some of the tests and methods most commonly applied in statistical practice. Deliberate stress has been placed on reasoning as opposed to cut and dried rules of procedure. Much of the background developed in previous chapters is presupposed; here matters are brought to a head in specific applications to statistics. The chosen material represents an important part, but a small part, of this subject.

The chapter is organized around conventional uses of four major distributions: the normal, chi-square, t, and F. Many problems of hypothesis testing can be solved in terms of these four distributions, because a great many other distributions tend toward these as limiting forms or simply are sufficiently well approximated by them.

The normal distribution applies mainly to tests on large samples, unless the variate in question is normal to start with, in which case the sample size can be arbitrary. Some of the uses of chi-square assume fairly large samples, while others do not; as a rule it is the magnitude of an expected absolute frequency, rather than the sample size itself, which is critical in uses of chi-square. With small samples, the t and F distributions fill the breach on certain tests to which otherwise the normal might be applied if the samples were larger; but they have broader uses as well.

The normal distribution is usually satisfactory for large-sample tests on percentages and means. Broadly speaking, hypotheses which characterize a distribution as a whole are tested by chi-square. For example, such hypotheses might define a distribution explicitly, assert that two or more variates have the same distribution without specifying its mathematical form, or state that certain attributes or variates are independent. Hypotheses which specify the mean value of one variate or the difference of the means of two variates are tested by t. Those which concern either the relative magnitudes of more than two means or the ratio of two variances are tested by F.

8-2. The Normal Tests. Use of the normal distribution as an approximation to the binomial distribution, in testing some hypothesized value of the probability of a given event, has been illustrated fully in Chap. 4. That topic will not be repeated in this chapter, but we shall take up two related topics which concern a pair of events. The first of these is the question as to whether two events have the same probability, or in sampling terms, whether two observed percentages are significantly different. This question was dealt with in Chap. 3 by employing the hypergeometric distribution. We shall see in Sec. 8-3 how the normal distribution can serve the same purpose as an approximation to the hypergeometric. The second topic is the test for association or independence of two events or attributes. This, also, is an application of the hypergeometric distribution, and consequently falls within the scope of normal tests when the sample size is sufficiently large. How large a sample has to be is a question to which, at present, we can give only the empirical sort of answer stated in Sec. 8-3. Later on in that section (when we consider how to compensate for the continuity of the normal curve, as contrasted with the discrete increments of the hypergeometric probabilities) we shall reason as we did previously for the binomial (Chap. 4) but shall arrive at a correction term which differs in magnitude from that of the binomial because the interval of the variate concerned is of different width.

8-3. The Normal Test for the Difference between Two Percentages. When both a and N_1 are large, the computation of $f(x)$ for the hypergeometric distribution becomes laborious. In that case, however, the hypergeometric distribution tends toward the binomial, and thence toward the normal. As n becomes large, the asymptotic form of the distribution of x/n (the relative frequency of a given attribute A in random samples of size n) is normal with $\mu = p$, $\sigma^2 = pq/n$.

Suppose that in sample 1 of size N_1, there are x_1 observations exhibiting attribute A and in sample 2 of size N_2, there are x_2. Under the null hypothesis, the two samples are drawn from the same population. Assume that both N_1 and N_2 are large enough to make x_1/N_1 and x_2/N_2 approximately normal. Then by the additive property of the normal distribution, the difference

$$d = \frac{x_1}{N_1} - \frac{x_2}{N_2} \qquad (8\text{-}1)$$

is approximately normal with $\mu = 0$ and $\sigma^2 = pq(1/N_1 + 1/N_2)$. Consequently the standardized variate

$$z = \frac{d}{\sqrt{pq(1/N_1 + 1/N_2)}}$$

can be referred to unit normal tables. However, since p is ordinarily unknown, it is replaced by its sample estimate p' where

$$p' = \frac{x_1 + x_2}{N_1 + N_2} \qquad \text{with } q' = 1 - p' \qquad (8\text{-}2)$$

and the test variate actually employed is

$$u = \frac{d}{\sqrt{p'q'(1/N_1 + 1/N_2)}} \qquad (8\text{-}3)$$

This, too, is treated as a unit normal variate, for

$$u \equiv z \sqrt{pq/p'q'}$$

and, in a probability sense, the ratio $pq/p'q'$ approaches unity as $N_1 + N_2$ becomes large. The accuracy of the normal approximation depends both on the sample size and the value of p. At present, rigorous proof as to safe magnitudes is lacking, but it has been found empirically that good results are obtained provided that $np' > 5$ (that is, $N_1p' > 5$ and $N_2p' > 5$).

Trying the normal approximation on Example 3-12, we have

$$p' = \frac{8}{4,694} \approx .0017$$

and $np' = 4$, which falls a little short of the recommended limit. From Table 4-4, we find that the boundary of the critical region for the significance level .05 is -1.64. The numerator of u is

$$d = 0 - \frac{8}{2,347} = -.0034$$

while the denominator is

$$\sqrt{(.0017)(.9983)(.00085)} = .0012$$

whereupon

$$u = \frac{-.0034}{.0012} = -2.83$$

which lies well within the critical region. The normal probability $P(u \leq -2.83)$, corresponding to $x = 0$ in the stocking group, is .0023 as opposed to the value .004 given by the hypergeometric distribution. The decision, nevertheless, is the same, even though the apparent rarity of the observed event is exaggerated with the normal approximation.

Example 8-1. The toy buyer of a department store observed that 8 out of 150 plastic dolls manufactured by company A were defective, while only 4 out of 130 manufactured by company B were defective. Is it reasonable to suppose that the two percentages represent a common level of quality?

Under the null hypothesis that both samples come from the same population, the difference

$$d = \frac{8}{150} - \frac{4}{130} = .053 - .031 = .022$$

represents a random draw from a distribution of possible differences for which the mean is zero and the variance is

$$\sigma^2 = pq(\tfrac{1}{150} + \tfrac{1}{130}) = pq(.0144)$$

where p is the proportion of defective articles in the common parent population and

$q = 1 - p$. Sample estimates of p and q are

$$p' = \frac{8 + 4}{150 + 130} = \tfrac{3}{70} \qquad q' = 1 - p' = \tfrac{67}{70}$$

whence the sample estimate of variance, say $\hat{\sigma}^2$, is

$$\hat{\sigma}^2 = p'q'(\tfrac{1}{150} + \tfrac{1}{130}) = (.0410)(.0144) = .000590$$

the corresponding square root being $\hat{\sigma} = .0243$.

Since the samples are fairly large and for both of them $np' > 5$, the test variate $u = d/\hat{\sigma}$ may be assumed to be unit normal in the sense that repeated independent trials would generate a series of values for which the true probability density function is adequately approximated by the unit normal. To decide whether an observed difference is consistent with the hypothesis that both samples represent a common population, we set up a two-sided critical region corresponding to the 5 per cent level of significance. Table 4-4 shows that $2R(x) = .05$ when $x = 1.96$. Hence we shall accept the null hypothesis provided that

$$-1.96 < u < 1.96$$

but otherwise reject it.

Here the sample value of the test variate is

$$u = \frac{.022}{.024} = .92$$

which lies well within the acceptance region. Therefore, we accept the null hypothesis and conclude that the observed difference in proportions of defective articles is readily explainable on the basis of sampling fluctuations around the average.

Example 8-2. Assuming equal sample sizes, how large must the sample size be in order that a given difference between two proportions will be judged significant?

Let N denote the sample size and p_1', p_2' (with $p_1' > p_2'$) the observed proportions. Assuming N sufficiently large and $Np' > 5$, the difference will be judged significant at the .05 level if $u \geq 1.96$, whence $u^2 \geq 3.8416$. With equal sample sizes, we have

$$p' = \frac{p_1' + p_2'}{2} \qquad q' = \frac{2 - p_1' - p_2'}{2} \qquad d = p_1' - p_2'$$

$$\hat{\sigma} = p'q'\left(\frac{1}{N} + \frac{1}{N}\right) = \frac{(p_1' + p_2')(2 - p_1' - p_2')}{2N}$$

$$u^2 = \frac{d^2}{\hat{\sigma}^2} = \frac{2N(p_1' - p_2')^2}{(p_1' + p_2')(2 - p_1' - p_2')}$$

Therefore, to reach the 5 per cent level of significance with a stated pair of proportions, the sample size must satisfy the following two conditions:

$$N \geq \frac{(1.9208)(p_1' + p_2')(2 - p_1' - p_2')}{(p_1' - p_2')^2}$$

$$N > \frac{10}{(p_1' + p_2')}$$

the first of which follows from the fact that $u^2 \geq 3.8416$ and the second from the fact that $Np' > 5$. The answer thus depends on both proportions and not merely on their difference.

As noted in Chap. 4 with reference to the normal approximation to the binomial distribution, a correction for continuity is a safeguard against an inflated estimate of significance. To arrive at a corresponding correction for the difference between relative frequencies, using the hypergeometric distribution, we recall that the difference d can be expressed in the form (Sec. 3-10)

$$d = \frac{N}{N_1 N_2}\left(x_1 - \frac{a N_1}{N}\right) \equiv \frac{N_1 + N_2}{N_1 N_2}(x_1 - N_1 p') \qquad (8\text{-}4)$$

Assume that our critical region is to be the right-hand tail of the distribution. Then in the binomial case we should reduce x_1 by one-half unit, and correspondingly, the value of d should be reduced by one-half times the coefficient of x_1, that is, $(N_1 + N_2)/2N_1 N_2$. (For it is to be noted that while x_1 is binomially distributed, d is not.) Thus, the revised measures d' and u' are

$$d' = d - \frac{N_1 + N_2}{2 N_1 N_2} \qquad u' = \frac{d'}{\hat{\sigma}} \qquad (8\text{-}5)$$

In the special case wherein $N_1 = N_2$ the correction reduces to $1/N_1$. For a left-hand region the correction is the same in magnitude, but is added to d instead of being subtracted. Thus, in applying the normal approximation once again to Example 3-12, we put

$$d' = \frac{-8}{2,347} + \frac{1}{2,347} = \frac{-7}{2,347} = -.0030$$

whence
$$u' = \frac{-.0030}{.0012} = -2.50$$

and $P(u' \leq -2.50) = .0062$ which differs from $.004$ about as much as the former approximate value $.0023$ but in the opposite direction.

For a two-sided region these corrections should be applied to both sides. Or, what amounts to the same thing, the boundaries of the critical region should be pushed tailward in both directions and then the values of d and u taken as originally given.

8-4. The Normal Test for Association or Independence. Two attributes A, B are independent in the probability sense when

$$P(A|B) = P(A)$$

otherwise they are associated. Therefore, although tests for association differ in motive from tests for independence, they are formally identical. Furthermore, in the case of only two attributes, the test is the same as that for the difference between two percentages. For if A and B are independent, the individuals exhibiting attribute B and those exhibiting the complementary one $\bar{B}$ may be regarded as making up independent samples as far as the relative frequencies of attribute A are concerned, because the observations themselves are random with respect to the two attributes, and by hypothesis, $p(A|B) = p(A) = p(A|\bar{B})$. Consequently, if the two conditional relative frequencies of A are significantly different, the two attributes A, B are significantly associated. Thus the hypergeometric test of Sec. 3-10 applies, and under the conditions stated in Sec. 8-3, the normal test can be used as an approximation. Ordinarily, a two-sided critical region would be appropriate. When there are more than two attributes, the test for association or independence is based on chi-square. The chi-square test is also applicable to two attributes, under the same conditions as the normal test, provided that the critical region is two-sided; for in that case, the chi-square test variate is identically the square of the normal test variate, assuming that continuity corrections are disregarded.

Example 8-3. At the beginning of a semester the instructor announced that assigned problems were intended mainly for the students' own benefit as learning exercises and would not be counted heavily toward the course grade. Unprepared for the wholesale hangings which his rope apparently invited, he decided to check up on the relationship, if any, between attention to homework in his course and the general average grade to date of the same students in their other courses, exclusive of his.

As an elementary procedure, he divided the class of 38 in half on the basis of homework performance (H = high, $\bar{H}$ = low) and, without reference to the first dichotomy, he divided the class in half also on the basis of general performance (G = high, $\bar{G}$ = low). Assuming independence, the four joint categories HG, $\bar{H}G$, $H\bar{G}$, $\bar{H}\bar{G}$ are equally likely. Letting x denote the number of individuals in one of these categories, say HG, the distribution of this symmetrical hypergeometric variate, under the null hypothesis, is

$$f(x) = \frac{C(19,x)C(19,\ 19 - x)}{C(38,19)} \qquad (x = 0, 1, \ldots, 19)$$

In this instance, because the parameters of the distribution are now known, we can establish the boundaries of the critical region without recourse to further data. From the lower half of the distribution, presented in Table 8-1, we find that for the .05 level of significance, the two parts of the critical region are $x \leq 6$, $x \geq 13$.

TABLE 8-1. LOWER HALF OF THE HYPERGEOMETRIC DISTRIBUTION WITH
$a = 19 = N_1$, $N = 38$

x	0	1	2	3	4	5	6	7	8	9
$f(x)$	.0000	.0000	.0000	.0000	.0004	.0038	.0208	.0718	.1616	.2414
$F(x)$	.0000	.0000	.0000	.0000	.0004	.0042	.0250	.0968	.2584	.4998

Let us now look at the data (Table 8-2) which, being real, are a bit astonishing. Not only does the observed value of x (17) lie well within the critical region, but the total probability of the numerical class it represents (17, 18, 19, 2, 1, 0) is less than 1.7×10^{-6}.

As far as it goes, the evidence for association is arresting; still, we must be circumspect in its interpretation. First, consider the sample. Random samples would

TABLE 8-2. CONTINGENCY TABLE FOR EXAMPLE 8-3

Group	G	$\bar{G}$	Total
H	17	2	19
$\bar{H}$	2	17	19
Total..........	19	19	38

rarely give such an appearance of association if the attributes were, in fact, independent. Since this sample, however, was not drawn at random, we may question how well it typifies the academic population at large. We do not know and can only say that, while the results bear notice, they lack the essentials for valid inference. Suppose that the sample were not open to this very damaging objection, and let us grant that a high degree of association exists. Association per se does not imply a casual mechanism whereby one attribute can be acquired by cultivating the other; both may be outcomes of more basic conditions. So long as the population itself is not disturbed, the two attributes will continue hand in hand; but a deliberate change in one need not produce a corresponding change in the other. In particular, the instructor, in this example, has caught the students off guard and induced them to reveal their habits of work without inhibition. Perhaps, therefore, he has unintentionally measured their personal drive, which is reflected simultaneously in diligence and achievement. On the other hand, human behavior tends to support the belief that a favorable attitude of mind for success can be stimulated by activity characteristic of successful people. At any rate, the material for practice is presumably an aid to learning, and this is our assumption in furnishing exercises.

As an illustration of the normal approximation in this same example, we have $p = q = \frac{1}{2}$; $\sigma^2 = pq(\frac{2}{19}) = \frac{1}{38}$. To establish the inside boundary of the right half of the critical region we put $d \sqrt{38} = 1.9600$, $d = .3180$. The corrected value of d will then be $d' = d + \frac{1}{19} = .3706$ and for the corresponding limit on x we put

$$d' = \frac{2}{19}(x - 19\frac{1}{2}) \qquad x = (9.5)(1.3706) = 13.02$$

Taken literally, this limit would exclude 13, but since we know that the continuity adjustment overcorrects somewhat, we ignore the .02 and arrive at the same region as before, $x \leq 6$, $x \geq 13$. Needless to say, the labor is far less.

8-5. The Chi-square Tests. The distribution of chi-square was first derived by the mathematician-physicist, F. R. Helmert, in 1875 and was rediscovered independently by K. Pearson in 1900. Pearson was the first to realize the practical importance of chi-square. The principal uses of chi-square are (a) testing a hypothesis as to the mathematical form of a single distribution, (b) testing the hypothesis that two or more variates are identically distributed, and (c) testing the hypothesis that certain variates or attributes are independent. In applying these tests it is *not* assumed that the original populations are normal. The conventional process of eliminating unknown parameters, however, leads to a sum of positive quantities, the sampling behavior of which is closely approximated by that of the sum of squares of an appropriate number of independent unit normal variates. Hence, for practical purposes, the test variate may be regarded as chi-square.

In most applications of chi-square, we use a one-sided critical region of the form $\chi^2 \geq a$, where a is determined from the condition that $\int_a^{\infty} f(\chi^2)\, d\chi^2 = \alpha$ and α is the chosen level of significance. The lower extreme of the distribution is rarely of interest, because departures from the hypothesized form of distribution tend to increase the value of chi-square. Extremely small values of chi-square indicate abnormally close agreement of the sample with the hypothesized population, but argue against the randomness of the sample rather than against the assumed type of population.

8-6. The Chi-square Test for Goodness of Fit. The problem of testing the agreement of a sample frequency table with a hypothesized form of distribution was solved in the main by Karl Pearson in 1900, although R. A. Fisher later contributed the important idea of "degrees of freedom," by which proper account is taken of parameters estimated from the same data. Let the total range of possibilities be divided into k mutually exclusive and exhaustive categories. Denote the observed frequencies by O_i $(i = 1, 2, \ldots, k)$ and the expected frequencies (as determined by the hypothesis) by E_i. The joint distribution of the frequencies in repeated independent trials is multinomial, and even if the use of this distribution were not prohibitively laborious (which it is), we would still have the problem of deciding on the multiple regions of acceptance and rejection. A general theory of critical regions, based on likelihood ratios, has been developed by J. Neyman and E. S. Pearson (the son of Karl Pearson) but its application in this connection yields substantially the same outcome as the earlier work of Karl Pearson. Using the expected value E_i as the norm for any category, it is reasonable to choose the quantity $(O_i - E_i)^2$ as a measure of departure from the norm. However, the raw magnitudes of the squared deviations would not be comparable from one category to another, inasmuch as the scale of each is nearly proportional to E_i. Therefore, a suitable measure is $(O_i - E_i)^2/E_i$, and the measure of total discrepancy becomes

$$\hat{\chi}^2 = \sum_1^k \frac{(O_i - E_i)^2}{E_i} \tag{8-6}$$

By expanding the quadratic and simplifying, we obtain the following equivalent expression, which is sometimes more convenient for computational purposes:

$$\hat{\chi}^2 = \sum_1^k \frac{O_i^2}{E_i} - N \tag{8-7}$$

TABLE 8-3. CRITICAL VALUES OF CHI-SQUARE FOR ONE-SIDED CRITICAL REGIONS AT STATED SIGNIFICANCE LEVELS

Degrees of freedom	Right-hand tail			Left-hand tail†		
	$\alpha = .10$	$\alpha = .05$	$\alpha = .01$	$\alpha = .10$	$\alpha = .05$	$\alpha = .01$
1	2.71	3.84	6.64	.02	.0039	.00016
2	4.61	5.99	9.20	.21	.10	.02
3	6.25	7.82	11.34	.58	.35	.12
4	7.78	9.49	13.28	1.06	.71	.30
5	9.24	11.07	15.09	1.61	1.15	.55
6	10.65	12.59	16.81	2.20	1.64	.87
7	12.02	14.07	18.48	2.83	2.17	1.24
8	13.36	15.51	20.09	3.49	2.73	1.65
9	14.68	16.92	21.67	4.17	3.33	2.09
10	15.99	18.31	23.21	4.87	3.94	2.56
11	17.28	19.68	24.73	5.58	4.58	3.05
12	18.55	21.03	26.22	6.30	5.23	3.57
13	19.81	22.36	27.69	7.04	5.89	4.11
14	21.06	23.69	29.14	7.79	6.57	4.66
15	22.31	25.00	30.58	8.55	7.26	5.23
16	23.54	26.30	32.00	9.31	7.96	5.81
17	24.77	27.59	33.41	10.09	8.67	6.41
18	25.99	28.87	34.81	10.87	9.39	7.02
19	27.20	30.14	36.19	11.65	10.12	7.63
20	28.41	31.41	37.57	12.44	10.85	8.26
21	29.62	32.67	38.93	13.24	11.59	8.90
22	30.81	33.92	40.29	14.04	12.34	9.54
23	32.01	35.17	41.64	14.85	13.09	10.20
24	33.20	36.42	42.98	15.66	13.85	10.86
25	34.38	37.65	44.31	16.47	14.61	11.52
26	35.56	38.89	45.64	17.29	15.38	12.20
27	36.74	40.11	46.96	18.11	16.15	12.88
28	37.92	41.34	48.28	18.94	16.93	13.57
29	39.09	42.56	49.59	19.77	17.71	14.26
30	40.26	43.77	50.89	20.60	18.49	14.95

† Left-hand tail used mainly for confidence limits on variance.

NOTE: For degrees of freedom $n > 30$ the variate $\sqrt{2x^2} - \sqrt{2n - 1}$ is approximately unit normal.

where $N = \Sigma O_i = \Sigma E_i$. We showed in Chap. 7 (Sec. 7-13) that this statistic is distributed asymptotically as chi-square. If the population parameters have not been estimated from the sample, there are $k - 1$ degrees of freedom. As a rule, however, only the general form of the distribution is hypothesized, so that in order to evaluate the expected frequencies, it is necessary to estimate the parameters from the data. In that case, the number of degrees of freedom is diminished by the number of parameters estimated; if h parameters are estimated, there are $k - 1 - h$ degrees of freedom. The extent to which the true distribution of χ^2, under the given hypothesis, is approximated by that of chi-square is affected primarily by the size of the *expected* frequencies (not the observed frequencies), and although the evidence on this score is partly empirical, it does seem safe to apply the chi-square tables when none of the expected frequencies is less than five.

The logic of testing goodness of fit is the same as that of any other type of hypothesis test. We decide arbitrarily upon the value of α and thus determine the corresponding limit of the critical region. The rules of decision are then fixed; a sample value either does or does not fall within the acceptance region, and the issue is closed. Whether or not the majority of random samples would yield a better fit is beside the point; we first decide on what will be judged acceptable and then abide by the decision. On the other hand, when the sample value lies within the acceptance region, the result is often amplified by citing the further fact that there is (perhaps) a considerable margin of safety. In view of the fact that the test itself is only approximate, this practice is perfectly legitimate and even desirable; for it is relevant to note that the decision would still hold good even making liberal allowances for errors of approximation.

Example 8-4. Using the data of Example 7-19, let us test whether the normal hypothesis is tenable as a description of the distribution of annual rainfall over the Susquehanna Valley.

In order to use the chi-square test for goodness of fit, the distribution of rainfall should be classified into mutually exclusive and exhaustive categories so chosen that random samples of N observations from the hypothetical population will, in the long run, yield an average of at least five observations in each category. Letting p_i represent the theoretical probability that an observation drawn at random will fall into category i, we must make this category broad enough so that $Np_i > 5$. Thus, with $N = 92$, the minimum value of p_i is $\frac{5}{92}$, or .0543.

To choose categories for a normal distribution, we begin with the tail area and work inward (Fig. 8-1). Representing a unit normal variate by z to avoid confusion with the notation x used for rainfall, we find from Table 4-4 that $R(z) = .0668$ when $z = 1.5$. True, the next higher value in the table, $z = 1.6$, yields $R(z) = .0548$, which would satisfy the minimum requirement, but to be on the safe side, let us decide upon $z = 1.5$. This means that the highest category will be $z > 1.5$ and the lowest category will be $z \leq -1.5$. While there is no set rule for subdividing the intermediate range, equal intervals on the abscissa are most commonly employed, although a division into equal areas is sometimes preferred. Here, to make this illustration easy to follow computationally, let us divide the range $-1.5 < z \leq 1.5$ into three equal intervals of z. We thus arrive at the expected numbers shown in Table 8-4.

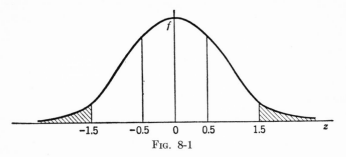

FIG. 8-1

Since the parameters μ and σ of the normal distribution have been estimated from the data, and we have decided to use five categories, χ^2 will be distributed as chi-square with $(5 - 1) - 2 = 2$ degrees of freedom. Using a one-sided critical region and the 5 per cent level of significance, the acceptance region is $\chi^2 < 5.99$.

TABLE 8-4. THEORETICAL PROBABILITIES AND EXPECTED NUMBERS

i	Category	p_i	$E_i = Np_i$
1	$z \leq -1.5$	.07	6.4
2	$-1.5 < z \leq -.5$	.24	22.1
3	$-.5 < z \leq .5$	.38	35.0
4	$.5 < z \leq 1.5$	.24	22.1
5	$z > 1.5$	.07	6.4
Total....................		1.00	92.0

In this example, the variate z is defined as $(x - \bar{x})/s$ where $\bar{x} = 39.492$, $s = 3.657$. The corresponding values of x and z are shown in Table 8-5.

TABLE 8-5. CORRESPONDING VALUES OF x AND z

z	-1.5	-0.5	0.5	1.5
x	34.007	37.663	41.321	44.977

Hence, in terms of actual rainfall, the categories are (1) $x \leq 34.00$; (2) $34.01 < x \leq 37.66$; (3) $37.67 < x \leq 41.32$; (4) $41.33 < x \leq 44.97$; (5) $x \geq 44.98$. The computation of chi-square is exhibited in Table 8-6, the actual numbers of observations in the categories being found from Table 7-4.

We accept the hypothesis and conclude that the distribution of annual rainfall is approximately normal, for the obtained value of χ^2 falls well within the acceptance region. Noticing that $O - E$ is positive for category 3 and negative for the other four categories, one is tempted to say that the normal curve must be too low in the immediate vicinity of the mean and too high elsewhere. This feature, however, should be discounted as an accidental property of the sample itself, at least as far as

TABLE 8-6. COMPUTATION OF CHI-SQUARE

i	O_i	E_i	$O_i - E_i$	$(O_i - E_i)^2$	$(O_i - E_i)^2/E_i$
1	5	6.4	−1.4	1.96	.306
2	20	22.1	−2.1	4.41	.200
3	43	35.0	8.0	64.00	1.829
4	18	22.1	−4.1	16.81	.761
5	6	6.4	−.4	.16	.025
Total........	92	92.0	.0	.....	$\hat{\chi}^2 = 3.121$

the present statistical evidence is concerned; for this pattern is merely one of the many whereby a random sample can yield a run of the mill value of $\hat{\chi}^2$. Obviously the distribution of rainfall could not be exactly normal, because the lower limit is zero and the upper limit is certainly not infinity. Nevertheless, the normal distribution seems to be a satisfactory approximation within the operating range of the variate. Few theoretical models are all-inclusive.

8-7. The Chi-square Test for Homogeneity. The problem is to decide whether s independent samples can be regarded as belonging to a common population. Divide the total range of possibilities into k mutually exclusive, exhaustive categories ($i = 1, 2, \ldots, k$), each having the same definition with respect to all samples. Let N_j denote the total number of observations in sample j ($j = 1, 2, \ldots, s$), E_{ij} the expected number of observations in Category i for a sample of size N_j, and O_{ij} the corresponding observed number. Then the test variate

$$\hat{\chi}^2 \equiv \sum_j \sum_i \frac{(O_{ij} - E_{ij})^2}{E_{ij}} \tag{8-8}$$

is distributed approximately as chi-square, with degrees of freedom governed by the number of estimates made from the data. As in testing goodness of fit, we may rewrite the above in the following equivalent form:

$$\hat{\chi}^2 \equiv \sum_j \sum_i \frac{O_{ij}^2}{E_{ij}} - N \tag{8-9}$$

where $N \equiv \sum_j N_j$.

By hypothesis, the probability that a random observation will fall in category i has the same value, say p_i, for all samples, and of course, $\Sigma p_i = 1$. If the individual probabilities are known in advance, the expected number of observations in category i for sample j can be evaluated, for $E_{ij} = N_j p_i$. In that event, since the samples are assumed independent, we may express $\hat{\chi}^2$ of the above equations as the sum of s independent components:

$$\hat{\chi}^2 = \sum_{j=1}^{s} \hat{\chi}_j{}^2 \qquad \hat{\chi}_j{}^2 \equiv \sum_{i=1}^{k} \frac{(O_{ij} - N_j p_i)^2}{N_j p_i} \qquad (8\text{-}10)$$

Here the effect of the test is the same as though each sample were tested separately for goodness of fit and the respective chi-squares added together. (Note analogy with pooling evidence from independent samples.) Each $\hat{\chi}_j{}^2$ has approximately the chi-square distribution with $k - 1$ degrees of freedom, and so the pooled result $\hat{\chi}^2$ is distributed approximately as chi-square with $s(k - 1)$ degrees of freedom. Commonly, however, the individual probabilities are not known in advance, and it is necessary to substitute sample estimates, $p_i' \equiv \sum_j O_{ij}/N$. To reckon degrees of freedom, therefore, we must diminish the quantity $s(k - 1)$ by the number of parameters estimated. Effectively, there are only $k - 1$ parameters, inasmuch as $\Sigma p_i = 1 = \Sigma p_i'$. Consequently, the number of degrees of freedom in the corresponding $\hat{\chi}^2$ is given by the following equation:

$$\text{Degrees of freedom} = s(k - 1) - (k - 1) = (s - 1)(k - 1) \qquad (8\text{-}11)$$

Hence, in the typical situation, $\hat{\chi}^2$ is given by

$$\hat{\chi}^2 = \sum_j \sum_i \frac{(O_{ij} - N_j p_i')^2}{N_j p_i'} \qquad (8\text{-}12)$$

and is distributed approximately as chi-square with $(s - 1)(k - 1)$ degrees of freedom. An alternative computational formula is

$$\hat{\chi}^2 = \sum_j \sum_i \frac{O_{ij}{}^2}{N_j p_i'} - N \qquad (8\text{-}13)$$

Example 8-5. Table 8-7 summarizes the distributions of first-term ratings of four classes of M.I.T. freshmen, exclusive of war veterans. Test for homogeneity.

The probability p_i that a random observation will fall into category i ($i = 1, 2, \ldots, 9$) being unknown, we shall substitute the sample estimate $p_i' = \sum_j O_{ij}/N$

where $N = 2{,}065$ is the size of the composite sample made up of the four classes combined. Accordingly, with 9 categories and 4 samples there will be $(9 - 1)(4 - 1) = 24$ degrees of freedom. Using the 5 per cent level of significance, the critical region will be $\hat{\chi}^2 \geq 36.42$, whence the acceptance region will be $\hat{\chi}^2 < 36.42$.

The expected number of observations (expected frequency) in category i for sample j is estimated from the equation $E_{ij} \approx N_j p_i'$. These estimates are shown in Table 8-8, and the other computations leading to $\hat{\chi}^2$ are exhibited in Tables 8-9 and 8-10.

TABLE 8-7. OBSERVED FREQUENCIES

Category	I	II	III	IV	Composite
0–1.00	12	8	13	5	38
1.01–1.50	23	10	27	26	86
1.51–2.00	39	32	49	29	149
2.01–2.50	58	39	48	38	183
2.51–3.00	101	89	106	66	362
3.01–3.50	112	136	135	110	493
3.51–4.00	92	88	123	72	375
4.01–4.50	51	79	63	61	254
4.51–5.00	25	35	37	28	125
Total.........	513	516	601	435	2,065

TABLE 8-8. ESTIMATES OF EXPECTED FREQUENCIES

Category	I	II	III	IV	Composite
0–1.00	9.4	9.5	11.1	8.0	38.0
1.01–1.50	21.4	21.5	25.0	18.1	86.0
1.51–2.00	37.1	37.2	43.4	31.4	149.1
2.01–2.50	45.5	45.7	53.3	38.5	183.0
2.51–3.00	89.9	90.5	105.4	76.3	362.1
3.01–3.50	122.5	123.2	143.5	103.9	493.1
3.51–4.00	93.2	93.7	109.1	79.0	375.0
4.01–4.50	63.1	63.5	73.9	53.5	254.0
4.51–5.00	31.1	31.2	36.4	26.3	125.0
Total.........	513.2	516.0	601.1	435.0	2,065.3

TABLE 8-9. VALUES OF $O - E$

Category	I	II	III	IV	Total
0–1.00	2.6	−1.5	1.9	−3.0	.0
1.01–1.50	1.6	−11.5	2.0	7.9	.0
1.51–2.00	1.9	−5.2	5.6	−2.4	−.1
2.01–2.50	12.5	−6.7	−5.3	−.5	.0
2.51–3.00	11.1	−1.5	.6	−10.3	−.1
3.01–3.50	−10.5	12.8	−8.5	6.1	−.1
3.51–4.00	−1.2	−5.7	13.9	−7.0	.0
4.01–4.50	−12.1	15.5	−10.9	7.5	.0
4.51–5.00	−6.1	3.8	.6	1.7	.0
Total.........	−.2	.0	−.1	.0	−.3

TABLE 8-10. VALUES OF $(O - E)^2/E$

Category	I	II	III	IV	Total
0–1.00	.719	.237	.325	1.125	2.406
1.01–1.50	.120	6.120	.160	3.448	9.848
1.51–2.00	.097	.727	.723	.183	1.730
2.01–2.50	3.434	.982	.527	.006	4.949
2.51–3.00	1.371	.025	.003	1.390	2.789
3.01–3.50	.900	1.330	.503	.358	3.091
3.51–4.00	.015	.347	1.771	.620	2.753
4.01–4.50	2.320	3.783	1.608	1.051	8.762
4.51–5.00	1.196	.463	.010	.110	1.779
Total..........	10.172	14.014	5.630	8.291	38.107

Since this value 38.107 of $\hat{\chi}^2$ falls in the *critical* region, we *reject* the hypothesis of homogeneity and conclude that the first-term ratings of these freshman classes at M.I.T. do not behave as random samples from a common population.

8-8. The Chi-square Test for Association or Independence. Association might be the object of investigation in one instance and independence in another, but in any event, the null hypothesis is that the variates or attributes are independent. This implies that their joint distribution is the product of the corresponding marginal distributions. The logic of the test applies equally well to quantitative and qualitative material or combinations of both, and there is no definite[1] restriction as to the number of dimensions or characteristics which can be analyzed simultaneously; but, for simplicity, we shall consider merely two variates or attributes A, B. Since these need not be commensurable, the categories into which each is subdivided are not assumed to be similarly defined.

Divide A into k mutually exclusive, exhaustive categories A_1, A_2, ..., A_k and B into s mutually exclusive, exhaustive categories B_1, B_2, ..., B_s. If α_i denotes the probability that a random observation will fall in category A_i and if β_j denotes the probability that a random observation will fall in category B_j $\left(\text{where } \sum_i \alpha_i = 1 = \sum_j \beta_j \right)$, then, by hypothesis, the probability of observing A_i and B_j simultaneously is the product $\alpha_i \beta_j$. The joint distribution is indicated schematically in Table 8-11. In successive random samples of N observations the joint distribution of the observed numbers O_{11}, ..., O_{ij}, ..., O_{ks} in categories A_1B_1, ..., A_iB_j, ..., A_kB_s will be multinomial of the order ks, and with a fixed value of N, there will be $ks - 1$ independent quantities since $\Sigma O_{ij} = N$. The problem thus becomes one of testing the goodness of fit

---

[1] Practical limitations are imposed by the size of the sample needed in order that the distribution be approximated by chi-square.

TABLE 8-11. JOINT DISTRIBUTION

Class	B_1	B_2	$\cdots$	B_s	Total
A_1	$\alpha_1\beta_1$	$\alpha_1\beta_2$	$\cdots$	$\alpha_1\beta_s$	α_1
A_2	$\alpha_2\beta_1$	$\alpha_2\beta_2$	$\cdots$	$\alpha_2\beta_s$	α_2
$\cdots$	$\cdots$	$\cdots$	$\cdots$	$\cdots$	$\cdots$
A_k	$\alpha_k\beta_1$	$\alpha_k\beta_2$	$\cdots$	$\alpha_k\beta_s$	α_k
Total........	β_1	β_2	$\cdots$	β_s	1

of the assumed bivariate distribution of A, B. The expected value of O_{ij} is simply $N\alpha_i\beta_j$ and so the statistic

$$\hat{\chi}^2 \equiv \sum_i \sum_j \frac{(O_{ij} - N\alpha_i\beta_j)^2}{N\alpha_i\beta_j} \tag{8-14}$$

is distributed approximately as chi-square with $ks - 1$ degrees of freedom. When the individual probabilities are unknown, sample estimates are substituted in the usual way. The estimates a_i, b_j of α_i, β_j are

$$a_i = \sum_{j=1}^{s} \frac{O_{ij}}{N} \qquad b_j = \sum_{i=1}^{k} \frac{O_{ij}}{N} \tag{8-15}$$

There are only $(k - 1) + (s - 1)$ independent parameters because $\Sigma\alpha_i = 1 = \Sigma\beta_j$. Hence

Degrees of freedom $= (ks - 1) - (k - 1) - (s - 1)$
$$= (k - 1)(s - 1) \tag{8-16}$$

and the resulting test variate

$$\hat{\chi}^2 \equiv \sum_i \sum_j \frac{(O_{ij} - Na_ib_j)^2}{Na_ib_j} \tag{8-17}$$

is distributed approximately as chi-square with $(k - 1)(s - 1)$ degrees of freedom. For computational purposes it is more convenient to define

$$N_j \equiv Nb_j \equiv \sum_{i=1}^{k} O_{ij} \qquad Na_ib_j \equiv N_ja_i \tag{8-18}$$

Then, by expanding the quadratic in Eq. (8-17) and simplifying, we obtain

$$\hat{\chi}^2 = \sum_i \sum_j \frac{O_{ij}^2}{N_ja_i} - N \tag{8-19}$$

a form clearly equivalent to that obtained for testing homogeneity. Thus, several uses of chi-square, while logically distinct, are mathematically identical.

TABLE 8-12. CHRONOLOGICAL LISTING OF ANNUAL AMOUNTS OF RAINFALL OVER
THE SUSQUEHANNA VALLEY

Year	Amount	Class†	Year	Amount	Class†	Year	Amount	Class†
1860	39.74	C	1891	41.96	D	1921	38.86	B
1861	38.91	B	1892	38.51	B	1922	35.76	A
1862	36.63	A	1893	39.13	B	1923	36.35	A
1863	44.82	D	1894	40.14	C	1924	39.99	C
1864	38.89	B	1895	31.21	A	1925	37.79	B
1865	41.45	C	1896	38.07	B	1926	40.60	C
1866	38.08	B	1897	37.79	B	1927	45.06	D
1867	42.26	D	1898 c	41.72	D	1928	40.08	C
1868	40.40	C	1899 b	37.13	A	1929	42.85	D
1869	42.09	D	1900	34.34	A	1930	28.04	A
1870	40.41	C	1901	42.03	D	1931	35.43	A
1871	37.72	B	1902	44.56	D	1932	39.08	B
1872 b	37.15	A	1903	43.44	D	1933	43.38	D
1873	44.76	D	1904	36.86	A	1934	37.96	B
1874	37.00	A	1905	41.18	C	1935	38.81	B
1875	36.70	A	1906	40.14	C	1936	40.67	C
1876	40.75	C	1907	40.57	C	1937	44.46	D
1877	36.65	A	1908	36.62	A	1938	37.77	B
1878	40.78	C	1909	34.25	A	1939	34.59	A
1879	32.11	A	1910	37.33	B	1940	41.23	C
1880	33.02	A	1911	40.15	C	1941	31.63	A
1881	36.39	A	1912 c	41.85	D	1942	46.51	D
1882	35.11	A	1913	40.54	C	1943	38.04	B
1883	38.15	B	1914	38.18	B	1944	38.43	B
1884	40.23	C	1915	43.17	D	1945	48.61	D
1885	· 36.62	A	1916	40.48	C	1946 c	39.55	B
1886	39.82	C	1917	38.65	B	1947	40.62	C
1887	37.57	B	1918 c	39.56	B	1948	44.34	D
1888 c	41.80	D	1919	41.12	C	1949	36.68	A
1889	48.22	D	1920	40.06	C	1950	45.89	D
1890	47.31	D				1951 c	41.90	D

† A = 37.15 or less; B = 37.16 to 39.56; C = 39.57 to 41.45; D = 41.46 and over.

Example 8-6. A chronological listing of annual amounts of rainfall over the Susquehanna Valley for a series of 92 years (1860–1951) is presented in Table 8-12. Test for significant association between the amounts observed in consecutive years.

Here the direct antithesis of the working hypothesis that consecutive annual amounts are associated is that they are independent. A more interesting and somewhat stronger null hypothesis would be that all observations (consecutive or not) are random draws from a common population. With a total of 92 observations we cannot test the latter hypothesis exhaustively, but we shall incorporate it as far as we can into the null hypothesis we actually do test. Considering successive pairs of observations (1860, 1861; 1862, 1863; etc.), we shall test the null hypothesis that both members of any pair are random draws from the same population and that this population is common to all pairs. Even if this hypothesis proves tenable, it will still be conceivable that other significant patterns not reflected in successive pairs exist in the data.

Let us try to divide the rainfall amounts into four exhaustive, equally likely categories A, B, C, D. Since there are 92 observations in all, each category should contain 23 cases. Referring to Table 7-4, we find that 23 of the observed amounts are less than or equal to 37.15 in., 46 are less than or equal to 39.56 in., and 69 are less than or equal to 41.45 in. Therefore, if we define category A as $x \leq 37.15$, category B as $37.15 < x \leq 39.56$, category C as $39.56 < x \leq 41.45$, and category D as $x > 41.45$, we shall have four exhaustive, mutually exclusive categories, each containing 23 cases. Table 8-12 indicates the classification of each year of record; the lower-case letters occurring in eight places will be explained presently.

Under the null hypothesis the time sequence is unimportant; therefore, we are interested in 10 combinations of categories: AA, AB, AC, AD, BB, BC, BD, CC, CD, DD. No distinction being made as to order of occurrence, the probability for each of the six mixed combinations (AB, AC, etc.) is $\frac{1}{8}$, and for each of the four duplicate combinations (AA, BB, etc.) the probability is $\frac{1}{16}$. Since there are 46 pairs of observations, the expected frequency of any duplicate combination is only $\frac{46}{16} = 2.875$. Therefore, we combine these into two composite classes ($AA + BB$), ($CC + DD$), thus doubling the expected frequency in order to obtain a satisfactory approximation of the $\hat{\chi}^2$ distribution by chi-square. Accordingly, we have eight categories, and the expected frequency of each is $\frac{46}{8} = 5.75$. Since E_i is constant, we may express the formula for $\hat{\chi}^2$ in the following simplified form, wherein the categories are numbered serially 1 through 8:

$$\hat{\chi}^2 = \frac{8}{46}\Sigma O_i{}^2 - 46$$

In determining class limits, we have estimated three fractiles from the data, namely, those corresponding to $F = .25, .50, .75$ (where F denotes cumulative probability). Hence there will be $8 - 1 - 3 = 4$ degrees of freedom, and the acceptance region for the .05 level of significance is $\hat{\chi}^2 < 9.49$. The observed frequencies are shown in Table 8-13.

TABLE 8-13

Category	$(AA + BB)$	AB	AC	AD	BC	BD	CD	$(CC + DD)$	Total
Frequency	8	2	6	5	10	5	5	5	46
Square	64	4	36	25	100	25	25	25	304

The calculations are as follows:

$$\hat{\chi}^2 = \frac{8(304)}{46} - 46 = 52.87 - 46 = 6.87$$

Since this value falls well within the acceptance region, we accept the hypothesis that the paired values are random draws from a common population which is the same for all the years tested. Thus, if any association whatever exists, it is not demonstrated in consecutive pairs of years.

Let us now examine a somewhat more specific hypothesis. Having shown that the distribution is approximately normal, let us determine the class limits from our normal fit, thereby gaining one degree of freedom. For the unit normal distribution the quartiles are $-.6745, 0, .6745$, and for a normal distribution with $\mu = 39.492$, $\sigma = 3.657$, the quartiles are $37.025, 39.492, 41.959$. The four classes are thus defined as follows:

$$A: \qquad x \leq 37.025$$
$$B: \qquad 37.025 < x \leq 39.492$$
$$C: \qquad 39.492 < x \leq 41.959$$
$$D: \qquad x > 41.959$$

It turns out that 84 of the years fall into the same categories as before, while the remaining eight differ by one category, as indicated by lower-case letters. Since we have fitted but two constants $\bar{x}$ and s to the data, we now have five degrees of freedom and the acceptance region is $\hat{\chi}^2 < 11.07$. The revised frequencies are shown in Table 8-14, and the calculation of $\hat{\chi}^2$ follows the table.

TABLE 8-14

Category	$(AA + BB)$	AB	AC	AD	BC	BD	CD	$(CC + DD)$	Total
Frequency	8	2	6	3	9	6	6	6	46
Square	64	4	36	9	81	36	36	36	302

$$\hat{\chi}^2 = \frac{8(302)}{46} - 46 = 52.52 - 46 = 6.52$$

This time we obtain very nearly the same value of $\hat{\chi}^2$ as before (actually, a trifle smaller) and yet have a broader acceptance region. Therefore, we accept the more specific hypothesis that the pairs are all drawn at random from the same normal population, with $\mu = 39.492, \sigma = 3.675$.

8-9. The Distributions of $\bar{x}$ and s^2 in a Normal Population. The threefold object of this section is to show that $\bar{x}$ and s^2, computed from the same random sample of size n from a *normal* population, are *independently* distributed in repeated independent trials to derive the distribution of s^2/σ^2 and to relate these results to t and F.

In repeated independent trials the joint distribution of the observations $x_1, x_2, \ldots, x_n$ is

$$f(x_1, x_2, \ldots, x_n) = K_0 e^{-Q_0/2} \qquad (-\infty, \infty \text{ all variates})$$

where

$$K_0 = (\sigma \sqrt{2\pi})^{-n} \qquad Q_0 = \frac{\sum_1^n (x_i - \mu)^2}{\sigma^2}$$

Making the change of variables

$$\bar{x} = \frac{x_1 + x_2 + \cdots + x_n}{n} \qquad u_i = x_i - \bar{x} \qquad (i = 1, 2, \ldots, n-1)$$

we have

$$x_i = \bar{x} + u_i \quad \text{for } i = 1, 2, \ldots, n - 1 \quad \text{and} \quad x_n = \bar{x} - \sum_1^{n-1} u_i$$

The equation for x_n is obtained from the fact that $\sum_1^n (x_i - \bar{x}) = 0$, whence

$$x_n - \bar{x} = - \sum_1^{n-1} (x_i - \bar{x}) = - \sum_1^{n-1} u_i$$

The Jacobian, which we simplify by adding the first $n - 1$ rows to the last row, is

$$J = \begin{vmatrix} 1 & 1 & 0 & 0 & \cdots & 0 & 0 \\ 1 & 0 & 1 & 0 & \cdots & 0 & 0 \\ \cdot & \cdot & \cdot & \cdot & & \cdot & \cdot \\ 1 & 0 & 0 & 0 & \cdots & 0 & 1 \\ 1 & -1 & -1 & -1 & \cdots & -1 & -1 \end{vmatrix} = \begin{vmatrix} 1 & 1 & 0 & 0 & \cdots & 0 & 0 \\ 1 & 0 & 1 & 0 & \cdots & 0 & 0 \\ \cdot & \cdot & \cdot & \cdot & & \cdot & \cdot \\ 1 & 0 & 0 & 0 & \cdots & 0 & 1 \\ n & 0 & 0 & 0 & \cdots & 0 & 0 \end{vmatrix}$$

and when this is expanded on the minors of its last row, the absolute value is found to be simply n. By virtue of the identity

$$\sum_1^n (x_i - \mu)^2 \equiv n(\bar{x} - \mu)^2 + \sum (x_i - \bar{x})^2$$

the quantity Q_0 may be expressed as a sum of two components:

$$Q_0 = \frac{n(\bar{x} - \mu)^2}{\sigma^2} + Q_1$$

where

$$Q_1 = \frac{\sum_1^n (x_i - \bar{x})^2}{\sigma^2} = \frac{\sum_1^{n-1} u_i{}^2 + \left(\sum_1^{n-1} u_i \right)^2}{\sigma^2}$$

Therefore, the joint distribution of the new variates is

$$g(\bar{x}, u_1, u_2, \ldots, u_{n-1}) = \left(\frac{\sqrt{n}}{\sigma \sqrt{2\pi}} e^{-n(\bar{x}-\mu)^2/2\sigma^2} \right) (K_1 e^{-Q_1/2}) \quad (-\infty, \infty \text{ all})$$

where $K_1 = (\sigma \sqrt{2\pi})^{-(n-1)} \sqrt{n}$. Since the first factor of this expression is the marginal density function of $\bar{x}$, the second factor $K_1 e^{-Q_1/2}$ must necessarily be the joint density function of the u's; and from the fact that s^2 is a pure function of the latter, it follows that $\bar{x}$ and s^2 are independent. While this strict independence of $\bar{x}$ and s^2 is a unique property of the normal population, the degree of dependence in many non-normal populations is often slight enough to be negligible.

Because the definition of s^2 formally contains $\bar{x}$, students are often puzzled by the assertion that s^2 and $\bar{x}$ are independent. It must be remembered that we are considering the behavior of two computed quantities in an infinite number of independent trials. Imagine all samples for which the mean $\bar{x}$ lies between any given values $\bar{x}'$ and $\bar{x}' + d\bar{x}$, and for this subset consider the conditional distribution of s^2. The quantity s^2 depends upon n terms of the type $x_i - \bar{x}$, and fixing the value of $\bar{x}$ still allows $n - 1$ of these deviations to assume any values whatever. Thus it is clear that s^2 is very far from determined by $\bar{x}$, and our proposition asserts that for a normal population the conditional distribution of s^2 is the same as its marginal distribution.

The distribution of s^2/σ^2 can now be ascertained from the moment-generating function. Let us put

$$S_0 = \frac{\Sigma(x_i - \mu)^2}{\sigma^2} \qquad S_1 = \frac{n(\bar{x} - \mu)^2}{\sigma^2} \qquad S_2 = \frac{\Sigma(x_i - \bar{x})^2}{\sigma^2}$$

Then, for any distribution whatever, we have the identity $S_0 \equiv S_1 + S_2$, but for the normal distribution S_1 and S_2 are independent and

$$M(\theta:S_0) = M(\theta:S_1)M(\theta:S_2)$$

whence
$$M(\theta:S_2) = \frac{M(\theta:S_0)}{M(\theta:S_1)}$$

Since $(x_i - \mu)/\sigma$ is unit normal, S_0 is distributed as chi-square with n degrees of freedom. Moreover, S_1 is distributed as chi-square with 1 degree of freedom. Now the moment-generating function of chi-square with, say, k degrees of freedom is given by $(1 - 2\theta)^{-k/2}$. Consequently,

$$M(\theta:S_2) = \frac{(1 - 2\theta)^{-n/2}}{(1 - 2\theta)^{-1/2}} = (1 - 2\theta)^{-(n-1)/2}$$

Therefore $S_2 = \Sigma(x_i - \bar{x})^2/\sigma^2$ is distributed as chi-square with $n - 1$ degrees of freedom, and s^2/σ^2 is distributed as the mean square with $n - 1$ degrees of freedom. By the same token, s/σ has the root-mean-square distribution with $n - 1$ degrees of freedom.

We are now in a position to construct test variates for several purposes. Recalling the definition of t (Chap. 6, Sec. 6-10), it follows at once that the ratio

$$\frac{(\bar{x} - \mu)\sqrt{n}}{s} \equiv \frac{(\bar{x} - \mu)\sqrt{n}/\sigma}{s/\sigma} \qquad (8\text{-}20)$$

is distributed as t with $n - 1$ degrees of freedom; for the variate $(\bar{x} - \mu)\sqrt{n}/\sigma$ is unit normal and the independent variate s/σ is distributed as the root-mean-square with $n - 1$ degrees of freedom. Moreover, if $\bar{x}_1$, $s_1{}^2$ and $\bar{x}_2$, $s_2{}^2$ are computed from two random samples of respectively n_1 and n_2 independent observations of the same normal variate x—that is, $\bar{x}_1 = \Sigma x_{1i}/n_1$, $s_1{}^2 = \Sigma(x_{1i} - \bar{x}_1)^2/(n_1 - 1)$ and $\bar{x}_2 = \Sigma x_{2j}/n_2$, $s_2{}^2 = \Sigma(x_{2j} - \bar{x}_2)^2/(n_2 - 1)$—then the ratio

$$\frac{s_1{}^2}{s_2{}^2} \equiv \frac{s_1{}^2/\sigma^2}{s_2{}^2/\sigma^2} \qquad (8\text{-}21)$$

will be distributed as F with $n_1 - 1$ and $n_2 - 1$ degrees of freedom. (Refer to Chap. 6, Sec. 6-11.) It is for this reason that F is called the "variance ratio." Let us now modify the previous conditions to the extent that the two samples are taken from normal populations with possibly different means μ_1, μ_2, but still with the same variance σ^2. Then, since the distribution of s^2 is independent of the population mean, the ratio $s_1{}^2/s_2{}^2$ will still be distributed as F with $n_1 - 1$ and $n_2 - 1$ degrees of freedom. Under the same conditions, the quantity

$$\frac{(n_1 - 1)s_1{}^2 + (n_2 - 1)s_2{}^2}{\sigma^2} \equiv \frac{\Sigma(x_{1i} - \bar{x}_1)^2 + \Sigma(x_{2j} - \bar{x}_2)^2}{\sigma^2} \qquad (8\text{-}22)$$

will be distributed as chi-square with

$$(n_1 - 1) + (n_2 - 1) = n_1 + n_2 - 2 \qquad \text{degrees of freedom}$$

by the additive property of chi-square. Therefore, denoting the pooled estimator of variance as s^2, where

$$s^2 \equiv \frac{(n_1 - 1)s_1{}^2 + (n_2 - 1)s_2{}^2}{n_1 + n_2 - 2} \equiv \frac{\Sigma(x_{1i} - \bar{x}_1)^2 + \Sigma(x_{2j} - \bar{x}_2)^2}{n_1 + n_2 - 2} \qquad (8\text{-}23)$$

it follows that the statistic s^2/σ^2 will have the mean-square distribution with $n_1 + n_2 - 2$ degrees of freedom and its square root s/σ will have the root-mean-square distribution with $n_1 + n_2 - 2$ degrees of freedom. The pooled estimator of variance s^2 will be independent of both sample means $\bar{x}_1$, $\bar{x}_2$, and likewise independent of any fixed function of them because $s_1{}^2$ and $s_2{}^2$ are independent of both. Consider, now, the difference $(\bar{x}_1 - \mu_1) - (\bar{x}_2 - \mu_2)$. Its variance is $\sigma^2(1/n_1 + 1/n_2)$, so that the ratio

$$\frac{(\bar{x}_1 - \mu_1) - (\bar{x}_2 - \mu_2)}{\sigma \sqrt{1/n_1 + 1/n_2}} \qquad (8\text{-}24)$$

will be unit normal. When the latter expression is divided by s/σ, the unknown parameter σ cancels, with the result that the ratio

$$\frac{(\bar{x}_1 - \mu_1) - (\bar{x}_2 - \mu_2)}{s \sqrt{1/n_1 + 1/n_2}} \qquad (8\text{-}25)$$

is distributed as t with $n_1 + n_2 - 2$ degrees of freedom. Much of the remainder of this chapter will be devoted to putting these results to work.

8-10. The t Tests. Prior to the work of W. S. Gosset in 1908, tests on sample means were made by replacing the unknown parameter σ^2 by a sample estimate and regarding the resulting variate as unit normal. Inexact as this approach was, it gave good results for large samples; but for small samples it gave (as is now known) an exaggerated impression of significance. Gosset (under the pseudonym "Student") cited several experimental situations wherein large samples could not be obtained, and propounded the problem of determining the exact distribution of the test variate in samples from a normal population. In solving this problem, Gosset found that the exact distribution was free from unknown parameters—a fact of primary importance in the modern theory of hypothesis testing. Gosset's discovery was not appreciated until its implications were ably expounded and developed by R. A. Fisher, who, however, modified Gosset's test variate slightly to obtain the variate t as now used. Fisher's own contributions to hypothesis testing as well as to the entire field of statistics are conceded to be the greatest of any single individual.

Although there are other applications of t, we shall confine our attention to its use in testing the significance of a single sample mean or the difference between two sample means, and its use in setting confidence limits for estimating the population mean.

The t tests are exact when the parent population is normal, but approximate otherwise. That is to say, the sampling behavior of the computed statistic is accurately described by the t distribution only in the case of a normal population. Empirical studies on non-normal populations, however, have tended to show that the tests are not very sensitive to moderate departures from normality. Similar remarks apply to F, except that F seems to be even less affected than t by non-normality.

8-11. The t Test for a Single Mean. The problem is to decide whether we can accept the hypothesis that the population mean equals some stated value μ_h. The answer is found by obtaining a random sample of n observations $x_1, x_2, \ldots, x_n$, computing their average $\bar{x}$ and the unbiased estimate of variance s^2, and then computing the statistic t defined as

$$t = \frac{\bar{x} - \mu_h}{\sqrt{s^2/n}} \tag{8-26}$$

Since there are $n - 1$ degrees of freedom associated with s^2, we refer to the t tables under $n - 1$ degrees of freedom. Ordinarily we have equal interest in negative and positive deviations from μ_h, in which case we use a two-sided critical region such that $\int_{-\infty}^{-a} f(t)\,dt + \int_{a}^{\infty} f(t)\,dt = \alpha$. On the other hand, if the working hypothesis is one-sided, as it would be if the

TABLE 8-15. CRITICAL MAGNITUDES OF t AT STATED SIGNIFICANCE LEVELS

Degrees of freedom	One-sided region		Two-sided region	
	$\alpha = .05$	$\alpha = .01$	$\alpha = .05$	$\alpha = .01$
1	6.31	31.82	12.71	63.66
2	2.92	6.97	4.30	9.93
3	2.35	4.54	3.18	5.84
4	2.13	3.74	2.78	4.60
5	2.02	3.37	2.57	4.03
6	1.94	3.14	2.45	3.71
7	1.90	3.00	2.37	3.50
8	1.86	2.90	2.31	3.36
9	1.83	2.82	2.26	3.25
10	1.81	2.76	2.23	3.17
11	1.80	2.72	2.20	3.11
12	1.78	2.68	2.18	3.06
13	1.77	2.65	2.16	3.01
14	1.76	2.62	2.15	2.98
15	1.75	2.60	2.13	2.95
16	1.75	2.58	2.12	2.92
17	1.74	2.57	2.11	2.90
18	1.73	2.55	2.10	2.88
19	1.73	2.54	2.09	2.86
20	1.73	2.53	2.09	2.85
21	1.72	2.52	2.08	2.83
22	1.72	2.51	2.07	2.82
23	1.71	2.50	2.07	2.81
24	1.71	2.49	2.06	2.80
25	1.71	2.49	2.06	2.79
26	1.71	2.48	2.06	2.78
27	1.70	2.47	2.05	2.77
28	1.70	2.47	2.05	2.76
29	1.70	2.46	2.05	2.76
30	1.70	2.46	2.04	2.75
∞	1.64	2.33	1.96	2.58

object were to achieve a significant improvement over a standard performance, the practical implication of a deviation in the opposite direction is much the same as a confirmation of the null hypothesis proper, for the new technique will be abandoned. The critical region will then be $t \geq a'$ where $\int_{a'}^{\infty} f(t)\, dt = \alpha$. In either case, of course, the equation for

t is the same, and for computational purposes it is convenient to write

$$\frac{s^2}{n} = \sum \frac{(x - \bar{x})^2}{n(n - 1)}$$

whence $\qquad\qquad t = \dfrac{\bar{x} - \mu_h}{\sqrt{\Sigma(x - \bar{x})^2/n(n - 1)}}$ $\qquad\qquad$ (8-27)

Example 8-7. A diet published in a newspaper is advertised as resulting in an average weight loss of 10 lb over a period of three weeks. Six persons who tried the diet reported the decreases shown in Table 8-16. Is the mean of this sample consistent with the published average of 10 lb?

TABLE 8-16

Person	A	B	C	D	E	F
Weight loss	10.1	6.3	7.4	11.4	11.9	5.7

With six observations there will be five degrees of freedom. Using a two-sided critical region, the acceptance region for the 5 per cent level of significance of t with five degrees of freedom is $-2.57 < t < 2.57$. The sample value of t is computed as follows:

$$\Sigma x = 52.8 \qquad n = 6 \qquad \bar{x} = 8.8$$
$$\Sigma x^2 = 500.52 \qquad \Sigma(x - \bar{x})^2 = \Sigma x^2 - \bar{x}\Sigma x = 35.88$$
$$\frac{s^2}{n} = \frac{\Sigma(x - \bar{x})^2}{n(n - 1)} = \frac{35.88}{30} = 1.196$$
$$t = \frac{8.8 - 10.0}{\sqrt{1.196}} = \frac{-1.2}{1.094} = -1.1$$

Since the sample value of t lies inside of the critical limits, we accept the hypothesis $\mu = 10$ lb.

8-12. The t Test for the Means of Paired Observations. When two processes are being compared, the technique of eliminating irrelevant sources of variation often calls for an experimental design in which paired observations are secured under controlled conditions. The two observational mates cannot be considered independent, but their difference is independent of a common mean value, and the mean difference can be tested as in a single sample.

Suppose we have n independent pairs of observations x_1, y_1; x_2, y_2; . . . ; x_n, y_n, and the hypothesis is that $\mu_x - \mu_y = \delta$. Put

$$d_i = x_i - y_i \qquad (i = 1, 2, \ldots, n) \qquad\qquad \bar{d} = \frac{\Sigma d_i}{n}$$

Compute t as follows:

$$t = \frac{(\bar{d} - \delta)}{\sqrt{\Sigma(d_i - \bar{d})^2/n(n - 1)}} \qquad\qquad (8-28)$$

Under the hypothesis $\mu_x - \mu_y = \delta$ this will be distributed as t with $n - 1$ degrees of freedom. Usually a one-sided region is appropriate.

Example 8-8. Let us apply the t test to the shellac problem introduced in Example 3-5. In this problem, we have six paired measures of wear under alternative treatments; hence the t test for related samples will be based on five degrees of freedom. The null hypothesis is that $\delta = 0$, whereas the working hypothesis is that $\delta > 0$, and this implies that we want a one-sided critical region. For five degrees of freedom the 5 per cent level of t with a one-sided criterion is 2.02 and the acceptance region for the null hypothesis is $t < 2.02$. The data and computations are as follows:

TABLE 8-17

Bldg.	Percentage damage		
	Reg.	Fort.	Diff.
1	5	2	3
2	11	7	4
3	4	5	−1
4	14	8	6
5	9	4	5
6	12	11	1

$$n = 6 \quad \Sigma d = 18 \quad \bar{d} = 3 \quad \Sigma d^2 = 88$$
$$\Sigma(d - \bar{d})^2 = \Sigma d^2 - \bar{d}\,\Sigma d = 88 - 54 = 34$$
$$\frac{\Sigma(d - \bar{d})^2}{n(n - 1)} = {}^{34}\!/_{30} = 1.133$$

The sample value of t is

$$t = \frac{3.0}{\sqrt{1.133}} = \frac{3}{1.064} = 2.82$$

Since this value lies outside the acceptance region, we reject the null hypothesis and conclude that the added ingredient improves the wearing quality of shellac. In this connection the t test is more sensitive than the magnitude test used in Chap. 3, for the probability of obtaining $t > 2.82$ is actually less than .02, as compared with the significance level of .047 reached with the magnitude test. The latter is sometimes advantageous, however, inasmuch as no appeal is made to the assumption of normality of sample means.

8-13. The t Test for the Difference of the Means of Two Independent Samples. When it is reasonable to assume common background conditions for all observations, the comparison of two means can be made with independent samples. This does not repudiate the logic of the previous section because uniform background conditions will not contribute to the variations among individual observations, and so we may legitimately regard the latter as independently distributed. With a fixed total number of observations, the precision is maximized by taking equal sample sizes. However, if there are practical limitations on the size of one sample while the other can be made larger, the larger number of observations should be taken in the latter. Hence, for generality, we allow for different sample sizes n_1, n_2.

Having independent samples $(x_1, x_2, \ldots, x_{n_1})$ and $(y_1, y_2, \ldots, y_{n_2})$ we wish to test the hypothesis that $\mu_x - \mu_y = \delta$. The test of this hypothesis by t presupposes equal variances, that is, $\sigma_x^2 = \sigma_y^2 = \sigma^2$. Denote the sample means as $\bar{x} = \Sigma x / n_1$, $\bar{y} = \Sigma y / n_2$. An unbiased estimate of σ^2 is given by

$$s^2 = \frac{\Sigma(x - \bar{x})^2 + \Sigma(y - \bar{y})^2}{n_1 + n_2 - 2} \tag{8-29}$$

and the test variate

$$t = \frac{(\bar{x} - \bar{y}) - \delta}{\sqrt{s^2(1/n_1 + 1/n_2)}} \tag{8-30}$$

will be distributed as t with $n_1 + n_2 - 2$ degrees of freedom. The critical region includes either one tail or two, depending upon the working hypothesis.

Example 8-9. A factory has two machines both of which make $\frac{1}{8}$-in. steel washers. Thicknesses of independent samples of each machine were measured to the nearest thousandth of an inch, with the following results. Are the mean thicknesses significantly different?

Machine I: .117, .130, .122, .139, .132
Machine II: .120, .127, .133, .115, .137, .126

Since the sample taken from machine I has five observations and that from machine II has six observations, the t test for independent samples will be based on $5 + 6 - 2 = 9$ degrees of freedom. Using a two-sided critical region, the acceptance region for t with nine degrees of freedom is $-2.26 < t < 2.26$ at the 5 per cent level of significance. The computations are as follows:

For machine I we have

$$n_1 = 5 \quad \Sigma x = .640 \quad \bar{x} = .128$$
$$\Sigma x^2 = .082218 \quad \Sigma(x - \bar{x})^2 = .000298$$

For machine II we have

$$n_2 = 6 \quad \Sigma y = .758 \quad \bar{y} = .126$$
$$\Sigma y^2 = .096088 \quad \Sigma(y - \bar{y})^2 = .000327$$

The combined estimate of variance is $s^2 = \dfrac{.000625}{9} = .0000694$ whence

$$s^2 \left(\frac{1}{n_1} + \frac{1}{n_2} \right) = .0000254 \qquad \sqrt{s^2 \left(\frac{1}{n_1} + \frac{1}{n_2} \right)} = .00504$$

Here we hypothesize that $\mu_x = \mu_y$, that is, $\delta = 0$. The difference of the means is $\bar{x} - \bar{y} = .002$, and so

$$t = \frac{.002}{.005} = .4$$

Since this value of t falls inside the acceptance region, we accept the null hypothesis and conclude that the two machines are producing washers of equal average thickness.

Those who are ignorant of the vagaries of arithmetic sometimes laugh at the number of decimals carried in a statistical computation. The student is warned not to confuse precision of measurement with precision of arithmetic; rounding errors can be devastating. As a case in point, we note that the correct value of $\Sigma(y - \bar{y})^2$ to three significant figures is .000327, this value being obtained from the formula

$$\Sigma(y - \bar{y})^2 = \frac{n\Sigma y^2 - (\Sigma y)^2}{n}$$

On the other hand, using the alternative formula $\Sigma(y - \bar{y})^2 = \Sigma y^2 - \bar{y}\Sigma y$ and retaining three decimals in $\bar{y}$, we get .000580. In order to obtain the correct result to three significant figures by the latter formula, it turns out that we must carry seven decimals in $\bar{y}$.

A common hypothesis is that $\delta = 0$, that is, $\mu_x = \mu_y$. In that case, students often object to the estimate of σ^2 on the grounds that it would be more logical to carry out the full implications of the null hypothesis by employing a variance estimate based on a combined estimate of the mean. This point merits investigation. Suppose we put

$$m = \frac{\Sigma x + \Sigma y}{n_1 + n_2} = \frac{n_1\bar{x} + n_2\bar{y}}{n_1 + n_2} \tag{8-31}$$

$$V = \Sigma(x - m)^2 + \Sigma(y - m)^2 \qquad S = \Sigma(x - \bar{x})^2 + \Sigma(y - \bar{y})^2 \tag{8-32}$$

We then find identically

$$V \equiv S + n_1(\bar{x} - m)^2 + n_2(\bar{y} - m)^2$$

$$\equiv S + \frac{n_1 n_2(\bar{x} - \bar{y})^2}{n_1 + n_2} \tag{8-33}$$

Therefore, although V is independent of m, it is not independent of $\bar{x} - \bar{y}$ and could not be used for t. A perfectly usable parameter-free test variate could be derived from V, but it would not have the t distribution. As a matter of fact, if we put $v^2 = V/(n_1 + n_2 - 1)$ and define the statistic

$$w = \frac{\bar{x} - \bar{y}}{\sqrt{v^2(1/n_1 + 1/n_2)}} \tag{8-34}$$

which is clearly analogous to Eq. (8-30) when $\delta = 0$, we find that the distribution of w is

$$f(w) = k\left(1 - \frac{w^2}{n_1 + n_2 - 1}\right)^{(n_1 + n_2 - 3)/2}$$

$$(-\sqrt{n_1 + n_2 - 1} \leq w \leq \sqrt{n_1 + n_2 - 1}) \tag{8-35}$$

where
$$k = \frac{\Gamma[(n_1 + n_2)/2]}{\Gamma[(n_1 + n_2 - 1)/2]\sqrt{\pi(n_1 + n_2 - 1)}}$$

The test variate given by Eq. (8-30) is distributed as t only if $\sigma_x^2 = \sigma_y^2$; for if the variances are not equal, these parameters do not cancel. To gain qualitative insight into further effects of unequal variances, let us examine the correct formulation of t in this case. The variance of the quantity $(\bar{x} - \bar{y}) - (\mu_x - \mu_y)$ will be $\sigma_x^2/n_1 + \sigma_y^2/n_2$, and in order to obtain a denominator which is distributed as the root-mean square, we must replace s^2 by

$$\frac{(n_1 - 1)s_1^2/\sigma_x^2 + (n_2 - 1)s_2^2/\sigma_y^2}{n_1 + n_2 - 2}$$

Putting $\lambda = \sigma_x^2/\sigma_y^2$ and simplifying, we obtain

$$
\begin{aligned}
t &= \frac{[(\bar{x} - \bar{y}) - (\mu_x - \mu_y)]\sqrt{n_1 + n_2 - 2}}{\sqrt{\sigma_x^2/n_1 + \sigma_y^2/n_2}\sqrt{(n_1 - 1)s_1^2/\sigma_x^2 + (n_2 - 1)s_2^2/\sigma_y^2}} \\
&= \frac{[(\bar{x} - \bar{y}) - (\mu_x - \mu_y)]\sqrt{n_1 + n_2 - 2}}{\sqrt{\lambda/n_1 + 1/n_2}\sqrt{(n_1 - 1)s_1^2/\lambda + (n_2 - 1)s_2^2}}
\end{aligned}
\tag{8-36}
$$

If $\lambda = 1$, we have the same formula as before, Eq. (8-30). If $\lambda \neq 1$, one factor of the denominator is smaller than before and the other is larger, so that the resultant effect may go either way, depending upon the particular n's and s^2's. To be on the safe side in applying Eq. (8-30), therefore, we should first test for equality of variances. This test is described in Sec. 8.16.

Several approximate tests have been proposed in case $\sigma_x^2 \neq \sigma_y^2$. Because of its comparative simplicity, we have chosen to present the method of Cochran and Cox.[1] Put

$$t' = \frac{(\bar{x} - \bar{y}) - \delta}{\sqrt{s_1^2/n_1 + s_2^2/n_2}} \tag{8-37}$$

For a two-sided critical region the acceptance region is $-a < t' < a$, where a is a certain weighted function [Eq. (8-38)] of tabular values. Let a_1 be the right-hand limit of the two-sided critical region for t with $n_1 - 1$ degrees of freedom and a_2 the corresponding limit for t with $n_2 - 1$ degrees of freedom. Also put $w_1 = s_1^2/n_1$, $w_2 = s_2^2/n_2$. Then

$$a = \frac{w_1 a_1 + w_2 a_2}{w_1 + w_2} \tag{8-38}$$

For a one-sided critical region we have an analogous definition of the acceptance region. Thus, if b_1, b_2 are the respective limits with $n_1 - 1$ and $n_2 - 1$ degrees of freedom, then the limit b appropriate to t' is

$$b = \frac{w_1 b_1 + w_2 b_2}{w_1 + w_2} \tag{8-39}$$

[1] W. G. Cochran and G. M. Cox, "Experimental Designs," pp. 91–93, John Wiley & Sons, Inc., New York, 1950.

By way of heuristic justification of the Cochran-Cox test, let us examine the case of equal sample sizes $n_1 = n_2 = n$. The two limits a_1, a_2 are then identical, and a (being the same) becomes the ordinary limit for $n - 1$ degrees of freedom. Moreover, the quantity $s_1^2/n_1 + s_2^2/n_2$ reduces to $(s_1^2 + s_2^2)/n$, whence

$$t' = \frac{(\bar{x} - \bar{y}) - \delta}{\sqrt{(s_1^2 + s_2^2)/n}} \tag{8-40}$$

Since the samples are independent, there is no logical basis for pairing.[1] Nevertheless, we can form the differences $d_i = x_i - y_i$ ($i = 1, 2, \ldots, n$) between the two sets of observations in whatever order they happen to occur. By the assumption of independence, all of the d's (in repeated sampling) have the same distribution; their expected value is $\mu_x - \mu_y$, and their sample mean value is $\bar{d} \equiv \bar{x} - \bar{y}$. Hence, a statistic t'' having the same formal definition as Eq. (8-28) could be employed here and (under the usual assumption that the parent populations are normal) would be rigorously distributed as t with $n - 1$ degrees of freedom. As to t', we note that since $s_1^2 + s_2^2$ is an unbiased estimate of $\sigma_x^2 + \sigma_y^2$, the true variance of the d's, an unbiased estimate of the variance of $\bar{d}$ is $(s_1^2 + s_2^2)/n$. True, the quantity $(s_1^2 + s_2^2)/(\sigma_x^2 + \sigma_y^2)$ is not distributed as the mean square, and as a consequence, t' is not distributed as t. But of all the quantities $\Sigma(d_i - \bar{d})^2/(n - 1)$ that could be formed by distinct rearrangements of the original data, the mean value is $s_1^2 + s_2^2$. Hence we should expect the distribution of t' to fall off more rapidly than that of t'' itself, and we infer that the stated limits of acceptance are on the conservative side, that is, broader than the true limits. If $n_1 \neq n_2$, the behavior of t' would follow some middle way between what would happen if both sample sizes were equal to n_1 and if both were equal to n_2. The weights of the critical limits are proportional to the estimated variances of the respective means; although somewhat arbitrary, this scheme is altogether reasonable.

8-14. Respective Confidence Limits for μ and σ^2. In random samples of n observations from a normal population, we have seen that the statistic $(\bar{x} - \mu)\sqrt{n/s^2}$ is distributed as t with $n - 1$ degrees of freedom, while $(n - 1)s^2/\sigma^2$ is distributed as chi-square with $n - 1$ degrees of freedom. From these statistics we may obtain separate pairs of confidence limits for μ and σ^2; and although separate limits suffice for most purposes, they are not the same as simultaneous limits, for which a different approach is needed.

---

[1] The argument we are about to give shows that pairing produces a valid test variate, but the student is warned that it has less precision than the standard t test for independent samples when equal variances can be assumed.

Adopting the confidence probability $1 - \alpha$, let $a < b$ denote any pair of values for which $\int_a^b f(t)\, dt = 1 - \alpha$, where $t = (\bar{x} - \mu) \sqrt{n/s^2}$; that is $P(a \le t \le b) = 1 - \alpha$. Substituting for t and simplifying, we find that the inequality $a \le t \le b$ implies that $(sa/\sqrt{n} - \bar{x}) \le -\mu \le (sb/\sqrt{n} - \bar{x})$ whence

$$\bar{x} - \frac{sb}{\sqrt{n}} \le \mu \le \bar{x} - \frac{sa}{\sqrt{n}} \tag{8-41}$$

When we assert that the latter inequality represents confidence limits for μ corresponding to a confidence probability $1 - \alpha$, we mean that in repeated independent trials the *variable interval* $\bar{x} - sb/\sqrt{n}$ to $\bar{x} - sa/\sqrt{n}$ will include the true value of μ a certain percentage of the time, and in the long run, the relative frequency with which such intervals include μ will be $1 - \alpha$. This statement must not be construed as implying that μ itself is distributed or subject to variation.

Since the requirement that $P(a \le t \le b) = 1 - \alpha$ does not suffice to determine the limits a, b, further criteria are in order. A criterion with intuitive appeal is that the confidence interval be as short as possible. Accordingly, representing the interval by D, where

$$D = \left(\bar{x} - \frac{sa}{\sqrt{n}} \right) - \left(\bar{x} - \frac{sb}{\sqrt{n}} \right) \equiv \frac{s}{\sqrt{n}} (b - a) \tag{8-42}$$

we minimize D subject to the requirement that $\int_a^b f(t)\, dt = 1 - \alpha$. The latter requirement yields

$$f(b)\, db - f(a)\, da = 0 \tag{8-43}$$

The unimodal form of the distribution permits us to minimize D by setting $dD = 0$, whence $da = db$. Accordingly, $f(a) = f(b)$, and since the distribution of t is symmetrical about zero, it follows that $a = -b$. Therefore, the upper limit b is determined from the relation $\int_b^\infty f(t)\, dt = \alpha/2$, and the confidence limits are $\bar{x} - sb/\sqrt{n}$ to $\bar{x} + sb/\sqrt{n}$; that is,

$$\bar{x} - \frac{sb}{\sqrt{n}} \le \mu \le \bar{x} + \frac{sb}{\sqrt{n}} \tag{8-44}$$

If the distribution had been J-shaped, the minimization of D would have required an examination of the sign of the derivative.

At this point the student might feel that he has been put through an involved process only to reach an obvious conclusion. We are about to discover that the conclusion is not so obvious when the distribution is skewed, and we shall need the method we have just applied.

With regard to σ^2, the direct probability statement is

$$P\left[a \leq \frac{(n-1)s^2}{\sigma^2} \leq b\right] = 1 - \alpha$$

and by transforming the bracketed inequality we obtain, as confidence limits,

$$\frac{(n-1)s^2}{b} \leq \sigma^2 \leq \frac{(n-1)s^2}{a} \tag{8-45}$$

Again representing the confidence interval by D, where

$$D = \frac{(n-1)s^2}{a} - \frac{(n-1)s^2}{b} \equiv (n-1)s^2\left(\frac{1}{a} - \frac{1}{b}\right) \tag{8-46}$$

we minimize D subject to the requirement that $\int_a^b g(\chi^2)\,d\chi^2 = 1 - \alpha$. The intermediate equations are

$$g(a)\,da = g(b)\,db \qquad \frac{da}{a^2} = \frac{db}{b^2} \tag{8-47}$$

and the result is

$$a^2g(a) = b^2g(b) \tag{8-48}$$

Unfortunately, convenient tables for the determination of these limits are not widely available, so that for practical purposes other limits are often substituted. For small to moderate numbers of degrees of freedom, it turns out that nearly optimum results can be obtained by putting $b = \infty$. That is, we use only the left-hand tail of chi-square, with the result that $D = (n-1)s^2/a$, and the corresponding confidence limits are

$$0 \leq \sigma^2 \leq \frac{(n-1)s^2}{a} \tag{8-49}$$

Example 8-10. Suppose that a random sample of 11 observations from a normal population yields $\Sigma x = 37.4$, $\Sigma x^2 = 251.73$. Then

$$\bar{x} = 3.4 \qquad \Sigma(x - \bar{x})^2 = \Sigma x^2 - \bar{x}\Sigma x = 251.73 - 127.16 = 124.57$$

$$s^2 = \frac{\Sigma(x - \bar{x})^2}{10} = 12.457 \qquad s = 3.53 \qquad \frac{s}{\sqrt{11}} = 1.06$$

With a confidence probability of .95, the limits for t with 10 degrees of freedom are $t = \pm 2.23$, from which we obtain $(2.23)s/\sqrt{11} = 2.36$. Therefore the .95 confidence limits for μ are 3.4 ± 2.36, whence

$$1.04 \leq \mu \leq 5.76$$

With regard to σ^2, we note that for 10 degrees of freedom the distribution of χ^2 is

$$g(\chi^2) = \frac{1}{2^5\Gamma(5)}(\chi^2)^4 e^{-\chi^2/2} \qquad (0, \infty)$$

Whence Eq. (8-48) becomes

$$a^6 e^{-a/2} = b^6 e^{-b/2}$$

or
$$\ln \frac{b}{a} = \frac{b - a}{12}$$

Solving for a and b by successive approximations, we obtain

$$a = 3.8845 \qquad b = 27.2638$$

which corresponds to splitting the specified area .05 between the extremes of chi-square in such a way that the portion in the lower tail has an area of .0476 while the portion in the upper tail has an area of only .0024. These values of a and b yield

$$\frac{(n-1)s^2}{a} = 32.0685 \qquad \frac{(n-1)s^2}{b} = 4.5691 \qquad D = 27.4994$$

Therefore, the .95 confidence limits for σ^2 are

$$4.57 \leq \sigma^2 \leq 32.07$$

Had we simply applied Eq. (8-49) with $a = 3.94$, our confidence interval would have been $0 \leq \sigma^2 \leq 31.62$, which compares favorably with the shortest interval.

8-15. The F Tests. Nearly all of the problems to which the F distribution applies were originally solved by R. A. Fisher, who constructed an appropriate parameter-free variate, derived its distribution, provided the necessary tables, and in all respects made it available as a research tool of extraordinary versatility. The variate introduced by Fisher was actually $(\frac{1}{2}) \ln F$, but F itself is now commonly used because it is easier to compute.

In view of its definition as the ratio of two mean squares, the most direct use of the variate F lies in testing whether two independent sample values of s^2 may be considered representative of a common variance. Although not obvious from the definition, the F ratio is also appropriate for testing the significance of the difference between two sample means, in this capacity serving as an alternative to the t test, or, what is much more important, testing the significance of the differences between *several* sample *means*, thus going *beyond* the *scope* of the t test. This, the principal use of F, has a wide range of application, the elaboration of which comes under the heading of *analysis* of *variance*.

At this point we call the student's attention to a widespread misuse of the t test by research workers with scanty training in statistics. A succession of t tests on the means of several samples is not a substitute for the F test applied simultaneously to the entire data. The separate t's are not independently distributed; therefore the evaluation of their combined significance must take proper account of their joint distribution. Fortunately, however, this end is accomplished automatically by using the F test in the first place.

Standard tables of the F distribution give limits for one-sided critical regions. Most tables give critical values for 5 per cent and 1 per cent levels of significance, but limits for intermediate levels can be approximated by linear interpolation. When a two-sided critical region is appropriate, the *lower* critical limit c can be found from tabulated values by virtue of the relation

$$\int_0^c f(F)\, dF = \int_{1/c}^\infty g\left(\frac{1}{F}\right) d\left(\frac{1}{F}\right) \qquad (8\text{-}50)$$

the second member of which is simply a transformation of the first. But from the definition of F with a and b degrees of freedom, it follows immediately that the reciprocal variate $1/F$ is analogously distributed with b and a degrees of freedom. Hence, by taking the reciprocal of the upper critical limit $1/c$ of the F with interchanged degrees of freedom, we obtain the lower limit c for the F in question.

8-16. Tests for Equality of Variances. The technical term "homoscedasticity" is used to denote "equality of variances." The appropriate test for homoscedasticity depends on whether there are two or more samples involved. The F test applies if there are two samples, but not otherwise. Several tests, based on suitable ratios or their logarithms, have been devised for more than two samples. The one we have selected yields a variate which is distributed approximately as chi-square.

Before applying any significance test, one should decide upon an appropriate critical region. Let us examine this issue with reference to supporting the t test by a check on homoscedasticity. Since very small values of the variance ratio and very large values are both unfavorable to the hypothesis of homoscedasticity, it is plausible that the critical region should be two-sided. Further arguments, which we are about to present, lead to the conclusion that the two portions of the critical region should have equal areas.

We reason to equal subdivision of area as follows: Defining the ratios $F = s_x{}^2/s_y{}^2$, $F' = s_y{}^2/s_x{}^2$, it is purely arbitrary whether we choose to compute F or F'. Consequently, if B is that value such that $P(F \geq B) = \epsilon$, and also B' is that value such that $P(F' \geq B') = \epsilon$, then there is neither more nor less logical justification for attaching significance to the event $F \geq B$ than to the event $F' \geq B'$, for both events are equally rare and both are damaging to the hypothesis that $\sigma_x{}^2 = \sigma_y{}^2$. But $F \leq 1/B'$ whenever $F' \geq B'$. Therefore, the logical implications of large or small ratios are essentially equivalent with reference to this particular hypothesis, and for its test of significance the critical region should be divided equally between the upper and lower tails of the F distribution.

Tables of F at the levels .005 and .025 have been constructed for use

TABLE 8-18. CRITICAL VALUES OF F WITH n_1 AND n_2 DEGREES OF FREEDOM. ONE-SIDED CRITICAL REGION (RIGHT TAIL) WITH $\alpha = .05, .01$
(Upper half, $\alpha = .05$; lower half, $\alpha = .01$)

Upper half, $\alpha = .05$

n_2 \ n_1	1	2	3	4	5	6	7	8	9	10	15	25	50	100	∞
1	161	200	216	225	230	234	237	239	241	242	246	249	252	253	254
2	18.51	19.00	19.16	19.25	19.30	19.33	19.36	19.37	19.38	19.39	19.43	19.45	19.47	19.49	19.50
3	10.13	9.55	9.28	9.12	9.01	8.94	8.88	8.84	8.81	8.78	8.70	8.64	8.58	8.56	8.53
4	7.71	6.94	6.59	6.39	6.26	6.16	6.09	6.04	6.00	5.96	5.86	5.77	5.70	5.66	5.63
5	6.61	5.79	5.41	5.19	5.05	4.95	4.88	4.82	4.78	4.74	4.62	4.53	4.44	4.40	4.36
6	5.99	5.14	4.76	4.53	4.39	4.28	4.21	4.15	4.10	4.06	3.94	3.84	3.75	3.71	3.67
7	5.59	4.74	4.35	4.12	3.97	3.87	3.79	3.73	3.68	3.63	3.50	3.41	3.32	3.28	3.23
8	5.32	4.46	4.07	3.84	3.69	3.58	3.50	3.44	3.39	3.34	3.21	3.11	3.03	2.98	2.93
9	5.12	4.26	3.86	3.63	3.48	3.37	3.29	3.23	3.18	3.13	3.00	2.89	2.80	2.76	2.71
10	4.96	4.10	3.71	3.48	3.33	3.22	3.14	3.07	3.02	2.97	2.84	2.73	2.64	2.59	2.54
15	4.54	3.68	3.29	3.06	2.90	2.79	2.70	2.64	2.59	2.55	2.41	2.28	2.18	2.12	2.07
25	4.24	3.38	2.99	2.76	2.60	2.49	2.41	2.34	2.28	2.24	2.08	1.95	1.84	1.77	1.71
50	4.03	3.18	2.79	2.56	2.40	2.29	2.20	2.13	2.07	2.02	1.87	1.73	1.60	1.52	1.44
100	3.94	3.09	2.70	2.46	2.30	2.19	2.10	2.03	1.97	1.92	1.77	1.62	1.48	1.39	1.28
500	3.86	3.02	2.62	2.39	2.23	2.12	2.03	1.96	1.90	1.85	1.69	1.53	1.38	1.28	1.12
1,000	3.85	3.00	2.61	2.38	2.22	2.10	2.02	1.95	1.89	1.84	1.67	1.52	1.36	1.26	1.08
∞	3.84	2.99	2.60	2.37	2.21	2.09	2.01	1.94	1.88	1.83	1.66	1.51	1.35	1.24	1.00

Lower half, $\alpha = .01$

n_2 \ n_1	1	2	3	4	5	6	7	8	9	10	15	25	50	100	∞
1	4,052	4,999	5,403	5,625	5,764	5,859	5,928	5,981	6,022	6,056	6,158	6,238	6,302	6,334	6,366
2	98.49	99.01	99.17	99.25	99.30	99.33	99.34	99.36	99.38	99.40	99.43	99.45	99.48	99.49	99.50
3	34.12	30.81	29.46	28.71	28.24	27.91	27.67	27.49	27.34	27.23	26.87	26.58	26.30	26.23	26.12
4	21.20	18.00	16.69	15.98	15.52	15.21	14.98	14.80	14.66	14.54	14.19	13.91	13.69	13.57	13.46
5	16.26	13.27	12.06	11.39	10.97	10.67	10.45	10.27	10.15	10.05	9.72	9.45	9.24	9.13	9.02
6	13.74	10.92	9.78	9.15	8.75	8.47	8.26	8.10	7.98	7.87	7.56	7.30	7.09	6.99	6.88
7	12.25	9.55	8.45	7.85	7.46	7.19	7.00	6.84	6.71	6.62	6.31	6.05	5.85	5.75	5.65
8	11.26	8.65	7.59	7.01	6.63	6.37	6.19	6.03	5.91	5.82	5.52	5.27	5.06	4.96	4.86
9	10.56	8.02	6.99	6.42	6.06	5.80	5.62	5.47	5.35	5.26	4.96	4.72	4.51	4.41	4.31
10	10.04	7.56	6.55	5.99	5.64	5.39	5.21	5.06	4.95	4.85	4.56	4.32	4.12	4.01	3.91
15	8.68	6.36	5.42	4.89	4.56	4.32	4.14	4.00	3.89	3.80	3.52	3.27	3.07	2.97	2.87
25	7.77	5.57	4.68	4.18	3.86	3.63	3.46	3.32	3.21	3.13	2.85	2.61	2.40	2.29	2.17
50	7.17	5.06	4.20	3.72	3.41	3.18	3.02	2.88	2.78	2.70	2.42	2.17	1.94	1.82	1.68
100	6.90	4.82	3.98	3.51	3.20	2.99	2.82	2.69	2.59	2.51	2.22	1.96	1.73	1.59	1.43
500	6.69	4.65	3.82	3.36	3.06	2.84	2.68	2.55	2.45	2.36	2.07	1.81	1.56	1.41	1.18
1,000	6.66	4.62	3.80	3.34	3.04	2.82	2.66	2.53	2.43	2.34	2.05	1.79	1.54	1.38	1.11
∞	6.64	4.60	3.78	3.32	3.02	2.80	2.64	2.51	2.41	2.32	2.03	1.77	1.52	1.36	1.00

NOTE: Missing values may be filled in by linear interpolation with respect to reciprocals of degrees of freedom. Accuracy improved by interpolating on log F instead of F itself.

with two-sided critical regions corresponding to the conventional significance levels, $\alpha = .01$ and $\alpha = .05$ respectively. Without deprecating the construction of such tables, we think that in the present context it is desirable to enlarge the critical region. When the object of the test for equal variances is to complement the t test on the difference of two means, one cannot afford to be quite so liberal as usual with regard to accepting the hypothesis of homoscedasticity, because an erroneous assumption here might vitiate the test on the means. Therefore, in making the F test, it is advisable to increase the probability of rejecting the null hypothesis that the variances are equal by choosing a somewhat lower level of significance. For instance, one might take α as .10 instead of .05. Accordingly, if B and B' represent the upper .05 levels of F and F' respectively, then the acceptance region of F at the .10 level of significance is given by $1/B' < F < B$.

Example 8-11. Using the data of Example 8-9, test the hypothesis that $\sigma_x{}^2 = \sigma_y{}^2$. There will be 4 and 5 degrees of freedom if we take F as the ratio $s_x{}^2/s_y{}^2$, and so F' will have 5 and 4 degrees of freedom. Choosing $\alpha = .10$, the two critical values are $B = 5.19$ and $B' = 6.26$, corresponding respectively to the upper .05 levels of F and F'. Thus, the acceptance region $1/B' < F < B$ becomes $.160 < F < 5.19$. The computations are as follows:

$$s_x{}^2 = \frac{.000298}{4} = .0000745 \qquad s_y{}^2 = \frac{.000327}{5} = .0000654 \qquad F = \frac{.0000745}{.0000654} = 1.14$$

Since this value of F falls within the acceptance region, we accept the hypothesis of equal variances. Thus, in the t test of Example 8-9 we are justified in assuming that $\sigma_x{}^2 = \sigma_y{}^2$.

With regard to more than two variances an exact test for equality is lacking, but approximate tests have been devised by Neyman and Pearson, Bartlett, and others. The test we present here was proposed by M. S. Bartlett,[1] who showed that the distribution is approximately that of chi-square.

Given k independent, unbiased variance estimates $v_1, v_2, \ldots, v_k$ based respectively on $a_1, a_2, \ldots, a_k$ degrees of freedom. To test the hypothesis that the v's are all estimates of a common variance σ^2, put $A = \sum_1^k a_i$, $\bar{v} = \sum a_i v_i / A$, and compute the statistic Z defined thus:

$$Z = \frac{A \ln \bar{v} - \Sigma a_i \ln v_i}{C} \qquad (8\text{-}51)$$

where
$$C = 1 + \frac{\Sigma(1/a_i) - 1/A}{3(k - 1)} \qquad (8\text{-}52)$$

---

[1] M. S. Bartlett, Properties of Sufficiency and Statistical Tests, *Proc. Roy. Soc. (London)*, ser. A, vol. 160, p. 273, 1937.

The statistic Z is distributed approximately as chi-square with $k - 1$ degrees of freedom. The nature of the test is such that any differences among the v's tend to increase Z; therefore, the appropriate critical region is the right-hand tail of the chi-square distribution. Since $C > 1$, it is often possible to save arithmetic by noticing whether the numerator of Z would fall short of the critical limit before dividing by C.

In the special case of uniform sample size $a_i = a$ (all i), the quantity C [Eq. (8-52)] reduces to

$$C = \frac{1 + k(3a + 1)}{3ak} \tag{8-53}$$

and Z assumes the simple form

$$Z = \frac{3a^2k(k \ln \bar{v} - \Sigma \ln v_i)}{1 + k(3a + 1)} \tag{8-54}$$

The purpose of this test is usually to justify the assumption of homoscedasticity, which is involved in significance tests for the differences among several means. In this connection, it is well to choose .10 as the level of significance.

Example 8-12. In a study on ultraviolet irradiation of sterols to produce a form of vitamin D, Bunker, Harris, and Mosher[1] obtained the experimental data which is summarized in Table 8-19. The measure of effectiveness x was a quantitative rating

TABLE 8-19

Wave-length, A	Sample size n_i	$\Sigma_j x_{ij}$	$\Sigma_j x_{ij}^2$	$\bar{x}_i$	$\Sigma_j(x_{ij} - \bar{x}_i)^2$	v_i	$\ln v_i$	a_i
2,483	40	64.0	114.50	1.6000	12.1000	.3103	-1.1702	39
2,537	40	65.5	121.75	1.6375	14.4938	.3716	-0.9899	39
2,652	40	66.0	119.00	1.6500	10.1000	.2590	-1.3509	39
2,804	50	83.0	154.00	1.6600	16.2200	.3310	-1.1056	49
2,894	49	86.0	173.00	1.7551	22.0612	.4596	-0.7774	48
2,967	49	97.0	211.50	1.9796	19.4796	.4058	-0.9019	48
3,025	40	62.0	116.00	1.5500	19.9000	.5103	-0.6728	39
Sum.........	308	523.5	1,009.75	......	114.3546	.....	....	301

of healing response when the test animals, rachitic rats, were given doses of sterol (7-dehydrocholesterol) which had been irradiated at specified wave lengths. Later on, we shall test the mean healing rates for significant differences, but at present we shall test for equality of variances.

Since there are seven wavelength groups, $k = 7$ and chi-square has six degrees of freedom. At the .10 level, the acceptance region will be $Z < 10.65$. The computa-

[1] J. W. Bunker, R. S. Harris, and L. M. Mosher, Relative Efficiency of Active Wave Lengths of Ultraviolet in Activation of 7-Dehydrocholesterol, *J. Am. Chem. Soc.*, vol. 62, pp. 508–511, 1940.

tions are as follows:

$$A = \Sigma a_i = 301; \qquad \bar{v} = \frac{\Sigma a_i v_i}{A} \equiv \frac{\Sigma_i \Sigma_j (x_{ij} - \bar{x}_i)^2}{A} = \frac{114.3546}{301} = .3799$$

$$\ln \bar{v} = -0.9678 \qquad A \ln \bar{v} - \Sigma a_i \ln v_i = -291.3078 + 297.9490 = 6.6412$$

The fact that the latter value falls within the acceptance region as it stands means that we do not need to compute the denominator C in order to accept the hypothesis of equal variances. However, to complete the illustration, we do compute C as follows:

$$3(k - 1) = 18 \qquad \sum \frac{1}{a_i} = .1646 \qquad \frac{1}{A} = .0033$$

$$\frac{\Sigma(1/a_i) - 1/A}{3(k - 1)} = \frac{.1613}{18} = .0090$$

$$C = 1.0090 \qquad Z = \frac{6.6412}{1.0090} = 6.582$$

As anticipated, this value of Z falls within the acceptance region, and so the hypothesis of equal variances is sustained.

8-17. The F Test for Equality of More than Two Means. Given m independent samples, the question as to whether their means $\bar{x}_1$, $\bar{x}_2$, . . . , $\bar{x}_m$ are significantly different may become the deciding issue in a research problem. A major object of experimental science is to find relationships between variables or attributes. The mere existence of a significant association can be tested by chi-square, but contingency methods require very large samples if it is important to investigate the tail ends of the distributions. Usually large samples are unavailable, and in any event, it is often sufficient to determine the answer to a more specific question—namely, whether the mean value of a variate x assumes significantly different levels depending upon the particular level (or category) assumed by another variate (or attribute) A. This question can be answered by the *analysis of variance*, which is due in the main to R. A. Fisher. Variance analysis has been developed extensively in the theory of experimental design, but we shall consider only the simplest case.

Suppose A is divided into m discrete levels or categories a_1, a_2, . . . , a_m. For each class of A take independent observations of x, letting n_1, n_2, . . . , n_m be the respective numbers of such observations and $N = \Sigma n_i$. Let x_{ij} be any observation of x when $A = a_i$, and let

$$\bar{x}_i = \frac{1}{n_i} \Sigma_j x_{ij}$$

be the computed mean value of x for this class. The problem is then to decide whether the several mean values $\bar{x}_1$, $\bar{x}_2$, . . . , $\bar{x}_m$ are significantly different.

The actual differences among the means can be measured by the weighted sum of squares of their deviations from the pooled sample mean $\bar{x}$, where $\bar{x} \equiv (1/N)\Sigma_i\Sigma_j x_{ij} \equiv (1/N)\Sigma_i n_i \bar{x}_i$. This measure of variability is

$$S_1 = \Sigma_i n_i(\bar{x}_i - \bar{x})^2 \qquad (8\text{-}55)$$

The question now hinges on whether S_1 falls within acceptable limits as fixed by the null hypothesis. If the samples are all drawn from a common normal population, it can be shown by the methods employed in Sec. 8-9 that $\bar{x}$ and S_1 are independent and that S_1/σ^2 is distributed as chi-square with $m - 1$ degrees of freedom. However, as we shall presently see, if the populations from which the samples are drawn have unequal means, then S_1 will tend to be greater than the value expected when the population means are equal.

Our test for equality of means presupposes equality of variances. To eliminate the parameter σ^2, we compute an unbiased estimate by combining the sums of squares about the respective sample means. Put $W_i = \Sigma_j(x_{ij} - \bar{x}_i)^2$ and

$$S_2 = \Sigma_i W_i = \Sigma_i\Sigma_j(x_{ij} - \bar{x}_i)^2 \qquad (8\text{-}56)$$

For any class the statistic W_i is independent of its own class mean $\bar{x}_i$ and certainly independent of the mean of any other class. Hence, the statistic S_2 is independent of all the class means and, therefore, independent of S_1. Now W_i/σ^2 is distributed as chi-square with $n_i - 1$ degrees of freedom, and by the additive property of chi-square (since the W's are mutually independent) it follows that S_2/σ^2 is distributed as chi-square with $N - m$ degrees of freedom [that is, $\Sigma_i(n_i - 1) = N - m$]. Therefore the variance ratio

$$\frac{S_1/(m - 1)\sigma^2}{S_2/(N - m)\sigma^2} \equiv \frac{S_1/(m - 1)}{S_2/(N - m)} \qquad (8\text{-}57)$$

will be distributed as F with $m - 1$ and $N - m$ degrees of freedom; and this statistic provides a test of the null hypothesis.

Now suppose that the samples are, in fact, drawn from populations with different means, $\mu_1, \mu_2, \ldots, \mu_m$. Then the weighted sum of squares S_1 can be expressed identically as follows, where $\bar{\mu} = \Sigma_i n_i \mu_i/N$:

$$S_1 \equiv \Sigma_i n_i[(\bar{x}_i - \mu_i) - (\bar{x} - \bar{\mu}) + (\mu_i - \bar{\mu})]^2 \qquad (8\text{-}58)$$

the expected value of which is

$$E(S_1) = (m - 1)\sigma^2 + \Sigma_i n_i(\mu_i - \bar{\mu})^2 \qquad (8\text{-}59)$$

Thus, any differences among the μ's will tend to increase S_1, so that the critical region will be the upper right-hand tail of F.

The reason for the name "analysis of variance" lies in the separation of the total sum of squares about the grand mean into additive components. Thus, denoting the total sum of squares by S_0 where

$$S_0 = \Sigma_i \Sigma_j (x_{ij} - \bar{x})^2 \qquad (8\text{-}60)$$

we have identically

$$S_0 \equiv S_1 + S_2 \qquad (8\text{-}61)$$

The student is invited to establish this identity on his own by putting $x_{ij} - \bar{x} \equiv (x_{ij} - \bar{x}_i) + (\bar{x}_i - \bar{x})$, squaring both sides, and noting that the cross-product term on the right sums to zero.

Computational Procedure. Although the foregoing definitions arise naturally out of the theoretical development, it is advantageous to work with algebraically simpler (although identical) terms for computational purposes. We shall present the procedure itself first and later on prove its validity. Define class totals $T_1, T_2, \ldots, T_m$ and the grand total T as follows:

$$T_i = \sum_{j=1}^{n_i} x_{ij} \qquad \text{whence } \bar{x}_i = \frac{T_i}{n_i}$$

$$T = \Sigma_i T_i \equiv \Sigma_i \Sigma_j x_{ij} \qquad \text{whence } \bar{x} = \frac{T}{N}$$

Compute these totals, the corresponding means, and the raw sum of squares:

1. $T_i, \bar{x}_i, T, \bar{x}$.

2. $\Sigma_i \Sigma_j x_{ij}^2 \equiv \Sigma_i (\Sigma_j x_{ij}^2)$. It is advisable to record subtotals of squares by classes to facilitate the test for uniform variability within classes. Next compute the grand mean times the grand total as well as the sum of the products of class means and class totals:

3. $\bar{x}T, \Sigma_i \bar{x}_i T_i$. In the special case of constant sample size, that is, $n_1 = n_2 = \cdots = n_m = n$, the sum of products of class means and class totals reduces to

$$\Sigma_i \bar{x}_i T_i \equiv \frac{1}{n} \Sigma_i T_i^2 \qquad \text{(constant sample size only)}$$

This formula promotes arithmetical accuracy and saves work, but must not be used unless all of the n's are equal.

From the quantities thus far computed derive the conventional terms of the analysis of variance table. These are:

4. The "total sum of squares," $S_0 = \Sigma_i \Sigma_j x_{ij}^2 - \bar{x}T$. This term equals $\Sigma_i \Sigma_j (x_{ij} - \bar{x})^2$, which is the total sum of squares of deviations from the grand mean.

5. The "sum of squares between classes," $S_1 = \Sigma_i \bar{x}_i T_i - \bar{x}T$, or, where applicable, $S_1 = (1/n)\Sigma_i T_i^2 - \bar{x}T$. This term equals $\Sigma_i n_i (\bar{x}_i - \bar{x})^2$, which is the weighted sum of squares of class means about the grand mean.

6. The "sum of squares within classes," $S_2 = S_0 - S_1$. This term equals $\Sigma_i\Sigma_j(x_{ij} - \bar{x}_i)^2$, which is the pooled sum of squares of individual values about the means of their respective classes.

Compile the results in the form of an analysis-of-variance table as follows:

TABLE 8-20. ANALYSIS OF VARIANCE

Source	Degrees of freedom	Sum of squares	Mean square
Between classes...........	$m - 1$	S_1	$S_1/(m - 1)$
Within classes............	$N - m$	S_2	$S_2/(N - m)$
Total.................	$N - 1$	S_0	Not done

$$F = \frac{S_1/(m - 1)}{S_2/(N - m)}$$

Look up F under $m - 1$ and $N - m$ degrees of freedom. As a rule we are interested only in the one-sided alternative $S_1/(m - 1) > S_2/(N - m)$ and so would not bother to compute F if it were obvious by inspection that the ratio is less than unity.

Example 8-13. Using the healing response data of Example 8-12, Table 8-19, test the means for significant differences. Carrying four decimals in the means, but rounding the product sums to two decimals, we obtain the following results:

$$T = 523.5 \quad N = 308 \quad \bar{x} = 1.6997 \quad \bar{x}T = 889.79$$
$$\Sigma_i\Sigma_j x_{ij}{}^2 = 1009.75 \quad S_0 = 1009.75 - 889.79 = 119.96$$
$$\Sigma_i\bar{x}_iT_i = 895.40 \quad S_1 = 895.40 - 889.79 = 5.61$$
$$S_2 = S_0 - S_1 = 119.96 - 5.61 = 114.35$$

The analysis of variance is presented compactly in Table 8-21. There being 6 and 301 degrees of freedom, the critical region with $\alpha = .05$ is $F \geq 2.13$. From Example 8-12 we already know that the assumption of homoscedasticity is justified.

TABLE 8-21. ANALYSIS OF VARIANCE OF HEALING RESPONSE DATA

Source	Degrees of freedom	Sum of squares	Mean square
Between Wavelength classes......	6	5.61	0.935
Within Wavelength classes........	301	114.35	0.380
Total......................	307	119.96	

$$F = \frac{.935}{.380} = 2.46$$

Since this value of F falls in the critical region, we reject the null hypothesis and conclude that activation at different wavelengths produces significantly different mean healing responses.

Justification of Computational Procedure. We first verify the computational formulas for S_0 and S_1 and then show that $S_0 \equiv S_1 + S_2$. Expanding the quadratic in the definition of S_0, identifying notation, and collecting terms, we have at once

$$S_0 \equiv \Sigma_i\Sigma_j(x_{ij} - \bar{x})^2 \equiv \Sigma_i\Sigma_j x_{ij}^2 - \bar{x}T$$

Next
$$S_1 \equiv \Sigma_i n_i(\bar{x}_i - \bar{x})^2 \equiv \Sigma_i(n_i\bar{x}_i^2 - 2\bar{x}n_i\bar{x}_i + n_i\bar{x}^2)$$

Now
$$n_i\bar{x}_i \equiv T_i \qquad n_i\bar{x}_i^2 \equiv \bar{x}_i T_i$$

Thus
$$S_1 \equiv \Sigma_i\bar{x}_i T_i - 2\bar{x}\Sigma_i T_i + \bar{x}^2\Sigma_i n_i$$
$$= \Sigma_i\bar{x}_i T_i - 2\bar{x}T + \bar{x}^2 N = \Sigma_i\bar{x}_i T_i - \bar{x}T$$

as was to be proved. Finally, to justify the formula for

$$S_2 \equiv \Sigma_i\Sigma_j(x_{ij} - \bar{x}_i)^2$$

we put
$$x_{ij} - \bar{x} \equiv (x_{ij} - \bar{x}_i) + (\bar{x}_i - \bar{x})$$

whereupon
$$S_0 \equiv \Sigma_i\Sigma_j(x_{ij} - \bar{x})^2 \equiv \Sigma_i\Sigma_j[(x_{ij} - \bar{x}_i) + (\bar{x}_i - x)]^2$$

When we expand the latter quadratic, the cross-product term vanishes, for

$$\Sigma_i\Sigma_j(\bar{x}_i - \bar{x})(x_{ij} - \bar{x}_i) \equiv \Sigma_i[(\bar{x}_i - \bar{x})\Sigma_j(x_{ij} - \bar{x}_i)] = 0$$

since $\Sigma_j(x_{ij} - \bar{x}_i) \equiv 0$. Therefore

$$S_0 = \Sigma_i\Sigma_j(x_{ij} - \bar{x}_i)^2 + \Sigma_i\Sigma_j(\bar{x}_i - \bar{x})^2$$

But
$$\Sigma_i\Sigma_j(\bar{x}_i - \bar{x})^2 \equiv \Sigma_i n_i(\bar{x}_i - \bar{x})^2 \equiv S_1$$

Therefore $S_0 \equiv S_1 + S_2$, which completes the proof.

Analysis of variance forms the backbone of a large part of statistical methodology. Hand in hand with the development of the theory of experimental design, the subject of variance analysis has broadened and deepened to such an extent that it deserves specialized study. We do not pursue this subject further here, because an adequate treatment of its theoretical and practical aspects requires an entire book, whereas a sketchy treatment gives the misleading impression of pat answers.

EXERCISES

1. According to theory the probability of a certain trait is .25. Taking .05 as the level of significance and using the normal approximation corrected for continuity, establish the limits of a two-sided critical region to which the absolute frequency of the trait in a sample of 192 random observations can be referred directly.

Ans. $x < 36$, $x > 60$.

2. The variate x is binomially distributed with parameters p, N. (a) Assuming the normal limit of the binomial distribution, explain why the sample relative frequency $(p' = x/N)$ of occurrences may be regarded as normally distributed with $\mu = p$, $\sigma^2 = pq/N$. (b) Derive appropriate corrections for continuity.

Ans. (a) Theorem 6-1. (b) If $p' \geq p + 1/2N$, use $p' - p - 1/2N$; if $p' \leq p - 1/2N$, use $p - (p' + 1/2N)$.

3. Given a binomial distribution with $p = \frac{1}{2}$, how large a sample must be taken in order that the probability shall be at least .98 that the sample relative frequency p'

will not deviate from $\frac{1}{2}$ by more than .05?   Assume the normal approximation, but disregard the correction for continuity.   *Ans.* $N = 542$.

4. For a certain binomial variate x the true value of the parameter p is unknown, and it is desired to determine the minimum sample size N such that the probability will be at least as great as some specified value P that the sample relative frequency $p' = x/N$ will not deviate from p by more than some specified magnitude $h > 0$. (a) Assuming the normal approximation, but disregarding the correction for continuity, determine N as a function of p, h, and k, where k is that value of a unit normal variate such that $W(k) = P$.   (b) If h is small compared to k^2pq, show that the correction for continuity would increase the required value of N by an amount approximately equal to $1/h$.

Ans. (a) $N = k^2pq/h^2$.   (b) Since the larger value of N must be allowed for in considering positive versus negative deviations from p, the required value is the greater root of the equation $4h^2N^2 - 4(k^2pq + h)N + 1 = 0$ rather than the greater root of the alternative equation $4h^2N^2 - 4(k^2pq - h)N + 1 = 0$.   Simplification of the radical by neglecting the term $-h^2$ yields the stated result.

5. Random samples of five observations each are taken from two populations in order to test the hypothesis that a certain attribute A has the same probability in the two populations.   Assuming the populations so large that sampling depletions are negligible, use the normal approximation corrected for continuity to estimate the areas of appropriate two-sided regions associated with (a) relative frequencies of 0 and 1 respectively, and (b) relative frequencies of .2 and .8 respectively.   (c) Compare with corresponding probabilities computed from the hypergeometric distribution in Exercise 23 of Chap. 3.   *Ans.* (a) .011, (b) .206, (c) .008 and .206.

6. First-term grades in mathematics and physics for a class of 728 freshmen showed the following joint frequencies of A's and non-A's where the first symbol of any pair designates the grade in mathematics.   Consider two groups: AA, $\bar{A}A$ and $A\bar{A}$, $\bar{A}\bar{A}$.

Combination............	AA	$A\bar{A}$	$\bar{A}A$	$\bar{A}\bar{A}$	Total
Frequency.............	53	57	27	591	728

(a) Choosing the .05 level of significance, determine the limits on the difference between the relative frequencies of AA and $A\bar{A}$ for a two-sided critical region based on the normal test for association, incorporating the continuity correction.   (b) Is the observed degree of association significant?   (c) What assumption is being made with regard to the sample?   (d) If we were interested in whether or not the percentages of A's in mathematics and physics are significantly different, what would be wrong with applying the same form of normal test to this sample?

Ans. (a) $\pm.09$.   (b) Yes.   (c) Drawn at random from a hypothetical general population of this school's freshmen.   (d) Condition of independence not satisfied.

7. The problem of testing the difference between two percentages pertaining to the same set of individuals was solved by McNemar.[1]   Assume that a given individual may exhibit either, or both, or neither of two traits A and B, and suppose that in a sample of N individuals there are n_{11} instances of AB, n_{12} instances of $A\bar{B}$, n_{21} of $\bar{A}B$, and n_{22} of $\bar{A}\bar{B}$.   Then, McNemar has shown that the appropriate test of the difference between the proportion of A's and the proportion of B's is given by $\chi^2 = (n_{12} - n_{21})^2/(n_{12} + n_{21})$, a statistic which may be regarded as having the chi-square distribution with one degree of freedom.   Provided that $n_{12} \neq n_{21}$, the continuity correction would be made by subtracting $\frac{1}{2}$ from the absolute value of the difference before taking the square; that is, $\chi^2 = (|n_{12} - n_{21}| - \frac{1}{2})^2/(n_{12} + n_{21})$.   (a) Using Table 8-3, apply the

[1] McNemar, *Psychometrika*, vol. 12, no. 2, p. 153, June, 1947.

latter form of this test to the data of Exercise 6 to decide whether there is a significant difference between the percentage of A's in mathematics and the percentage of A's in physics. (b) If one preferred to use a unit normal test variate instead of chi-square, how should he go about it? (c) Using this normal variate, estimate the significance measure of the given sample.

Ans. (a) $\chi^2 = 10.3$, which is significant; hence the percentages are significantly different. (b) Compute $u = (|n_{12} - n_{21}| - \frac{1}{2})/\sqrt{n_{12} + n_{21}}$ and refer to $2R(u)$ in Table 4-4. (c) $2R(3.3) \approx .001$.

8. At a certain locality the probability of rain during any 24-hr period at a particular time of the year is .2. A random sample of 100 independent trials presented the following distribution of forecast and observed categories, where the subscripts f, o denote "forecast" and "observed" respectively.

Event	R_f, R_o	$R_f, \bar{R}_o$	$\bar{R}_f, R_o$	$\bar{R}_f, \bar{R}_o$	Total
Frequency	6	14	10	70	100

(a) Using the normal approximation corrected for continuity and setting the significance level at .05, test for significant association between forecast and observed categories of rainfall. (b) Compute the mean score m based on the scoring scheme of Table 7-3. (c) Applying the central-limit theorem, test for a significant degree of skill as compared to a random allocation of categories. (d) What accounts for the discrepancy between the conclusions of (a) and (c)?

Ans. (a) $u' = 1.57$, not significant. (b) $m = .175$. (c) $\sigma_m = .1$, $m/\sigma_m = 1.75$, which is significant at the .05 level. (d) The test for association takes the marginal totals for granted and employs a two-sided critical region. The test for skill leaves the marginal totals unspecified and uses a one-sided critical region, because only a positive degree of skill is relevant.

9. Contract specifications usually require the vendor to demonstrate a satisfactory level of quality by subjecting the articles offered for sale to certain prescribed tests. A typical specification reads: "The vendor shall establish, with a confidence coefficient of at least .90, that the fraction defective does not exceed .05." Since the manufacturer would ordinarily aim at a fraction defective appreciably lower than the maximum acceptable, in order to stand a good chance of passing the test, the numbers of defective items in random samples of constant size N may be assumed to be Poisson distributed with $\mu = Np$, where p is the true fraction defective in the population from which the samples are drawn. Special tables giving confidence limits for the Poisson and binomial distributions are available, but good results can be obtained also by applying normalizing transformations.[1] The advantage of the transformation lies not only in the applicability of readily available tables of the normal distribution but also in the fact that the variance becomes virtually independent of the mean. If x is Poisson distributed with parameter μ, the transformed variate $y = \sqrt{x + \frac{1}{2}}$ is approximately normal with mean equal to $\sqrt{\mu + \frac{1}{2}}$ and standard deviation equal to $\frac{1}{2}$. (a) Using this approximation, determine the maximum fraction defective in a random sample of 175 items for which it can be asserted with a confidence coefficient of .90 (i.e., the probability that statements of this sort will be correct is .90) that the fraction defective in the population does not exceed .05. Correct for continuity by adding one-half unit to the absolute frequency (besides the $\frac{1}{2}$ already called for by the equation for y), but otherwise neglect the discrete nature of the data. (b) Con-

[1] See M. S. Bartlett, The Use of Transformations, *Biometrics*, vol. 3, no. 1, p. 39, March, 1947, and J. H. Curtiss, On Transformations Used in Analysis of Variance, *Annals of Mathematical Statistics*, vol. 14, no. 2, p. 107, June, 1943.

sidering the fact that only discrete increments are possible, what would the actual upper limit of the fraction defective in a sample have to be? (c) Estimate the probability that the vendor will meet the specified standards with a random sample of 175 items if the true fraction defective in the population sampled is .02.

Ans. (a) .0272, (b) 4/175, (c) $F(.472) = .681$; the exact probability that x will not exceed 4 if $\mu = 3.5$ is .725.

10. The average weight of 100 regular-sized cigarettes is 4 oz. Hence, if .01 oz is chosen as the unit, the weight of individual cigarettes will average out to 4 units. Individual weights vary, of course, because the tobacco itself is not perfectly uniform, and even if it were, perfect precision could not be maintained in the mechanical processes of manufacture. Therefore, production standards prescribe certain control limits within which the individual weights are allowed to vary and still be judged acceptable; and weight uniformity is checked intermittently by random sampling. The general field of measuring the output and maintaining prescribed standards is called *quality control*. Assume that individual cigarette weights are normally distributed with $\mu = 4, \sigma = .15$. (a) Determine 95 per cent control limits for the mean weights of random samples of 5. That is, find a constant C such that $P(\mu - C < \bar{x} < \mu + C) = .95$, where $\bar{x}$ denotes the sample mean, and then compute $\mu - C$ and $\mu + C$. (b) Let $s^2 = \Sigma(x_i - \bar{x})^2/(n - 1)$. If the value of $\bar{x}$ were satisfactory, would there be any objection to an unusually small value of s? (c) Determine a one-sided control limit S for s such that $P(s < S) = .95$. (d) A random sample of 5 observations gave the following results: $\Sigma x = 20.40$, $\Sigma x^2 = 83.3162$. Compute $\bar{x}$ and s and decide whether the sample indicates satisfactory control.

Ans. (a) $3.87 < \bar{x} < 4.13$. (b) No, the smaller the better. (c) $s < .231$. (d) $\bar{x} = 4.08$, $s = .145$. Both statistics lie in their respective acceptance regions; hence, satisfactory control is indicated.

11. Five cigarettes were picked at random from the production run of a given hour, with sufficient spacing to justify the assumption of independence, and the sampling was repeated hourly. In samples from six consecutive hours, the individual weights in units of .01 oz were as follows:

1. 4.15, 4.04, 4.25, 4.10, 3.86; $\Sigma x = 20.40$, $\Sigma x^2 = 83.3162$
2. 4.01, 3.63, 4.09, 3.89, 4.08; $\Sigma x = 19.70$, $\Sigma x^2 = 77.7636$
3. 4.19, 3.81, 3.84, 4.20, 4.16; $\Sigma x = 20.20$, $\Sigma x^2 = 81.7634$
4. 4.02, 3.91, 3.80, 3.85, 4.07; $\Sigma x = 19.65$, $\Sigma x^2 = 77.2759$
5. 3.79, 3.66, 3.82, 4.21, 3.97; $\Sigma x = 19.45$, $\Sigma x^2 = 75.8371$
6. 4.03, 3.98, 4.05, 3.55, 3.64; $\Sigma x = 19.25$, $\Sigma x^2 = 74.3359$

(a) Compute $\bar{x}$ and s for each sample, and plot a control chart. Use the upper half of the chart for $\bar{x}$ and the lower half for s, with the control limits established in Exercise 10 indicated as horizontal lines. (b) When is lack of control definitely indicated? Ans. (a)

	Sample					
	1	2	3	4	5	6
$\bar{x}$	4.08	3.94	4.04	3.93	3.89	3.85
$\Sigma(x - \bar{x})^2$	.0842	.1456	.1554	.0514	.1766	.2234
s	.145	.191	.197	.113	.210	.236

(b) Lack of control indicated definitely in sample 6.

12. As a practical convenience in the cigarette industry, weights are customarily expressed in reciprocal units rather than in hundredths of an ounce. That is, the scale indicates the number of cigarettes, of a weight equal to the one on the scale, which would be needed in order to make up a total of 4 oz. Assuming a normal distribution of actual weights, would reciprocals be normally distributed?

Ans. Not exactly; but since the standard deviation is so small compared to the mean, the normal approximation can be justified by expanding the reciprocal in powers of $x - \mu$ and neglecting terms beyond the first degree.

13. The reliability of an electronic component is defined as the probability of continuous, satisfactory operation over a stipulated interval of time T. If initial defects are weeded out by the manufacturer's inspection of finished pieces and failure due to wear-out is prevented by maintenance inspection on the part of the user, the remaining causes of failure may be regarded as random phenomena. Under these circumstances failures per unit time arising from a large number of similar components exposed to comparable conditions typically conform to the Poisson distribution. Hence, by Example 4-8, the time between failures will follow the exponential distribution, and by a property unique to the exponential distribution (Exercise 24, Chap. 5), the distribution of service life is precisely the same as that of time between failures. Consequently, if the mean time between failures is equal to θ, then the distribution of service life t will be given by $f(t) = (1/\theta)e^{-t/\theta}$ $(0, \infty)$ and the reliability ρ will be given by $\rho = P(t \geq T) = e^{-T/\theta}$. An efficient test of reliability has been devised by Epstein and Sobel.[1] A convenient sample size n being chosen, n items are placed on test and the test is continued until a prescribed number k (determined in accordance with costs and available time) have failed. Denoting the failure times by $t_1, t_2, \ldots, t_k$ in ascending order, the maximum likelihood estimate of θ is given by

$$\hat{\theta} = \frac{t_1 + t_2 + \cdots + t_k + (n - k)t_k}{k} = \frac{t_1 + t_2 + \cdots + t_{k-1} + (n + 1 - k)t_k}{k}$$

and the corresponding estimate of reliability is $\hat{\rho} = e^{-T/\hat{\theta}}$. Confidence limits can be calculated from the critical levels of chi-square, for Epstein and Sobel have proved that the variate $2k\hat{\theta}/\theta$ is distributed as chi-square with $2k$ degrees of freedom. While the sampling distribution of the estimate depends on k, the average length of time one has to wait for the occurrence of k failures decreases as the sample size n is increased.

Suppose that contract specifications call for 5 hr of continuous performance with a reliability of at least .95 demonstrated with a confidence coefficient of .90. The vendor decides to place seven units on test and wait until the first four have run to failure. The test data (hours to failure) are 23.5, 52.8, 72.0, 158.8.

(*a*) Estimate the mean life and the reliability. (*b*) Find the lower confidence limit R on reliability such that the confidence coefficient is .90 that $\rho \geq R$. (*c*) On the strength of this sample, does the lot pass the test?

Ans. (*a*) $\hat{\theta} = 195.9$ hr, $\hat{\rho} = .975$. (*b*) $8\hat{\theta}/13.36 = 117.3$; $5/117.3 = .0426$; $R = .958$. (*c*) Yes, but just barely.

14. An operations research group studying the M.I.T. libraries found that the number of books withdrawn by individual users during any one visit to the Science Library was geometrically distributed with $p = .4$; that is,

$$f(x) = .4(.6^x) \qquad (x = 0, 1, \ldots)$$

Test this hypothesis for goodness of fit using the following data, which represent an independent random sample of 100 observations.

[1] See B. Epstein and M. Sobel, Life Testing, *Journal of the American Statistical Association*, vol. 48, no. 263, p. 486, September, 1953.

Value of x...........	0	1	2	3	≥ 4
Frequency..........	37	26	17	5	15

Ans. With 4 degrees of freedom the acceptance region is $\hat{\chi}^2 < 9.49$ at the .05 level of significance. The sample value of 2.68 falls within the acceptance region, and the hypothesis is sustained.

15. In terms of the sample estimates of the mean and standard deviation based on 310 independent observations, the frequency distribution of January temperatures (time: 1230 Z) at Bismarck, N.Dak. was found to be as summarized in the following table. On the hypothesis of a normal distribution, expected frequencies were computed to the nearest whole number. (*a*) Explain how the expected frequencies were obtained, and illustrate by calculating the expected frequencies in the intervals $> -.4$ to $\leq .4$ and $> .4$ to ≤ 1.2. (*b*) How many degrees of freedom are there? (*c*) Test the hypothesis that the temperature distribution is normal.

$(x - \bar{x})/s$..............	≤ -2.0	$> -2.0,$ ≤ -1.2	$> -1.2,$ $\leq -.4$	$> -.4,$ $\leq .4$	$> .4,$ ≤ 1.2	$> 1.2,$ ≤ 2.0	> 2.0
Observed frequency.....	7	34	67	87	78	32	5
Expected frequency.....	7	29	71	96	71	29	7

Ans. (*a*) $310W(.4) = 96$; $310[F(1.2) - F(.4)] = 71$. (*b*) There are $7 - 3 = 4$ degrees of freedom. (*c*) Acceptance region, $\hat{\chi}^2 < 9.49$; sample yields $\hat{\chi}^2 = 3.50$. Therefore the hypothesis of normal distribution is sustained.

16. The theoretical probabilities associated with the possible combinations of two attributes A and B are as follows:

Combination.....	A_1B_1	A_1B_2	A_1B_3	A_2B_1	A_2B_2	A_2B_3	A_3B_1	A_3B_2	A_3B_3
Probability.......	.20	.08	.04	.08	.20	.08	.04	.08	.20

The observed frequencies in a random sample of 100 were respectively 15, 12, 6, 11, 15, 10, 6, 10, 15. Is the theory tenable?

Ans. If 9 classes are used, there will be 8 degrees of freedom and the acceptance region at the 5-per cent level of significance will be $\hat{\chi}^2 < 15.51$. If the two smallest classes are combined, there will be 7 degrees of freedom and the acceptance region at the 5-per cent level of significance will be $\hat{\chi}^2 < 14.07$. It turns out that exactly the same sample value is obtained in either case, namely $\hat{\chi}^2 = 9.875$. Since this value falls within the acceptance regions, the theory is tenable.

17. In a particular city, the sales of a certain commodity are dominated by 4 leading brands A, B, C, D, while all other brands combined (represented by E) account for only 10 per cent of the sales. Initially, the percentage distribution of market shares was as follows:

Brand........,....	A	B	C	D	E	Sum
Share..........	25	25	20	20	10	100

After vigorous sales campaigns put on by the manufacturers of C and D, a random sample of 1000 sales showed the following breakdown:

Brand..........	A	B	C	D	E	Sum
Sales...........	232	228	229	227	84	1000

Has the distribution undergone a statistically significant change?

Ans. With 4 degrees of freedom, the critical region is $\hat{\chi}^2 \geq 9.49$ at the 5 per cent level of significance.   The sample value 13.64 falls in the critical region and indicates a significant change in the distribution.

18. Annual sales of a certain type of sporting goods to individual retail dealers in a large eastern city have a markedly skewed distribution.   With economic data it is often found that the logarithm of the initial variate is approximately normal.   In that case, the initial variate is said to have a log-normal distribution.   Another transformation worth considering is the cube root; for if the initial variate has the gamma distribution, its cube root will be approximately normal.   Both transformations were tried on the same sample of 150 observations, and in each case the mean and variance of the transformed variate were estimated from the sample.   Letting u represent the deviation from the mean in units of s, nine categories were defined thus: $\text{I}(u \leq -1.75)$, $\text{II}(-1.75 < u \leq -1.25)$, $\text{III}(-1.25 < u \leq -.75)$, $\text{IV}(-.75 < u \leq -.25)$, $\text{V}(-.25 < u \leq .25)$, $\text{VI}(.25 < u \leq .75)$, $\text{VII}(.75 < u \leq 1.25)$, $\text{VIII}(1.25 < u \leq 1.75)$, $\text{IX}(u > 1.75)$.   The sample gave the following results:

Comparison	Category									
	I	II	III	IV	V	VI	VII	VIII	IX	Sum
Normal relative frequency..........	.04	.07	.12	.17	.20	.17	.12	.07	.04	1.00
Expected normal frequency..........	6.0	10.5	18.0	25.5	30.0	25.5	18.0	10.5	6.0	150
Observed frequency with logarithm......	9	9	10	21	31	35	24	9	2	150
Observed frequency with cube root......	4	11	20	27	29	27	16	7	9	150

Test each transformation for normality.

Ans. With $9 - 3 = 6$ degrees of freedom, the acceptance region at the 5 per cent level of significance is $\hat{\chi}^2 < 12.59$.   The log gives $\hat{\chi}^2 = 14.55$, which indicates a significant departure from normality.   The cube root gives $\hat{\chi}^2 = 4.01$, which lies well within the acceptance region and shows that the distribution is approximately normal.

19. Over the course of the year, the climatological "normal" temperature (normal in the sense of population average) from day to day exhibits, as one might expect, a pronounced seasonal cycle which is approximately sinusoidal.   The standard deviation has a seasonal cycle also, but the curve is flat compared with that of the "normal." It turns out that, if the daily mean temperature is expressed as a deviation from normal and the difference is standardized by dividing by the standard deviation based on the climatological record for the whole month, the resulting standard score has very nearly the same (slightly non-Gaussian) distribution in large samples, irrespective of season and location, within North America.   The time dependence among consecutive observations still remains, nevertheless, and shows up in a tendency (called "persistence") for one day's score to deviate less from that of the previous day than from the population mean of zero.   This fact, of course, is valuable from the viewpoint of weather forecasting, but it complicates a statistical analysis.   The general effect of persistence is illustrated by the following example.

Standard scores of daily mean temperature for three years x, y, z at Station W during the month of September were classified into three categories: high, medium, low.

Year	Category			Total
	High	Medium	Low	
x	0	20	10	30
y	8	18	4	30
z	10	13	7	30

(a) Assuming independence, would these three years be considered a homogeneous group, or would the differences between them be judged significant? (b) Keeping the observed *relative* frequencies the same, determine the greatest number N (in place of 30) for which the samples would be regarded homogeneous.

Ans. (a) With 4 degrees of freedom, the acceptance region is $\hat{\chi}^2 < 9.49$ at the .05 level of significance. Hence the sample value 13.43 would be judged significant. (b) $N = 30(9.49)/13.43 = 21.2$; i.e., $N = 21$.

20. The chi-square tests for association, independence, or homogeneity in the case of two samples with k categories each can be simplified by applying a formula due to Brandt and Snedecor. One way of writing this is as follows:

$$\hat{\chi}^2 = \frac{1}{pq} \sum r_i - \frac{a.}{q} \qquad (k - 1 \text{ degrees of freedom})$$

wherein a_i = observed frequency of category i in sample 1; b_i = observed frequency of category i in sample 2; $c_i = a_i + b_i$; $r_i = a_i^2/c_i$; $a. = \Sigma a_i$; $b. = \Sigma b_i$; $c. = \Sigma c_i$; $p = a./c.$, $q = b./c.$

(a) Derive this formula by showing first that in category i, the combined contribution to chi-square can be expressed as

$$\frac{(a_i - pc_i)^2}{pc_i} + \frac{(b_i - qc_i)^2}{qc_i} = \frac{(a_i - pc_i)^2}{pqc_i}$$

Complete the proof by expanding the quadratic and simplifying the summation. (b) In case the sample sizes are equal ($p = \frac{1}{2}$), derive the still-simpler formula $\hat{\chi}^2 = \Sigma(d_i^2/c_i)$, where $d_i = a_i - b_i$; $c_i = a_i + b_i$.

21. Two discrete variates x, y have the same set of possible values, and random samples of each turned out as follows:

	Possible values					Total
	1	3	6	9	11	
x	5	13	64	13	5	100
y	9	2	78	2	9	100

Test the hypothesis that the distributions are the same.

Ans. At the .05 level of significance, the acceptance region with 4 degrees of freedom is $\hat{\chi}^2 < 9.49$. Since the sample value 19.80 falls in the critical region, we conclude that the distributions are different.

22. In attempting to judge a certain forecaster's ability to forecast cloud coverage 24 hr in advance, the following information was compiled from a series of independent trials.

Category observed	Category forecast			Total
	Cloudy	Scattered	Clear	
Cloudy..............	12	28	3	43
Scattered...........	8	55	24	87
Clear...............	1	8	36	45
Total..............	21	91	63	175

(*a*) Is there a significant degree of association between the forecast and observed categories of cloudiness? (*b*) What would you say about the forecaster's ability?

Ans. (*a*) At the .05 level of significance, the acceptance region with 4 degrees of freedom is $\hat{\chi}^2 < 9.49$. The sample value 62.61 falls in the critical region, thereby indicating a significant degree of association between the forecast and observed categories of cloudiness. (*b*) An analysis of marginal totals by formula (*b*) of Exercise 20 reveals significant differences. At the .05 level of significance, the acceptance region with 2 degrees of freedom is $\hat{\chi}^2 < 5.99$, whereas the sample value is 10.65. Hence the sample excess of forecasts of "clear" and deficit of forecasts of "cloudy" must be judged significant departures from observation. Since errors of two categories are comparatively rare, we may surmise that when in doubt the forecaster tends to call "cloudy," "scattered" and "scattered," "clear."

23. The mean of Sample 6, Exercise 11, was found to differ significantly from the population value $\mu = 4$ when the standard deviation was known to be .15. If the standard deviation were unknown, would lack of control be detected with this sample at the same level of significance?

Ans. At the .05 level of significance, the acceptance region for t, corresponding to a two-sided critical region, is $-2.78 < t < 2.78$, with 4 degrees of freedom. Since the sample value $t = -1.42$ is not significant, lack of control would not be detected with this sample if the standard deviation were unknown.

24. Seven students were sent to a remedial reading clinic to improve their reading speed. Corresponding speeds in words per minute on standardized material at the start and after a short period of treatment are shown in the following table:

Speed	Student						
	A	B	C	D	E	F	G
Initial................	210	235	255	275	300	310	315
After treatment.........	255	260	310	260	330	355	375

(a) Test for a significant improvement.   (b) Why would a two-sided critical region be inappropriate?   (c) Does the lack of a control group vitiate the test of significance?

Ans. (a) At the .05 level of significance and a one-sided critical region, the acceptance region for the null hypothesis with 6 degrees of freedom is $t < 1.94$.   A significant improvement (on the average) is demonstrated, for the sample yields $t = 3.66$, which falls in the critical region.   (b) A two-sided critical region would not be appropriate because it would be incompatible with the working hypothesis that treatment would be beneficial.   (c) The test of significance, as such, is independent of a control group, for it depends solely on the probability distribution under the null hypothesis. A control group would, however, strengthen the argument that the established tendency to improve is due to the treatment.   But one need not confine his knowledge of a field to the evidence presented by a small sample.

25. In the manufacture of files, the teeth are cut on side A first, then on side B. The following data were taken on a random sample of six files and refer to weight in grams of filings removed from standard stock per 1000 strokes:

Side	File					
	1	2	3	4	5	6
A	8	6	5	9	11	10
B	7	4	3	10	9	12

(a) Do sides A and B differ significantly in the average weights of filings removed?
(b) Justify your method of calculation.

Ans. (a) The acceptance region for the null hypothesis at the .05 level of significance is $-2.57 < t < 2.57$, since the critical region is two-sided and there are 5 degrees of freedom.   The sample value, $t = 0.94$, falls in the acceptance region, thus sustaining the null hypothesis that the average weights, in the long run, are equal. (b) The method of paired comparisons is used to ensure independence in case the two sides of the same file mutually reflect common causes of variation.

26. A farmer grows the same crop on two fields A and B, of equal acreage.   On field A he puts an enriched fertilizer, but on field B an equal amount of standard fertilizer.   He continues this experiment for five years and gets the following yields in bushels per acre:

Field	Year				
	1	2	3	4	5
A	18	16	24	18	23
B	17	14	21	19	20

Does field A produce a significantly higher average yield?
Ans. The critical region being one-sided, in view of the working hypothesis, the acceptance region for t with 4 degrees of freedom is $t < 2.13$ at the .05 level of sig-

nificance.   Hence the sample value, $t = 2.14$, indicates a significantly higher average yield from field A.

27. Two random samples of size 10 and size 12 from normal populations gave the results $\bar{x}_1 = 19$, $s_1 = 5$; $\bar{x}_2 = 24$, $s_2 = 4$.   Are the means significantly different?

Ans. There are $9 + 11 = 20$ degrees of freedom, and the acceptance region for the .05 level of significance is $-2.09 < t < 2.09$.   Thus, the sample value $t = 2.60$ demonstrates a significant difference in the means.

28. As a step toward the optimum allocation of sales effort, the customers for a certain line of merchandise were classified according to various factors which seemed likely to affect sales volume by means of an objective system which did not depend on current sales data.   The classification scheme was then subjected to various tests; and because of the extreme skewness of the initial sales data, the cube root of amount purchased was used as a normalizing transformation (refer to Exercise 18).

Sample results for two of the classes were as follows: $n_1 = 10$, $\bar{x}_1 = 27.3$, $s_1 = 9.1$; $n_2 = 12$, $\bar{x}_2 = 20.1$, $s_2 = 4.6$.

(a) By interpolating on the reciprocals of degrees of freedom, find the .05 critical levels of F with 9 and 11 degrees of freedom and F with 11 and 9 degrees of freedom.

(b) Establish the acceptance region for the hypothesis of equal variances at the .10 level of significance, and decide whether the two variances can be considered equal.

(c) Test the hypothesis of equal means by the Cochran-Cox method.   (d) What simplification could you suggest?

Ans. (a) 2.90, 3.09.   (b) $.324 < s_1^2/s_2^2 < 2.90$, or equally well, $.345 < s_2^2/s_1^2 < 3.09$.   Sample value $s_1^2/s_2^2 = 3.91$ indicates a significant difference.   (c) At the .05 level of significance, the acceptance region for the hypothesis of equal means is $-2.25 < t' < 2.25$.   Sample value $t' = 2.27$ indicates a significant difference. (d) Before computing the weighted average a, check significance against the greater of the limits a_1, a_2.

29. A random sample of 10 observations from a normal population gave $\bar{x} = 40$, $s = 5$.   Determine 95 per cent confidence limits for μ.   *Ans.* $36.43 \leq \mu \leq 43.57$.

30. With reference to the data on weight of filings (Exercise 25), (a) test the variation of average weights removed by different files against the variation of weights removed by alternate sides of the same file.   (b) What simplification can be employed in computing the sum of squares "within files"?

Ans. (a) Under the null hypothesis that the average weights are equal, the acceptance region at the .05 level of significance for the variance ratio with 5 and 6 degrees of freedom is $F < 4.39$.   The sample value of 10.7 indicates that the means are significantly different.

Source	Degrees of freedom	Sum of squares	Mean square	Variance ratio
Between files..........	5	80.67	16.1	10.7
Within files...........	6	9.00	1.5	
Total..............	11	89.67		

(b) When there are two observations in a class, the sum of squares within the class is simply half the square of the difference of the two observations.

31. Three samples of six each were taken at different times by picking consecutive cigarettes from the production line.   The data on individual weights in units of .01 oz were as follows:

Sample 1	4.08, 3.81, 3.97, 3.78, 3.73, 4.03
Sample 2	4.28, 3.95, 4.15, 4.21, 3.91, 4.04
Sample 3	3.92, 4.05, 3.82, 3.80, 4.00, 3.75

(a) Test the hypothesis of equal variances. Note that natural logarithms can be obtained from an exponential table in case a convenient table of natural logarithms is not at hand. (b) Test the hypothesis of equal means, assuming the samples to be random. (c) Suppose that 30 per cent of the total variance of weight could be eliminated by a special attachment which regulates weights automatically. What are the chances that a random sample of 86 independent observations, when referred to a one-sided critical region, would indicate a significant reduction of variance at the .05 level of significance if the initial variance were known? (See note at foot of Table 8-3.)

Ans. (a) At the .10 level of significance with 2 degrees of freedom the acceptance region for the hypothesis of homoscedasticity is $Z < 4.61$. The sample value, $Z = .25$, falls in the acceptance region and sustains the hypothesis.

Sample	$\bar{x}$	$\Sigma(x - \bar{x})^2$	v	$\ln v$
1	3.90	.1056	.0211	−3.859
2	4.09	.1086	.0217	−3.830
3	3.89	.0712	.0142	−4.254
Total........	....	.2854	.....	−11.943

$$a = 5, \quad A = 15, \quad \bar{v} = .0190, \quad \ln \bar{v} = -3.963, \quad Z = .25$$

(b) Under the null hypothesis that the average weights are equal, the acceptance region at the .05 level of significance for the variance ratio with 2 and 15 degrees of freedom is $F < 3.68$. The sample value of 4.01 indicates that the means are significantly different and hence, that the samples are not random.

Source	Degrees of freedom	Sum of squares	Mean square	Variance ratio
Between samples........	2	.1524	.0762	4.01
Within samples.........	15	.2854	.0190	
Total...............	17	.4378		

(c) $\chi_0^2 = 64.5$; $\chi_1^2 = \chi_0^2/.7 = 92$; $P(\chi^2 < 92) \approx .7$.

32. A small job shop manufactures custom-built machinery, and a fixed price for each job is agreed upon with the customer before the work is started. Errors in cost estimation, therefore, cause a variation in profit from job to job, even though a constant per cent profit is intended. Apparently, the errors are roughly proportional to the contract price, although from one point of view, a downward trend, percentage-wise, might be expected. After the price range was divided into approximately equal intervals, 2 random samples of 10 were selected from each price group and the average price, average profit, and (approximate) average per cent profit on the selling price were computed, with the results as shown in the accompanying table. The per cent profit was actually estimated from the ratio of average profit to average price in each sample; but this figure was checked against the average of 10 individual ratios in the lowest price group, and the 2 estimates were found to agree to the number of figures exhibited.

(a) Spot-check a few values of v and ln v and test the hypothesis of homoscedasticity. (b) Test the hypothesis of uniform average per cent profit. (c) Assuming that the per cent profit on the selling price is normally distributed, what is the probability of suffering a loss on an individual job? (d) Assume a pricing formula of the type $S = (1 + m)C'$ where C' is the estimated cost, m the markup as a decimal fraction, and S the selling price. Judging from the data presented, what seems to be the value of m? (e) How large would m have to be in order to reduce the probability of loss to .01?

Price Group	Sample A		Sample B		Per cent profit				Estimates of variance	
	Mean price	Mean profit	Mean price	Mean profit	A	B	Sum	Difference	v	ln v
1	\$ 262	\$ 32	\$ 297	\$ 41	12.2	13.8	26.0	−1.6	1.28	0.247
2	703	83	808	76	11.8	9.4	21.2	2.4	2.88	1.058
3	1,242	166	1,191	167	13.4	14.0	27.4	−0.6	0.18	−1.715
4	1,790	301	1,757	246	16.8	14.0	30.8	2.8	3.92	1.366
5	2,212	230	2,250	351	10.4	15.6	26.0	−5.2	13.52	2.604
6	2,732	418	2,779	381	15.3	13.7	29.0	1.6	1.28	0.247
7	3,270	376	3,220	235	11.5	7.3	18.8	4.2	8.82	2.177
8	3,726	600	3,738	639	16.1	17.1	33.2	−1.0	0.50	−0.693
9	4,250	348	4,321	640	8.2	14.8	23.0	−6.6	21.78	3.081
10	4,776	602	4,681	562	12.6	12.0	24.6	0.6	0.18	−1.715
Totals	.....	....	.....	....	128.3	131.7	260.0	−3.4	54.34	6.657

Ans. (a) At the .10 level of significance, the acceptance region for the hypothesis of homoscedasticity with 9 degrees of freedom is $Z < 14.68$. The sample value of 7.51 falls in the acceptance region and sustains the hypothesis. (b) At the .05 level of significance, the acceptance region for the variance ratio with 9 and 10 degrees of freedom is $F < 3.02$. The sample value of 1.79 falls in the acceptance region, and so the hypothesis of uniform average per cent profit is tenable.

Source	Degrees of freedom	Sum of squares	Mean square	Variance ratio
Between price groups........	9	85.84	9.54	1.79
Within price groups..........	10	54.34	5.43	
Total...................	19	140.18		

(c) $P = .04$, (d) $m = .15$, (e) $m = .20$.

33. Industrial specifications for a certain manufactured article which must withstand repeated percussion stipulate a core of hard wood, with a protective coating of resilient plastic. Although the coating usually remains intact, it occasionally loses its adhesion to the core; and when the separation exceeds a certain limit, the article is no longer suitable for its purpose. Resistance to separation is tested in the factory by a mechanical device which delivers a given number of blows of fairly uniform intensity. The following data pertain to the unseparated area u per square inch of test surface at the termination of the impact test. For the experimental comparison of three coating processes, random samples of four articles made by the respective processes were subjected to the impact test.

Process A: .55, .44, .51, .42; $\Sigma u = 1.92$, $\Sigma u^2 = 0.9326$
Process B: .47, .58, .66, .53; $\Sigma u = 2.24$, $\Sigma u^2 = 1.2738$
Process C: .54, .59, .69, .74; $\Sigma u = 2.56$, $\Sigma u^2 = 1.6634$

Are the mean unseparated areas significantly different?

Ans. For the variance ratio with 2 and 9 degrees of freedom, the acceptance region, such that the null hypothesis of equal means will be sustained at the .05 level of significance, is $F < 4.26$. The sample value of 4.13 falls in the acceptance region and thus supports the null hypothesis.

Source	Degrees of freedom	Sum of squares	Mean square	Variance ratio
Between processes.......	2	.0512	.0256	4.13
Within processes........	9	.0554	.0062	
Total...............	11	.1066		

34. A fairly accurate representation of the trend in successive stages of coat separation in the context of Exercise 33 may be derived by assuming that the increment of separation per square inch on the nth impact is proportional to the fractional area u_{n-1} still unseparated after the $n - $1st impact. This means that $u_n - u_{n-1} = -kf_n u_{n-1}$ ($u_0 = 1$) where k is constant and f_n represents the effective intensity of the nth impact. This factor is subject to chance variations both in the blow delivered and in the material struck. The formal solution of the difference equation is $u_n = (1 - kf_1)(1 - kf_2) \cdots (1 - kf_n)$, provided all $f_i < 1/k$; or $u_n = 0$ if any $f_i \geq 1/k$. We arrive at a simplified probabilistic model by setting $h = 1 - kE(f)$ and defining a random variable y_n such that $u_n = h^n y_n$ ($0 \leq y_n \leq h^{-n}$). Here, the parameter h is a characteristic of the coating process (including the material used), while y_n may be regarded as having practically the same distribution for all coating processes, since the extreme limit h^{-n} would rarely have an effect. Thus it is clear that the variance of u_n will be a function of the coating process. This dependence can be avoided by transforming to logarithms. Define $m = -n \log h$, $z = -\log y_n$, $x = -\log u_n$. Then $x = m + z$ and the variance of x will equal the variance of z, independently of m. By this transformation the following set of data was obtained from that of Exercise 33:

Sample A .598, .821, .673, .868; $\Sigma x = 2.960$, $\bar{x} = .740$, $\Sigma x^2 = 2.2380$
Sample B .755, .545, .416, .635; $\Sigma x = 2.351$, $\bar{x} = .588$, $\Sigma x^2 = 1.4433$
Sample C .616, .528, .371, .301; $\Sigma x = 1.816$, $\bar{x} = .454$, $\Sigma x^2 = 0.8865$

Are the mean values of x significantly different?

Ans. The acceptance region at the .05 level of significance is $F < 4.26$. Therefore the sample value of 4.31 indicates significantly different means.

Source	Degrees of freedom	Sum of squares	Mean square	Variance ratio
Between processes.......	2	.1638	.0819	4.31
Within processes........	9	.1712	.0190	
Total...............	11	.3350		

35. When a machine has several cams on one shaft, the resultant eccentricity of the cam system must be kept below a prescribed upper limit for proper mechanical operation. Scaled to appropriate units, the resultant eccentricity x is distributed very nearly as a beta variate with parameters $\alpha = a - 1$, $\lambda = b - 1$, where a and b are usually nonintegral numbers and $a < 1$. In case tables of the incomplete beta function are either inapplicable or not readily available, the probability levels can be estimated with considerable accuracy by using a normalizing transformation due to Edward Paulson and originally derived for F with n_1 and n_2 degrees of freedom.[1] In connection with F, Paulson has shown that the variate u, given by the transformation $u = [(1 - w_2)q - (1 - w_1)]/(w_2 q^2 + w_1)^{1/2}$, where $q = F^{1/3}$, $w_1 = 2/9n_1$, and $w_2 = 2/9n_2$, is approximately unit normal, provided that $n_2 \geq 3$. If the lower tail of the distribution is also of interest, then a further restriction is that $n_1 \geq 3$.

(*a*) Show that if x is a beta variate with parameters $\alpha = a - 1$, $\lambda = b - 1$, then the variate $y = bx/a(1 - x)$ is distributed as F, with parameters (equivalent to degrees of freedom) given by $n_1 = 2a$, $n_2 = 2b$. (*b*) Hence, show that the same normalizing transformation holds for the beta variate if $q = [bx/a(1 - x)]^{1/3}$, $w_1 = 1/9a$, and $w_2 = 1/9b$—the restrictions being that $b \geq 3/2$ if only the upper tail is required, and $a \geq 3/2$ if the lower tail is required as well. (*c*) Estimate the upper .05 level of x if $a = 0.8$ and $b = 3.2$. That is, find X such that $P(x \geq X) = .05$.

Ans. (*a*) Univariate change of variable. (*b*) Direct substitution. (*c*) $X = .565$.

[1] Edward Paulson, An Approximate Normalization of the Analysis of Variance Distribution, *Ann. Math. Stat.*, vol. 13, no. 2, p. 233, June, 1942.

INDEX